EARTH
COULD BE
FAIR

Other Books by Pierre van Paassen:

DAYS OF OUR YEARS

THE TIME IS NOW

THAT DAY ALONE

THE FORGOTTEN ALLY

EARTH
COULD BE
FAIR

A Chronicle By

PIERRE VAN PAASSEN

The Dial Press ~~~ 1946 ~~~ New York

To avoid embarrassment or pain to surviving relatives and friends of persons mentioned in this chronicle, names of individuals and localities have been changed.

CONTENTS

BOOK I

BOOK II

BOOK I

Chapter I

THE NIGHT OF ALL SOULS

NOVEMBER came in that year in a gray mantle of fog. The ringer of Sint Jan, who was in the habit of watching the sky from his room in the belfry, remarked that it seemed as if a huge curtain of soiled wool was drawn over our town. For days the sun remained invisible. Every object turned dull and dark. The birds were song-choked, as if they had seen a portent. Even the crows left off cawing. Some cattle still remaining in the meadows outside the town walls stood with lowered heads along the moisture-dripping fences, or had sought shelter in the warming nearness of the haystacks. With a loud clatter of their mandibles that could be heard in the most remote quarters of the town, the last pair of storks bade us farewell from their nest on top of the chimney of the orphan asylum. This, according to the old people, was the never-failing signal that the equinoctial storms were not far off. Ashen was the earth that day and leaden the sky, with splashes of a tawny yellow light, the so-called sundogs flitting in and out of the blanket of shadows overhead, leaving a brief melting pool of green foam where they vanished.

In October there had been some sharp gusts of wind that stripped the elms in the church square of their leaves so that the massive old tower suddenly stood forth bare and lonely in the half-light of the sunless days. But there was no cold in the air as yet. When the fog lifted early on the day of the fourth of November the sky was a faint blue, which changed to a cool green beryl as the day wore on. Just before sunset these colors were blended with orange and purple until they swam together in one vast shimmering lake of gold that stretched across the entire expanse of the western horizon.

In that hour, seen from its high old ramparts, the town of Gorcum seemed to hang in the air as in a dream; pure, timeless, and still; a compact, walled-in little kingdom, where harmony reigned, and peace. The houses, seemingly glued together like toys and leaning on each others' shoulders, were ranged in wide circles around the Great Church, like children looking up to their mother's face. Only on the outskirts, at the foot of the ramparts, where narrow alleys crossed and crisscrossed in a labyrinthine maze of dwellings, was there any disorder in the ranks. Between these slum quarters and the ramparts lay a strip of green garden land enclosed in high stone walls topped with broken glass embedded in concrete. By the town's side the broad river moved almost imperceptibly. From a distance the stream looked more like a glassy, polished highway than a body of living water.

Beyond, on the farther shore, in Brabant, the church steeples of a dozen communes were sharply outlined against the somber mass of the Forest of Altena. On the east, at the confluence of the Meuse and the Rhine, the ancient Castle of Loevesteyn, once Holland's bastille, appeared as a gray dissolving shadow.

As night set in the skies' fading realm seemed to mingle with the smoke of darkening houses. From their dull-red roofs the pall slowly urged itself across deserted gardens and desolate lawns. Mauve pockets appeared under the eaves. The shadows on the church wall deepened to black. From the barracks came the strident blare of bugles sounding the lights-on signal. Then the gas lamps in the streets went on too, one after the other, in such intervals as the lamplighter required to walk from one post to the next. From the town wall it seemed as if some moving magic hand were placing candles in a row.

"There's water coming," said Jan Wynant, the night watchman. "Water and wind! There was a streak of blood in that sky just now which bodes nobody any good!"

Wynant was not wrong. But the storm he foresaw did not break till the evening of the seventh, when a sudden, heavy downpour drove lingering strollers from the small park by the river's shore into the deep, covered town-gate for shelter. The cloud banks which had been lying in the west all afternoon, now lifted by the wind, began rapidly to climb the arc of the sky. Presently they loomed threateningly over the earth. Driven upward and on, they assumed ever more ominous shapes like living monsters rolling out of dark caverns in black coils of destruction. Out of the gathering darkness the cold wind vaulted through the empty streets in long, blustering jumps, tearing at the roof tiles and rattling the glass in the street lanterns. There was still some light in the sky then, but it was more of a lambent outer radiance springing from some greater inner sea of light than a pure flame. The orange-tawny afterglow revealed a procession of low-hanging clouds flying by at fantastic speed, like the swollen sails of unseen ships scudding through froth and foam.

Before an hour had passed the wind was blowing a gale, booming over the roofs and through the narrow streets with the sustained roar of distant thunder punctuated, now and then, by a thudding clap such as can be heard in mountainous regions in wintertime when a slide of snow strikes the valley below. Invisible in the black face of the storm, the high church steeple of Sint Jan whistled with the shrill wail of a projectile cutting the air.

Now loosened tiles, hurtling through the air, shattered in a thousand fragments on the cobblestones. Chimneys collapsed and their bricks could be heard clattering through windows and into the streets. By eleven o'clock the old elms in the church square could no longer withstand the onslaught. They broke down, one by one, as if felled by giant ax blows. The oaks along the canal were torn up by their roots. Those who heard their fall said later that the trees shrieked like a man in death agony when their mighty branches cleft the air for the last time.

It was the night of All Souls and the worst storm the

oldest inhabitants could remember. In later years people reckoned the passage of time, their individual age, and the occurrence of important events in their lives from the night of that tempest. That storm cut people's lives in twain, as it were. There was a before and an after; the storm of November 1907 was the dividing point.

When a large piece of sculpture from the upper gallery in the ancient tower crashed through the roof of an adjacent schoolhouse shortly after midnight, the great bell Roelandt, suddenly and to the surprise of all, began to toll. Never before heard by living men, for it was said he would ring only if the country was in danger of invasion, Roelandt's deep monotonous boom, his moaning resonance, now heightened by the fury of the wind, now sinking to a mournful, muffled peal that seemed to come from far away, sounded like a frightened, anguished human voice insistently, almost hysterically, calling for help.

But now also the thumping rubadub of heavy boots could be heard moving over the cobblestones. The dike guards, dressed in their oilskins and swinging their hurricane lamps, hurried through the streets to answer the call. From every quarter, rich and poor, young and old, volunteers in the hour of danger like their fathers before them since times immemorial, all ran as by instinct in the general direction of the hereditary enemy, the water. For it soon became known that the flood had risen some thirty feet since sundown. Cologne telegraphed that the Rhine was in a frenzy. Flares sent up from the opposite shore in the small communes of Woercum and Sleeuwijk, two miles distant, reported that a break in the dikes had already occurred in or near those places. At regular intervals red glowing arrows shot up from the southern shore like those giant firecrackers the municipality set off on the night of the Queen's birthday. They lit up the dark and foaming river for an instant with the ruddy glare of Bengal fire only to sizzle out almost instantly in the driving sheets of rain. From time to time a brief flash of moonlight pierced the clouds. It was as if a weird, gigantic green-yellow bird suddenly flew over the river with broad sweeping wing-beat to return as swiftly into the utter darkness whence it came. The wind lashed the dikes as if the monster which lives in storms and water sought to make them loosen their grip in the soil. And all the time Roelandt tolled his deep-throated clangor.

The storm now had the force of a million battering-rams and was pounding furiously at buildings and bridges and sluice gates, tearing beacons and buoys from their moorings, toppling smokestacks and chimneys, clawing at shutters and window frames, flinging cornices and rain conduits and tree branches into the streets, along with glass and mortar and all manner of debris, in a roaring chaos of inscrutable confusion; raging, fighting, pummeling, and laughing—yes, laughing—like some invisible titan in the throes of delirium.

Every autumn brings its storms to the Lowlands. But once in a century perhaps do they attain the fury of that tempest which raged on All Souls night in 1907. That night is still remembered because then the waters rose almost to the heights they reached on those historic occasions when the Zuyder Sea and the Dollard Sea came into existence, or when, at another time, a third of the land of the Province of Zeeland was drowned, or yet still another autumn about five hundred years before the date of this chronicle when, in the so-called Flood of St. Elizabeth, an entire district not far from Gorcum itself, known as the Biesbosch, with its ninety-five villages and all their inhabitants, perished in the raging waters.

Nobody went to bed in Gorcum that night. Even the smallest children were kept dressed to be in readiness to leave for higher ground should the water enter the town. Where that higher ground may have been located or how far distant it was, I have never learned. Virtually the entire Province of South Holland, in which Gorcum is situated, lies below sea level while the Merwede River, which carries most of the waters of both the German Rhine and the French Meuse in its broad bosom, bears down precisely from the direction where some higher ground may be encountered.

Heedless of the falling masonry that littered the streets and the squares, men and boys were now running to and fro, ringing doorbells to warn housewives to put out fires in the kitchens and on the hearths. They swung their lanterns and shouted through cupped hands the ominous intelligence that the water was pouring in at the Dalem Poort, one of the five town gates. Most of the street lamps had been smashed and the flow of gas had been turned off at the source. Barrels of tar were therefore rolled into the principal square in front of the Town Hall and there set on fire to provide a lurid dipping light for the crews of burghers who set about digging up cobblestones and earth. Shoveled into sacks and loaded on carts, this material, along with baskets of sand and gravel, was hauled off to the spots indicated by the dike guards as the most seriously menaced. There it was heaped into barricades. You heard the drivers of the carts lashing their horses up the inclined streets that led to the gates near the river, the grating of the ironclad hoofs upon the pavement, the cracking of the whips and the shouts of the men; and you felt in the growing panic that an evil spirit was taking possession of the stoutest hearts.

Then, as if the steadily rising water did not cause enough anxiety, a fire broke out around midnight in a warehouse owned by one Gerrit de Visser, a prosperous dealer in groats. When discovered, the flames had already broken through the roof, and the neighborhood was bathed in a lurid, sinister glare. Our Burgomaster, Floris Karel de Bruyn, on learning of the new disaster decided to call upon the military to man the pumps, since the volunteers who would otherwise have operated the fire engines were busy fighting back the water.

The shrill cry of the bugles, strangely alarming in that night of booming tempest, was soon heard, and within a few minutes companies of artillerymen were dragging the hose wagons and the ladder trucks toward De Visser's warehouse. When the first soldiers arrived on the scene of the fire, which raged in a particularly narrow street, a mere alley, a broad column of flying sparks, hissing in the pelting rain above the housetops, showed the building to be a roaring furnace from top to bottom. There was not the least chance of saving it. Even while the soldiers were unwinding the hose, connecting it with the sprinklers, and priming the hand pumps, two

adjacent structures, a bakery and a public library, caught
fire. Fanned by the screaming wind that was sucked through
the alley with a force against which a strong man could
scarcely stand up, the fire was carried from house to house
by thousands of burning books and papers that flew into the
sky like so many fiery birds. In the twinkling of an eye roofs
were burning, two, three blocks distant.

So passed that night in alarm and trepidation. The Burgomaster and the Councilors ran to and fro between the
fire and the flood, here encouraging the dike workers, there
giving instructions to the military fire-fighters. And all the
time Roelandt tolled on, calling the inhabitants of outlying
villages to the rescue, and the wind yelled and moaned with
the mad, frenzied cry of a million souls in torment.

It must have been close to three o'clock in the morning
when my mother, who had grown anxious about her parents,
sent me to my grandfather's house. When I dropped the
metal knocker on the door it was my grandfather himself
who answered. He was dressed in a long coat with a hat
commonly known as a southwester pulled over his eyes. I
noticed that his beard was wet. He bade me follow him upstairs to a room in the rear of the house which, as I knew
well, looked on the town wall across a small garden. Behind
that granite barricade flowed the Merwede River. Grandfather opened one of the French windows but kept the
wooden shutters closed. At once the room was filled with
the thunder of the waves. The foam splashed through the
latticed woodwork.

"Come close now," said the old man, beckoning me to
the window, "and listen. A moment ago I thought I heard a
voice calling from there." He pointed in the direction of the
river. "It may have been my imagination playing me a
trick," he added, "but I feel almost sure. I have been hearing it all night. Now listen!"

I bent my head against the wood, but though I strained
my ears I could hear nothing distinct or human in that
frightening tumult of the wind and the waters. . . .

At that moment my Uncle Kees stamped into the room,

the rain streaming from his oilskins. He had come home
for another lantern, his first having been broken at the
Dalem Gate, where his duties as a volunteer dike guard
had called him.

"What are you doing in this room, standing by an open
window?" Kees asked his father in surprise. "Do you want
to catch your death of cold?" He was about to say more,
but Grandfather stopped him with a gesture of his hand and
quickly explained our presence by the open window.

"A voice? Out there?" Kees asked incredulously. "That's
impossible!"

But he too bent his head close to the shutters, and we
stood all three listening intently.

"I hear nothing in particular," said Kees, looking up
and shaking his head. But the next instant his jaw dropped
and his fists clenched as he turned back to the window.
"There," he whispered fiercely, "there it is. . . . You were
right, Father! Here, listen! There it is again. . . ."

I heard it too now, first indistinctly, then much clearer
as a blast of wind suddenly veered in our direction: *"Hilfe!
Hilfe!"*

"My God, that's a foreign language," said Grandfather,
stepping back from the window and looking at Kees and me
alternately with consternation and horror on his face.

"It's a cry for help," Kees came back curtly, his blue eyes
staring hard at his father. "How can a human being live in
such a storm? He must be out on the water. I'm going into
the garden to look over the wall. . . ."

With a bound he was out of the room and down the stairs.
My grandfather and I followed. We lit the lamps in the
living-room, which gave on the garden, and then moved the
curtains aside to provide Kees with all the light possible.
We could see that the water stood several feet high in the
garden. With every heave of the waves more tons of it
spilled over the wall. Presently we saw Kees struggling
through that swirling pool carrying a lantern in one hand
and dragging a ladder with the other.

He placed the ladder against the wall and started to
climb. First he raised his hurricane lamp above the parapet,

then his hands crept over the top groping for a hold so as not to be blown back by the bucking wind the moment his head and shoulders should come within its path. At last his head appeared for an instant in the circle of light cast by his lantern. But he ducked back instantly as a breaker smashed in with a clap of thunder and an avalanche of water poured over the wall, hiding him from our eyes for a moment. He must have seen something, for presently we saw his shoulders above the parapet again and this time he swung his lantern to and fro in two or three broad sweeps and we heard him shout into the darkness something about holding fast. . . .

"There is a man out there," said Kees, still gasping for breath and shaking the water from his face as he ran up the stone steps that led from the garden into the house. "He is clinging to the mast of a small vessel that is pounding to pieces against our wall. I'd say he's about fifty feet off. The ship is being pulled to and fro between the wall and the rocks out there. I am going to get him. Come, Pieter!"

We ran through the street and up an inclined passage to the Water Poort, which was the town gate on the river-bank nearest Grandfather's house. There, by the light of a dozen pitch flares we found a number of citizens building a barricade of sandbags in the deep portal of the gate.

"Ho!" shouted Kees to all and sundry. "Here men, listen a moment. . . . There is someone out there calling for help! He is holding onto the top of the mast of a sinking vessel . . . just east of here . . . back of my father's house, it's about a quarter of a mile. There isn't a moment to lose. We must go out there! We must launch a boat . . . !"

"Have you gone completely out of your mind?" called back Abraham van der Werff, the furniture-maker, as he stepped up to Kees. "No human creature can live out on that river for a minute in this tempest. This is the end of the world, man! To launch a boat means death for everyone in it. This storm is going to be the end of us all. God, you must be insane!" He tapped his forehead several times.

"Hold your tongue, *ongeluksprofeet*" (prophet of doom),

shot back Kees. "Nobody is asking for your advice!" Then turning to another man: "What do you say, Frerick? Can a boat be launched?" The man to whom he spoke was a fisherman, Frerick Mik by name, a giant with a weather-beaten face that might have been cut from a gnarled chunk of brierwood. Frerick spat out a lump of chewing tobacco and stepping up to Kees, looked my uncle straight in the eyes, and said gravely: "If you say it must be done, we will launch a boat, but we will need ten strong men." And turning around he called out: "Here you, Bakels, you are number one!"

These words were spoken to a flaxen-haired youth, a student at the local Latin School, who was considered one of Gorcum's best athletes and boatsmen.

"And you, Pudding Powder," called out Frerick, "you are number two!" This to another student by the name of Thompson, whose family lived in Amsterdam, where they owned a factory of jellies, cereals, and a famous brand of pudding powder to which the young man in question owed his nickname.

"You, Koos Verraay, you stand by here!" Frerick shouted to a fellow fisherman, another grim-faced citizen like himself, renowned in the community as a phenomenal drinker and fighter. In a few moments Frerick had his crew picked.

But the launching proved no easy undertaking. A boat was shoved through and over the wall of sandbags into the flagstone-covered, three-cornered space formed by the Water Poort's structure and the town's ramparts. The space itself and the small park right on the river's edge were under water and with each pounding wave further inundated by a fresh volume of spattering foam and drizzle. What lay beyond the gate was an inky blackness, a turmoil of crested waves, the howling chaos of the gates of hell. To venture upon that seething inferno seemed rankest folly.

Still the attempt was made. Vats of oil from Wouter Spronck's storehouse, located just inside the Water Poort, were rolled out through the opening that had quickly been made in the barricade of sandbags and pushed to the very edge of the foam-spattered quay. There the bottoms were stove-in and the contents poured upon the water. Then the boat was pushed out to the brink of the swirling river. More pitch flares were lit, and Frerick Mik shouted to his crew, who stood ready with the oars in their hands: "Now, men, when there is a high one" (he meant a particularly big wave) "push the boat in and at the same time jump aboard and row for all you're worth . . . !"

They stood watching the water and listening, tense, bracing themselves against the wind, their oilskins flapping about their legs. Once, twice the waves broke over the shore, but Frerick did not judge the moment opportune to push off. He held up his hand in a gesture ordering delay while he peered into the night. A minute or two may have passed that way in suspense when he suddenly bellowed: "Here she is! *Kerels, vooruit!* Forward, men!"

In a flash the boat was riding on what seemed the gleaming and twisting back of a monstrous jet-black sea serpent. But the men were aboard. The small craft flew out of sight of the onlookers as if it had been sucked down by a whirlpool. An instant later it appeared high above our heads on the crest of a towering breaker, which shot it back with the velocity of an arrow. It slid across the pavement of the quay with such violence that its bow was splintered to matchwood against the wall of the rampart. Before it crashed, even in that brief instant when it touched land, the men jumped out. The wreck itself was pulled back in the twinkling of an eye by the water and disappeared from view.

A second boat was at once brought to the water's edge and again the crew stood waiting for Frerick Mik's signal. By the glare of the pitch flares, which dipped so low at times that they seemed about to be extinguished, I saw that Kees' oilskins had been ripped to tatters. He was biting his mustache as Frerick shouted the signal to be off again. Only at the third try did the maneuver succeed. Then the boat shot away like a roller-coaster, flying sky-high as it climbed with incredible speed up the side of a heaving, angry mountain of water. In the same instant it plunged out of sight into the blackness of the night. For a few moments Frerick's voice could still be heard above the din calling out his hoarse rhythmic command of one-two, one-two to the rowers. Then more vats of oil were poured out and we stood watching for what was to come.

How long did we wait? Perhaps an hour, surely no more. But it seemed an eternity! Would they come back? Would the boat hold together in that hissing and boiling maelstrom? Would they reach the half-sunken ship and rescue the man whose voice had been heard? These were the questions in everyone's mind while we waited, and the clock in the Water Poort's superstructure boomed out the quarter-hours. All were silent. . . .

"There they are!" suddenly called out Dominie van Pelt, a young minister from the village of Dalem, which lies just outside Gorcum, a quarter of an hour's walk eastward in the Province of Gelderland. Dr. van Pelt was a volunteer dike guard and in the forefront of the watch that night.

"There they are! Everybody stand by!" shouted the Pastor. "Grab the men! Let the boat go!"

"Hold the boat, too!" called back Van der Werff. "Why let the boat go? Whose boat are you talking about, anyway?"

"Don't try to hold the boat, for heaven's sake," interrupted my grandfather, who had also appeared on the scene. "Don't try to hold the boat, you will be dragged back with it!"

There they were indeed, not rowing now but resting on their oars and looking around at the lighted quay. A few times their faces came quite near, only to drop out of sight again as the boat sank back into the hollow of an intervening wave. Then, with a crash that splintered the craft to bits, the boat dashed against the town wall. In a flash, too, the wreck was sucked back into the cavern of the flood. In the short interval the men had jumped out.

Uncle Kees was carrying a half-conscious young man in his arms. Grandfather put his hand on Frerick Mik's shoulder and walked off with him into the Water Poort. . . .

A few moments later the whole crew of the lifeboat and many of the barricade-builders were assembled in my grandfather's living-room, where the rescued lad had been placed on the sofa. His hands were badly cut and blistered, he had some minor injuries about the body, mostly bruises, but his face was swollen out of all human semblance. Doctor van Amstel, who had been sent for, and Dominie van Pelt were bent over him questioning him in a halting, groping way in German.

In answer the boy told how the skipper of the lugger from which he had been rescued, after casting anchor at one of the moles in the river on the previous afternoon, had gone ashore to look for a certain tavern, leaving his sole and youthful assistant alone on board. When the storm tore the craft loose from its mooring and dashed it against the town wall, it had sprung a leak causing it to sink, fortunately in shallow water. The boy, who was no more than sixteen, had climbed onto the mast and clung there to rope and tackle until at last he felt Uncle Kees' strong arms around him. Then he had fainted.

There was a general outburst of indignation against the absent skipper as soon as the boy's words had been translated into Dutch. Koos Verraay and Frerick Mik, who thought they knew the master of the sunken lugger from previous visits to our town, proposed to go and look for the man at once in the dives and stews of a certain neighborhood.

"The only treatment for such a rascal is a thrashing," said Verraay, "and I am the man to give it to him!" Others objected, saying that it was a matter for the police. The skipper was a German; to beat him up might precipitate an international incident. No, the police must be brought in. . . .

Well, then, why had the police not been notified? Why has the skipper not shown up at the Water Poort all night? Where could the man have been on such a night when he must have heard the storm and must have known his craft was in danger? Such conduct was the height of irresponsibility. The German should get a good lesson, at any rate. Verraay was still for going to look for the man.

"Ah," said Van der Werff, "and who is going to look after this boy? It will cost a pretty penny in medical fees to fix him up. And then, who is going to pay for his return to Germany now that he has obviously lost his livelihood?"

"We had better get started," assented Dominie van Pelt, "and call the police." But nobody left, seeing that my grandmother had just entered the room accompanied by Grietje, the servant girl, and the two began laying the big table for breakfast.

No sooner had the food appeared than Abraham van der Werff stepped up to the table and cut himself a slice of cheese. "We have well deserved a little bodily refreshment," he said unctuously, holding his head sideways and rubbing his hands. "There are a lot of scoundrels in this world and a good many of them are Germans. . . ." He paused to take a hot bun, splitting it open and smearing both halves with butter. He then placed a sausage between and pushed the stuffed roll into his mouth. "In fact such is life," he resumed his monologue, while chewing as if he were under contract. "Life is made up of coming and going, I always say. This boy comes to us and the skipper disappears, the one comes and the other goes. It's very simple, it's life's rhythm, the rule of life, coming and going. . . ."

"Like those buns you're stuffing into your pockets, I suppose," interrupted Kees, who had watched the speaker from the corner of his eye and who heartily detested the furniture-maker as a pathological, inquisitive, empty-headed, and altogether impossible person. "Leave something for others, man; there are at least twenty-five other persons here. . . ."

Grandfather put an end to the discussion by saying that the German lad would stay in his house for the time being and that he wanted him carried upstairs. . . .

Now it was morning, too. A sickly light seeped through the leaden, yellow clouds. The wind had died down, but not enough to warrant signaling the emergency's end. Dike guards were still working in the Town Square when I passed by on my way home. But the fire in De Visser's warehouse was out. Soldiers were rolling up the hose in front of the blackened and gutted buildings. As I stopped for a moment to look at the scene, from which fumed the acrid odor of

wet ashes and scorched bricks, a passing neighbor told me
that two girls, hatmaker De Hosson's daughters, had died
in the fire. The body of one, still holding a rosary in her
charred fingers, had just been found in the ruins. A little
farther down the street I noticed Major Seyffardt[1] in conversation with the bereaved father. . . .

Never did Gorcum look more disconsolate. From the
bulging, low-hanging clouds that rolled by in agitated procession like so many puffed-up woolsacks, fell a dreary,
powdery drizzle. The misty rain hung in the air like a transparent, smoky veil that blotted out the ends of streets and
made the town look even smaller and more compact than it
was. The light had a sulphurous tinge, a weird doomsday
color. I went up to my small room in the attic to change
my clothes and pick up my schoolbooks. For a moment I
stood by the window before going down. The town was a
riot of tiles and bricks and chimney pots.

In the murky panorama that I saw, every roof, every
window and wall, even the tufts of grass sprouting from
eaves and cracks and crevices, were familiar to me. Directly
across, phantomlike, its spire invisible in the mist, stood the
tower of Sint Jan, gnarled and bent like a weary old man
under its burden of nearly a thousand autumnal storms and
summer heat. Between the tower and my window lay the
roofs of the town's business quarter, an expanse of gray
and red tiles, pitted by the craters of the open squares and
the bottle-green, winding snake of the canal. A humid vapor,
smelling of mildew and decay, rose from the gardens and
back yards. A wisp of steam, but steam of a sepulchral chilli-
ness, enveloped the unclean quarter of the Melkpad, where
the alleys were so narrow the sun never penetrated to
the pavement, and the inhabitants dwelt in a perpetual
twilight.

On the left stood the weather-blackened stone block with
its long narrow slits of windows that housed the greater part

[1] Hendrik A. Seyffardt was a general in 1940, at the time of the invasion
of Holland by the German army. He joined the Nazis and tried to raise
a corps of volunteers to fight for Hitler on the Russian front. He was shot
dead by a patriot as he emerged from the War Office building in The Hague
in July 1942.

of the garrison. Its roof had been ripped off in the night. The broken rafters jutted upward into the yellow fog like the stiffened fingers on a dead man's hand. On the right, at the foot of another clock tower as slender as an Oriental minaret, were the high red-brick walls of the dreariest of all structures, the Convent of the Sacred Heart, the rebuilt remnant of an earlier medieval abbey demolished by Calvinist iconoclasts in the wars of religion. The raindrops grew larger again. Black smoke mixed with the fog. Shapeless bags of dirty yellow sailed by swiftly in the sky, leaving a pale streak of ocher on the white mist. Sadly the carillon of Sint Jan played the hourly tune as the melancholy scene melted away in a lurid, moist glimmer.

Do towns have feeling? Do they at times seek to communicate to us their weariness of spirit, a sentiment of resignation or of hope or joy? It may well be so. A great deal happens in the universe which can neither be explained by school learning nor made tangible and final by rational understanding. Why should an old town, old in human history, rich in human destinies, not produce something out of nothing, an atmosphere, an aura, an irresistible affirmation? I have nowhere else in later life, except in Ypres and Bruges, so clearly felt the impression of a town possessing a collective personality, with feelings and passions and senses of its own. That morning, I felt as if Gorcum spoke to me and prophesied. If towns prophesy, it is not that they know the future. They know the days gone by. They remember. They do not judge or condemn. They have seen. It is because of what they have seen and remember and feel and know that they suffer. Gorcum trembled that morning. Not the hollow roar of the tempest in the night, but the still, almost secret lament of the aftermath sounded like the sigh of someone who feels abandoned to his fate in an unfeeling and unresponsive universe. . . .

A new gust of wind splashed the rain with swishing sound over the window. A hundred nervous rivulets suddenly coursed down the panes as if a shivering, mobile curtain had hastily been drawn before the glass.

There remained just enough time before school to walk to the town wall for a look at the river. Hundreds of citizens were out on the ramparts, talking of the events of the night and peering into the wet mist. The Merwede was yellow and gray. The fog raced along with the waves, hovering over them in steamlike puffs. It was even then all you could do to keep your footing against the half-gale that blew with sudden, jerky blasts. Someone said the spire of Woercum's tower was missing. How he knew was a puzzle, inasmuch as Woercum, a small town directly across the river in Brabant Province, fully a mile distant, was as invisible as the top of the windmill a hundred yards down the street behind us. Another man said that a Rhine steamer of the Mannheim Line had just gone by downstream with all its lights burning, but its rudder damaged or out of commission. The big boat had managed to avoid the moles and breakwaters that jutted into the river, but could hardly hope to get by the great railway bridge at Sliedrecht with its broad granite pillars, a few miles downstream.

All I could see was wreckage floating by: tree trunks, cork jackets, roofs of houses, small river craft, here and there the bodies of horses and cattle, their legs pointing stiffly upward, looking like the inflated leather sacks that water-vendors carry in the East. Near by lay the sunken barge from which the German boy had been rescued in the night and, across a basalt pier or breakwater, like a broken, discarded toy, the ferryboat, its smokestack trailing in the current.

With the exception of the boys who lived in the communes on the southern side of the Merwede, all the students of the Latin School[1] gathered in the common room at nine, although it was obvious that no classes could be held that day, nor for several days to come. Nearly all the windows had been shattered and in several classrooms the

[1] A Latin School is known as a gymnasium in Holland. It has nothing to do with gymnastics, except perhaps that it is supposed to strengthen the mental fibers. It corresponds roughly to the French lycée, although the curriculum in a Dutch gymnasium is more exacting.

water stood ankle-deep. The old Rector, Dr. van Bergen, had lit a long clay pipe, as was his wont when disturbed or irritated. He was pacing up and down, shaking his immense white beard as he inspected the damage and sending up clouds of blue tobacco smoke. In appearance he resembled Count Tolstoi, except that he was of considerably larger bulk. He had the same small eyes as the Russian sage, the same thick, overhanging eyebrows and leonine mane. Several other instructors stood listening to Dr. Vossius, a red-bearded instructor of Greek who had been at the Water Poort the night before as a dike guard and watched the rescue of the German lad.

Among the boys, Bakels and Thompson were, of course, the heroes of the occasion for their part in the exploit. Bakels was showing the blisters on his hand and explaining that when he reached the shore he had only his trousers left, the rest of his clothing having been torn off his body by the wind.

In the meantime the custodian of the building, a man named Matthys Muller, who walked with a pronounced limp, brought the Rector a freshly filled pipe, held out a lighted match for him, and reported that not a single room could be utilized. For one thing all the chimneys were down, so that no fires could be laid in the stoves. As the Town Council, already in session at that early hour, had decreed that the damage to the elementary schools was to be repaired first, it looked as if the Gymnasium would not get its turn for several days.

We all heard Muller deliver the message and now looked hopefully to the Rector for his reply, fully expecting him to declare a holiday. Such thoughts, however, were far from the old man's mind. Dr. van Bergen was a believer in education though the heavens fall. A man who was to post a notice on the school gate on the morning when the guns announced the birth of a long-hoped-for heir to the House of Orange, stating that "the extraordinary event in the royal household shall in no way interfere with the regularity of classwork," such a man could not be expected to curtail the sacred curriculum for a mere tempest. He sucked some mighty drafts from his pipe until his Jovian head was wreathed in clouds, shrugged his shoulders, and announced that he saw no other issue from the calamitous situation but to shift the classes to the individual homes of the instructors. After these words he turned to Bakels and "Pudding Powder" with the remark that in spite of their "naval victory" he expected them and all others present to behave as Piet Hein[1] had done when he returned from the capture of the Spanish silver fleet, and cause as little inconvenience as possible to the instructors' wives and housekeepers.

Dr. van Bergen's decision meant that my class, one of the lowest grades, was to go out for the first hour to the home of Dr. Jan Snetlage, the *Conrector*. This man was the best-liked of all the fourteen instructors. He had traveled a great deal in the company of his illustrious brother, an architect of world renown, and never tired of telling of these expeditions. He had even visited America, a rare accomplishment in Europe half a century ago. The story of that trip, told in my hearing a dozen times, always excited the liveliest interest and amusement. But his chief geographic interest lay really in a totally different direction. Every second year during the summer vacation he went either to Greece, to Asia Minor, or to one of the Aegean Islands, for no other reason, as he said, but to tread the soil of the Hellenic people which through its thinkers, poets, artists, statesmen, and strategists had founded what was the spiritual birthplace of Europe.

The chief reason for his popularity lay in the fact, I think, that in his teaching Dr. Snetlage went beyond the rigidly scholastic requirements of the textbooks. He was a perfect raconteur and his stories showed that he understood the meaning of the world, which is faith in life and love of humanity. Besides being ever willing to help the students individually, he took a keen interest in their home

[1] It is said that when Admiral Piet Hein reached his mother's house in Delftshaven, after bringing in the captive Spanish galleons loaded with the annual output of the silver mines of the Americas, the old lady called out: "Don't come in, Piet, till you've wiped your feet on the door mat!"

life, in their intellectual doubts, in their artistic tastes, and even in their political views. Personally he was a socialist, as was his brother the architect, but both were far from being unbending doctrinaire Marxists. For one thing our *Conrector* frequently attended church, which was not exactly a habit among the red and liberal bourgeois intelligentsia in our town. He realized, as he told me many years afterward, when I met him unexpectedly one day strolling along the water front in the Crimean town of Yalta, that the genuine strength of an idea, the socialist idea included, subsists only during its nonfulfillment. He did not, like Lord Acton, say that power corrupts and that absolute power corrupts absolutely, but characteristic of the humanist that he was, he said that power as the result of the triumph of an idea is just, alas, to itself alone.

He differed also from the other instructors in that he did not belong to the *Societeit*, a sort of club of the liberal notables of our town. Whatever time of day one met Dr. Snetlage, one was sure to see him with a bundle of newspapers under his arm. This detail astonished us not a little. Our parents read one paper only, conservative or liberal according to their own political convictions. It was hard to believe that one man read all the papers and especially those that held extreme and contradictory opinions. Dr. Snetlage was as much interested in what liberals, antirevolutionaries, Christian Democrats, aristocrats, fundamentalists, or Roman Catholics had to say on international and national events, as in socialists, anarchists, or religious radicals, each of which groups and parties had its own organ. In addition he read foreign journals of opinion.

It was perhaps a pity that he taught Latin and not history. For he was never content to explain grammar and syntax. He added his comments on historical events, whether classical or contemporary. He argued. He disputed. He admired or he grew indignant. He was never impartial. He took sides: with Catiline against Cicero, with Pompey against Caesar, with the Prince of Orange against Philip of Spain, with Marx and Engels against Louis Bonaparte, with the people against the tyrants and oppressors. He taught us to form personal opinions and to dare to defend them.

Every month or so he invited his best pupils to dinner at his home, or at a restaurant. Though he had no other income than his salary, which was by no means fabulous, yet at these dinners he did not spare expense. He took us to the best place in town. As far as I am concerned, I was always deeply impressed with the luxury and ostentation of the dining-halls and the dishes and drinks. I should add that I had never eaten in a restaurant before. On those evenings, never to be forgotten, Dr. Snetlage discussed with us, in perfect freedom, all those intimate and undefinable disquietudes that harass and torment young men and which have generally to do with the most important problems of life and human destiny.

For adolescents are not troubled by trivialities. They are concerned with major questions and problems. There was nothing precocious or artificial about our thirst for knowledge. Young men are instinctively preoccupied with philosophy, which is not mere difficult language about matters of interest only to philosophers. Philosophy is concerned with what interests every human being: with the nature of man and the nature of the universe. Boys are often more philosophical than men. What they miss in their lessons, generally without knowing it, is in fact philosophy. I have seldom in later life met a man so intellectual as Dr. Snetlage, a man with so ready a command of the wealth of a well-stored memory. Everything about him seemed to breathe learning and profound thought. The awe in which he was held rose in time to almost idolatrous veneration. From him we learned what was the kernel of Nietzsche's philosophy and of Pascal's thoughts, what was Schleiermacher's conception of God, why Strauss and Renan had written their lives of Jesus, what was at stake in the Belgian revolt against the King of Holland, why the Communards lost out against Thiers, and why England annexed the Dutch republics in South Africa. All the vexing questions from which our parents and the other instructors generally steered away with a condescending word of reassurance, or with a superior smile, were taken up by Dr. Snetlage as naturally as if they were questions pertinent to everyday affairs.

Being a socialist did not mean that the *Conrector* was considered less of a good citizen than some of his thoroughly reactionary colleagues or than the generally rather conservative members of the middle class to which he belonged. It may well be that the issues were not yet so sharply drawn as they were in later years when the class struggle split humanity into two irreconcilable camps, but I have seldom, even in so small and intensely Calvinist a community as Gorcum, come across a sample of that poverty-stricken mentality which identifies love of country, patriotism, or good citizenship with attachments to any particular social or religious creed or to any particular mode of production. Political and religious freedom were anyone's prerogative so long as he admitted the common ideas of duty that are its basis. In spite of the tireless efforts in the opposite direction of the always powerful Calvinist faction, the Dutch state is not built on the principle of religious and political unity. Besides Calvin we also had Erasmus in our national historical formation and the works of Bayle, Rousseau, Voltaire, and Castalion had first been published in Holland. Nourished on the Protestant principle of the right to dissent and the right to heresy, the Dutch could not place intolerance on the ground of religious error or, which follows logically, on disagreement in economic and philosophical matters. The burghers had to put up with each other, so to speak, and with each other's ideas. Mutual respect, but not silence, had come to be regarded as the best assurance of social peace.

It would not have entered anyone's mind to discriminate against a person or speak less civilly to him because he happened to believe that a socialist organization of society would be a better and juster dispensation to the majority of the citizens than capitalism. He was free to hold that opinion and to seek to persuade others to embrace his views. The men of our community felt, almost instinctively and without giving specific utterance to this sentiment, that to differ on political, social, or philosophical grounds was in itself something of distinct cultural value; community in diversity. Moreover, the doctrine of evolution had seriously shaken the notion to which the orthodox divines still clung almost frantically: that history was fixed for all time by the mold set in the Book of Genesis and that man had come ready-made, as it were, from the hands of the Creator. We knew that human character does change, that it, and all human institutions, have not always been what they are; that man had once, in fact, been an anthropoid ape, that he had climbed up from the slime and was still climbing, and that all things therefore were subject to continual and endless change.

"If it is true, as the anthropologists say, that man has been on earth about a hundred thousand years or so," Dr. Snetlage used to say, "he is only in his infancy. The human species is not ten years old, you may say, by no means yet adult. Wait till man comes of age in another hundred thousand years from now and he will laugh at war and poverty as he now laughs in pity at his ancestors who crawled into the depth of a cave to hide from the voice of thunder. . . .

"All our human dignity resides in our capacity to think," he would quote from Pascal, and then with a characteristic sudden lift of the head, he would add solemnly: "Let us therefore, at no time in our lives, put the slightest obstacle in the way of any man's freedom of thought and expression, for thought is the sole basis from which he and all society can raise themselves."

I can see him yet, our *Conrector*: a man of medium height, who walked with a quick, nervous step, swinging a thick malacca cane. He affected a closely clipped mustache and combed his hair in a brush or, as the fashion was known then, in pompadour style. He had penetrating blue eyes, set in deep, square sockets, and a strong chin. As I have said, he had a peculiar way of throwing back his head as if he were suddenly roused from a reverie by someone calling his name.

He did not stay with us the full length of the six-year course. In 1912 he accepted the rectorship of the Gymnasium in the city of Zutphen. But as long as he remained in Gorcum he indulged in a peculiar devotion, which almost amounted to a cult, for the tower of Sint Jan. This idiosyncrasy he shared, among others, with my Uncle Kees, the painter. Dr. Snetlage's house stood in the very shadow of that hoary pile and he had it constantly before his eyes, but like Kees he would walk for miles and miles, in all directions, to Dalem, Vuren, Asperen, Goudriaan, and Vianen, and he would even journey across the Merwede to Werkendam and Giesendam, to see old Sint Jan from every possible angle and vantage point and under every conceivable shade of light. Distance seemed indeed, in the case of these men, to lend enchantment to the object of their admiration, for they returned from those trips of observation more in love than ever.

"Did you boys ever look at that tower?" the *Conrector* would suddenly ask us apropos of nothing in particular, after he had been silently gazing at the structure, which could be seen from the windows of several of the classrooms. And when we replied that we had looked at it a thousand times, he would interrupt: "Ah yes, of course you have! But have you ever looked at it with the eyes of faith, with feeling? Did you ever look at it with your hearts? Look at him now! Think of it, he is nearly a thousand years old! See that ray of light there now breaking through the clouds on those gargoyles of the second gallery. Those stones are alive, I tell you! They breathe. They feel us looking at them! Isn't he a treasure, our Sint Jan? So full of worldly wisdom and kindliness, the way he stands there bending slightly forward, as if he would speak to little children at his feet. And those house roofs clustered around him! Do they not make you think of that fine saying of Jesus about a hen wanting to gather her chicks under her wings? What comfort he spreads! There is so much gentleness and warmth and strength in that old pile of stones that in looking at it my eyes sometimes fill with tears. . . ."

Once the *Conrector* launched on the subject of Sint Jan, he could, and sometimes did, go on talking for hours. You would think that he spoke of some animate creature, a dear

human friend, or that our sagging old tower was another
architectural world-wonder like the Parthenon, the Cathedral of Chartres, or the Palace on the Dam in Amsterdam.
He defended Sint Jan, he boasted about him, he talked of
his height, his width, his age, his feelings and experiences,
until it sounded like a fairy story he was telling. . . .

Kees cherished the same loving sentiments toward that
gray monument, which was built, incidentally, in the reign
of Charlemagne, who had his court at a few hours' distance
from Gorcum in the Valkhof Castle near Nijmegen. When
I once mentioned to my uncle that the *Conrector* had been
absent a few days to attend some academic congress and that
upon his return from the university city of Utrecht he told
us that he had ascended the famous Dom tower there for no
other purpose but to see our own Sint Jan twenty-five miles
away, Kees asked eagerly: "And did he see him?"

"Yes," I replied, "he did. He said he had seen Sint Jan
standing like a battered sentinel on the shores of the Merwede facing Brabant, proud and yet sad. . . ."

"Sad?" interrupted Kees with a start. "Is that what he
said, sad?"

And without a moment's delay he put on his hat and
cloak to run into the street to have a look for himself, as if
he had never seen Sint Jan before. A few minutes later he
was back nodding his head meditatively. "It is true," he
said, "it's very true. Sad is the right word! Strange that I
have never noticed it myself. Sint Jan's sadness is in fact
overwhelming. Dr. Snetlage is a man of deep insight. . . ."

Such a man was the *Conrector*. In those years when the
clouds began to gather on the international horizon—they
were as yet no larger than a man's hand, far off in the
Balkans and scarcely discernible in an out-of-the-way, almost
medieval community like Gorcum—Dr. Snetlage was one
of the few who saw and understood the signs of the times.
He said to Ary Brandt, a fellow student, and myself one
day while we were walking home that we, in our day and
generation, were about to witness the accumulation of all the
latent contradictions in society and their violent clash.

"One, two, three, or five years more and the explosion

will come," he remarked. "Then the world will be in the
throes of an upheaval that may well last a century or more.
Some big change, as fundamental as the Peoples' Migration
of the seventh century or the Thirty Years' War, is on the
way. War will become as intermittently regular a phenomenon in society as thunderstorms in summertime. What
stands before the door, historically speaking, is wars and
still more wars by imperialist rivals to eliminate one another,
with a final terrific struggle between two or three Powers
for the mastery of the earth. In half a century the map of
Europe will be unrecognizable. . . ."

We did not believe him when he spoke in that vein. He
seemed to contradict his own expressed belief that history
was entering upon an age of reason and peaceful collaboration among the peoples. Ary argued back that there were
too many people in Europe now who placed human and
international values above the temporary values of fatherland and race for such an explosion to occur.

"The imperialisms will discover," said Ary, "that the
wars they unleash will turn into revolutions and their own
undoing. In all of Europe there are teachers like yourself
who are making citizens of the younger generation, not
soldiers. How many times have you not told us yourself that
the idea of a great international brotherhood is now too
firmly anchored in millions of hearts to be uprooted at the
mere beating of the drums? Who is going to fight in those
wars you speak of? I certainly will not," said Ary. "Pieter
here won't! Who will? Where are the patriots to bring on
such catastrophes? They will be overwhelmed by the common people in every land the moment they start their
clamor."

"Patriots?" exclaimed Dr. Snetlage with a gesture of
disgust. "You are going to see them sprout from the European soil like toadstools in the forest after a good night's
rain. It will astonish you how few men will maintain the
sobriety and freedom of an unclouded mind. And how many
of them will be former pacifists!"

Patriotism of that kind was as repugnant to the Doctor
as vulgarity of any kind. He said it limited his freedom of

outlook. "I strive for a view of the world," he said, "above
the mists of local falsehoods." This did not mean at all that
he despised Holland. He loved his country with all his
heart, its people, its history, its skies, its achievements, even
its faults. But there were also institutions in Holland he
detested as intensely. Not even for the sake of Holland
could he betray his own conscience. "I want to understand
everything," he said. "Loyalty to the truth is the only
loyalty."

I do not know what our parents or the school's supervisors would have said could they have heard Dr. Snetlage
hold forth about our being first men, cosmopolitans, inter-
nationalists, Europeans, and Dutchmen afterward. Doubt-
less we were to love our country, Dutch art and science, the
great civilizing tradition from which we sprang. It lived in
us and we in it. We could not have denied the Dutch spirit,
the taste for independence and the will to keep those good
things our fathers had conquered. But above our country
we were to put humanity, the *Conrector* said. Before everything else came the universal brotherhood of those who,
starting with opposition to the iniquities of their own
government, struggle in a manner worthy of man's dignity
to bring about a truly human society.

This was the man to whose house the members of our
small class were going that dreary, wet morning. Other
groups marched off to other homes. We were six boys and
one girl. Jetze Sissingha, the son of a pastor in a village of
Brabant, a boy of Frisian descent, as his name indicates, led
the way. Jetze was affectionately known to us as the
"Admiral," because of his surpassing interest in things nau-
tical and because the captain of the small river steamer on
which he traveled back and forth to school often allowed him
to take the wheel. Jetze knew his way on water far better
than in Latin grammar. He walked with David Dalmaden.
Behind them came Ary Brandt, Alfons Boogaert, Zeger
van Rietvelt, Adriana van Alphen, our only female classmate, and myself. Dr. Snetlage accompanied us and led the
way upstairs to his study. The first half-hour of the day had
been lost before we were finally seated in two rows on

either side of a long table with the *Conrector* at the head.

While poking up the fire in the coal stove he was saying that he had been afraid the night before that the house would tumble down. "There were some squalls," he said, "that literally shook the place on its foundations. This table actually moved, and above my head here, those old rafters and beams creaked and groaned as if someone were bending them for firewood over his knee and presently would break them in pieces."

Then, seating himself at the table, he went into an elaborate discourse as to where the storm had originated, why storms struck Holland so furiously, usually in the month of November; and said that our distant forebears, the primitive Chatti and Batavi, instead of being the stupid and helpless barbarians that certain Roman historians make them out to be, were in reality brave pioneers, heroes in fact, who began the construction, two thousand years before, of those very dikes to whose protection we owed our lives that very morning.

"Yes," he said, warming up to the subject, "and they built those dikes without the engineering experience and the tools of the modern Machine Age. Tacitus and other travelers in these parts may have turned up their fine Roman noses before those ancestors of ours. True, they were uncouth and clad only in deerskins. They had no soft linen togas or gold-embroidered, perfumed tunics like the patricians in the Eternal City. They smelled of sweat and mud and fish. It is also true that they did not dwell in marble halls but in huts of loam and branches, and they did not travel in cushioned litters but paddled and splashed about on the lakes and rivers in tipsy canoes hollowed out of the trunks of birch trees. But they faced storms as fierce as and undoubtedly a great deal fiercer than the one we have just passed through. This morning we ought to feel a new respect for those pioneers. They were not slaves at all, those Celtic, Slavonic, and Teutonic tribes who came here a hundred years before Caesar in search of freedom; and their vision of two thousand years ago sustains us to this day.

"There is," he went on, "perhaps no other people on earth whose character has been so clearly formed by the ground on which they stand as the Dutch. The very soil under our feet had to be created first. Our fathers made that soil with their own hands. It was not stolen from others. And that soil in turn made us what we are: stubborn, unbending, strong. Those storms made the race fearless. Those storms were our national teachers. They formed and molded the Dutch people, for they taxed the cunning and the ingenuity of our forebears. They made them vigilant, kept them on the alert from one season to the next, from one generation to the next, and so on, we hope, *per omnia saecula saeculorum,* defiant of the absolute, the avowed, never-resting foes of the elements. . . .

"Did you ever think of it," he asked, "that those Batavi whom Caesar encountered here must have looked almost amphibian, some superior kind of beavers, the way they swam and waded and splashed about in mud and swamp and water to build their dams and dikes and to tear this good land, which was to feed them and the generations to come, from the grasp of the sea? Didn't the Duke of Alva when he came here first to reconquer the provinces for Spain pronounce the inhabitants miracle-workers and magicians for living below sea level? Dante himself celebrated the fame of the Dutch dike in the fifteenth canto of the Inferno:

"Like the Flemings between Cadzant and Bruges,
Fearing the flood which advances upon them,
Build themselves a dike to push back the sea.

"Holland came into existence as the result of a flood," the *Conrector* said. "When that occurred, I mean in what epoch of history the ocean drove a channel between the European mainland and Britain, nobody really knows. All we know is that once Holland and England were one. Some geologists say that the separation took place some four thousand years before the Christian era. That would be about the time Hammurabi was codifying the law in Babylonia and some nomad tribes with leaders known as Abraham, Joseph, and Jacob were roaming the Syrian

Desert. One black night in that era of shadows, the ocean rose to mountainous heights and forced a passage through the western tip of the European continent. The next morning you had England on the one side and Holland on the other.

"Of course, I say this merely as a manner of speaking." He smiled. "Most likely the storm did not cut that channel and form the North Sea as easily and quickly as all that. The formation of that sea may well have come about through the corroding and sapping work of the water over a long course of time; decades, or perhaps even centuries, were involved. Still, in the end the job was done. Are you sorry for it?" he asked suddenly with an amused twinkle. "If it hadn't happened some of us might well be wearing monocles, or going to the football game this afternoon and drinking tea afterward. But we would also be calling Shakespeare our national poet, something not to be thought of lightly either."

And then, as if he suddenly remembered that he was to teach Latin and not to gossip about geology and history, he continued: "Since it is more important to know what others had to say about our valiant Batavian and Nervian ancestors, I will ask you, Sissingha, to read to us the passage in Pliny where that intrepid but shivering traveler speaks of this land and of the people he saw here."

And so Sissingha read and translated: ". . . there the ocean pours twice daily an immense flood over an immeasurable stretch of land in such a way that one is led to doubt in that eternal struggle in the affairs of nature whether the soil belongs to the earth or to the sea. There lives a miserable people on hills, or rather on mounds of earth which they have thrown up with their bare hands to such heights as previous experience has taught them to be the crest of the highest flood. On top of these mounds they build their huts. They are like sailors riding on the flood, as it were, when the water covers the environs, but really look more like castaways or shipwrecked persons.

"When the water has receded they can be seen around their huts chasing the fish which seek to escape with the tide

as it flows off. They possess no cattle and hence cannot feed
on milk as their neighbors do. They never capture a wild
animal because the sea as far as the eye can reach has
washed away all verdure, vegetation, and shrubbery. They
make a sort of rope out of reeds and rushes. These they
knot into crude fish nets. Clods of earth (peat) which they
dig up with their hands, they allow to dry more in the wind
than in the sun. These clods they burn in order to cook their
food and to warm their bodies stiffened by the glacial storms
from the North. And such tribes when they are conquered
by the Romans dare to call it slavery!"

"And slavery it was!" exclaimed the *Conrector*, interrupting Sissingha's reading. "Freedom is what they sought,
and not Roman overlordship. Glory and honor to the clods
of earth and the dirty hands of the Chatti and the Batavi!"

The hour had slipped by before we were aware of it.
The *Conrector* rose while we put our books in our satchels.
Quite a little journey lay before us to the house of the next
hour's instructor, Mr. Yssel Ponthieu, who taught history.
Dr. Snetlage still talked. *"Sakkerloot!"* he called out. "Sint
Jan strikes ten. Away with you!" The next instant we clat-
tered down the stairs.

IN AND OUT OF SCHOOL

HAD Ary Brandt, who was in a certain sense the leader of
our class, not been the motherless and pampered son
of a rural burgomaster in affluent circumstances, he would
probably never have given quite so free a rein to that
rebellious independence of speech and conduct which became
the dominant trait in his character. While still in knee pants,
he had already formed the wretched habit of giving expression to the most extravagant opinions and contradicting
his elders and superiors. It may well be true, as our Rector
surmised, that this unblushing frowardness on our friend's
part derived in a large measure from the fact that in his
native commune of Altena, a village numbering perhaps a
thousand souls, he was looked upon and treated as a little
tin god whose every wish and whim must be indulged. Certain it is that very early Ary acquired an uncommonly
exalted notion of himself. He was the only boy in Altena to
wear leather shoes and the only boy to own a bicycle.

The circumstance that at the age of three he had lost
the mother who could have put a curb on his youthful brash-
ness made him the object of general commiseration and
concern. All the women in Altena doted on him. He could
do as he pleased, and like the King he could do no wrong
in the eyes of all those female sympathizers. He admitted
later that before he had learned to read and write properly
he was ordering the servants around like a slave-driver, and
that he behaved in general like a little snob. Frequently left
to his own devices by reason of his father's absence on

official business, he took advantage of the situation, perhaps unconsciously, by assuming the melodramatic pose of a tragic hero.

He felt, I have good reason to think, that his mother's death had deprived him of the greatest value in life, and he secretly counted on the world to make up for that loss by treating him with special consideration. This secret expectation of his, I have since realized, was more of a subconscious desire on his part to be loved by others. He had self-mockery enough to save him from being barrenly vain, but a little vanity he had all his life. It is true he had good reason to be proud, for he had an independent mind and a fund of courage and conviction such as I never saw combined in any other man. Despite his sense of superiority, he would never trample on the humblest mortal or be tyrannous even to the basest scoundrel. As a man he was generous and just. But of that presumptuous overconfidence of his younger years he was not broken until he became aware that people no longer tolerated his idiosyncrasies as pranks of a highspirited although somewhat raw adolescent, but instead began to take him seriously, and with that inevitably took offense at his impudent sallies.

The Dutch on the whole, I am afraid, are not endowed with too much sense of humor.

When he came to the Gymnasium in Gorcum, after attending a similar institution elsewhere, he was still a confirmed contradicter. He distinguished himself at once by starting arguments with everybody in and out of season. On his very first day at school, for instance, in the course of the German lesson he put the master beside himself with rage by suddenly asserting apropos of nothing in particular that not Goethe, but Goethe's secretary, Eckermann, was the real light of the world. Had Eckermann, who was forced to earn his bread and butter, declared Ary Brandt, not been denied the opportunity of writing by the eternally dictating and gossiping *Herr Geheimrat*, we would in all probability have to give first place in world literature to the secretary.

The German master, a certain Dr. Schulting who hailed precisely from Goethe's Weimar and to whom Goethe was his all in all, reddened to the roots of his yellow hair on hearing such opinionated blasphemy. He did not say a word, although we who had known him longer than Ary could tell by the swelling veins in his neck, and by the dueling scars on his cheek suddenly growing livid, that he was nearly choked with indignation. When the German class was over and the Doctor had retired, Ary said coolly: "I think I reduced one *Mof*[1] to speechlessness that time." He then confided to us that he had heard his Uncle Maurits make that remark about Goethe in fun. He probably imagined that the German master would take it in the same spirit. But there he was wrong.

It has pleased God in His inscrutable wisdom to endow the Germans with even less of a sense of humor than the Dutch. Schulting held that flippant remark against Ary till the end of his days.

For provocations such as this Ary could never, even had he wanted to, be called a favorite of the instructors, who were mostly men of fixed ideas and habits of life, to whom the principal business in life seemed the preservation of their own ease in Zion. They taught with a certain routinelike devotion which, with its small cares and simple satisfactions, filled out their entire existence. After a long residence in our community, they had abandoned all hope of advancement. They had become mere functionaries, and like functionaries they had nothing more to look forward to but the next vacation and ultimately the year of their retirement on pension. When that hour of their release finally struck, they rushed off to The Hague, or to Arnhem, or to some other spot of beauty or social gaiety, frequently without even bidding their friends adieu in their eagerness to escape at last from the pettiness and monotony of existence in a small provincial town dominated by Puritan divines and the stamp of Calvin.

[1] The word *Mof* is a derogatory and contemptuous reference to a German. Germany, in the same way, is sometimes called *Mofrika* by the Dutch. The word came into use during the last Napoleonic campaign, when German soldiers fighting in the armies of the Holy Alliance passed through Holland in pursuit of the retreating Emperor of the French. To shield their hands against the cold, the German soldiers carried a muff (*mof*).

To such men the daily presence of a youth as mobile as quicksilver and of as unpredictable a temperament as Ary's was visibly disturbing. His laughter ringing through the halls and corridors made them glance about furtively, half-fearful that something they had said or done was the object of his glee. They did not know what to do with a student who was extraordinarily brilliant but who at the same time often disrupted the class. One day, having found a deserted wood finch's nest in the Forest of Altena, Ary carried the eggs in his pocket and kept them there until, right in the midst of one of the most impressive passages in the *Iliad*, feeling the chicks breaking their shells, he interrupted the pompous Dr. Vossius with the remark: "Oh, let old Homer snore for a while. I have something here that's alive!" Once he seriously asked the Rector if he didn't agree that Cicero, that truly sickening advertiser of his own virtues, was a base agent provocateur and Catiline, the genuine libertarian. On yet another occasion he startled the old gentleman with a question as to whether Jesus and Pontius Pilate might not perhaps have conversed in the sign language, seeing that Latin or Greek was out of the question for a Galilean carpenter's son and Aramaic was probably a barbarian abomination to a Roman proconsul.

To this question the Rector, caught off his guard, replied that it was likely *koine*, the universal pidgin Greek of the Mediterranean basin, that the two used in the memorable story.

"But, sir," came back Ary, "this is a pure supposition on your part. There was nobody else present during that interview, not a single witness, the New Testament says so specifically. Who, do you think, faked the story so convincingly, anyway?"

"*Os durum!* What confounded cheek! Brandt, go home! Get out of my sight! Three days—no, six days!"

"Gladly, sir, gladly! Thank you very kindly!"

Then there was the ever-recurrent case of the stray dogs. When one of them followed Ary, and they all seemed to take turns in following him, he would promptly go to the Rector's room, the so-called Chamber of Horrors, knock at the door, present the wanderer, and unabashed ask asylum for it until noon or four o'clock, when he would guarantee to find a home for the stranger or else take it home to Altena to be added to the collection of mongrels with which he had endowed his father's trans-Merwedian commune.

The Rector, a great dog-lover himself, would glance at the animal with suspicion and shake his head. "Don't bother me with such things. I'm busy!"

"Come, sir, look at his eyes, please. He seems to have complete confidence in you, sir. Look, puppy, that's Doctor van Bergen, our Rector. Nice man, isn't he?"

"Hell's bells, no!" the old man would snort in exasperation. "This is a Gymnasium, not a dog pound. Chase him out!"

"It's raining, sir, and besides we'd be breaking an old Dutch tradition. We have always welcomed refugees in this country!"

"Yes, but not dogs, damn it! Will you never learn to be serious?"

"I promise, sir. Shall I tell Muller, then" (the custodian of the building) "to keep him in the coal shed? I don't think he'll bark. I got him some bones. They're right here in my satchel with the immortal Virgil, sir."

In one way or another this dialogue would be repeated at least once a month. The Rector always gave in. Secretly he liked Ary, who in relating his triumphs to us would speak of having "sensitized the old boy's conscience with canine propaganda once more."

In his final months at school Ary took an impish delight in leaving radical tracts and books lying around where they would catch the eye of the most reactionary of the masters. Waiting until one of the gentlemen stumbled upon the document, he would ply him with questions, or start an argument.

"If we should follow the tactics of the Russian nihilists here in Holland, sir, whom would you suggest as the first grand duke to be removed?"

A question like that, asked in the most innocent and natural tone of voice, was enough to produce an explosion of wrath and indignation. That was Ary's moment of glory. Always starting arguments that way or asking embarrassing questions, pulling the old gentlemen's legs and upsetting their peace of mind, so that some of them tried to avoid him as if he were a noisome pestilence.

But that was only in school. Outside everybody liked Ary Brandt. The burghers greeted him as a grown-up equal, while the fishermen loitering by the waterside eyed him with silent respect because he was one of the few to have swum the Merwede River with its treacherous currents and undertow. When he performed that perilous feat one evening after missing the six o'clock ferryboat, which usually carried him to the shores of Brabant Province where the village of Altena is located, he was just sixteen. Endowed with uncommon physical strength, he stood shoulder-high above everyone else in the school, including the boys in the top classes and the instructors. His hands were those of a clean blacksmith and he threw his head back like a soldier when he walked. Unruly dark hair, gray-blue eyes of steely glint, and a nose slightly bent at the bridge gave him a somewhat alien, Southern appearance.

He had a habit in his younger years of looking past the face of the person he was addressing as if to a larger audience beyond. This was not done out of vanity but rather out of a certain reserve in the presence of strangers, especially those of whom he disapproved. For Ary Brandt was not everybody's friend. He could very well be a fierce enemy. In time, it is true, he learned to control the more tempestuous side of his nature, although he never equivocated when it came to matters of principle. After the turbulent period of his youth, he was distinguished by a quiet urbanity and grace of manners, which are the peculiar attributes of superior men. In serious controversy, not just in banter, his face grew as pale as marble and his eyes flared up, but to those who knew him, his mouth, which remained calm and benevolent, showed even in such moments the tenderness of his heart.

When the circumstances of his youth are taken into account, it becomes a mystery that this boy, the perennial

storm center of the school and sometimes of the town,
should in the end have chosen to enter the ministry of the
Reformed Church. In his home religion was not held in
high esteem. His father, the Burgomaster of Altena, an
appointee of a former Liberal government, was known as
an inveterate scoffer at all things sacred and ecclesiastical.
In addition he was a notorious drinker as well as an avowed
patron of a club of freethinkers and Freemasons known as
"The Dawn," which then flourished in Gorcum. The particular dawn to which these gentlemen looked forward was
an era in which all superstitions, including religious dogmas,
would have disappeared. In one of their annual reports,
which I recall reading by chance, it was stated that their
chief aim was to combat the phantasmal and soul-murdering
moonshine of the fundamentalists and obscurantists—or
militant words to that effect which sounded like a declaration of war.

I knew Burgomaster Brandt from seeing him pass
through Gorcum's streets on his way to the railroad station
where he took a train going in the direction of Rotterdam
and The Hague. Habitually dressed in a black frock coat,
a soft slouch hat of the same color pulled deep over his
eyes, and carrying an umbrella, he was as stalwart and
broad-shouldered as his son, but his face was disfigured by
a large, purple-tinted nose. It was an open secret that he
kept a mistress in one of the big cities, a circumstance sufficient in itself to damn him utterly in the eyes of the Puritan
majority of our town as a hopelessly depraved person
scarcely fit to bring up children, let alone stand at the head
of the Christian community of Altena to which a materialist,
anticlerical, Liberal administration, now happily superseded
by a Calvinist government of God's own elect, had appointed him—for life, of course.

If the elder Brandt was a perpetual source of annoyance
to the fundamentalist brethren and politicians, he enjoyed,
by contrast, a wide popularity among the liberals. To them
a certain amount of freedom in morals, if it caused nobody
any harm, rather passed as a true sign and token of social
emancipation. Laissez-faire, live and let live, was their edi-

fying slogan. Besides, they probably envied and admired Burgomaster Brandt for his frank avowal of what took him so frequently out of the district.

When I knew Ary first, he carried on a regular correspondence with the famous dramatist Louis Bouwmeester in Amsterdam and it was more or less understood that he was going to be an actor himself. It goes without saying that he was to be a great actor, not just an entertainer, but an artist whose performances would purify the souls of men and urge them into new paths of righteousness. As time went on the sacred enthusiasm for the theater—the church of the future, he called it—grew unaccountably but markedly thin and in the end evaporated altogether. After that, painting was chosen as our friend's future mode of expression. But when I left Holland the brush and palette in turn had been forgotten. At that time Ary had his mind set on studying medicine, specializing in tropical diseases with the intention of eventually joining Albert Schweitzer in the heart of Africa. This change of direction came about shortly after Dr. Schweitzer's visit to Gorcum, where the renowned Biblical exegete gave an organ recital in the Great Church in the interest of his mission station at Lambaréné. Ary, then twenty years of age, had a long talk with the Doctor and was completely captivated by his gentle manners, his erudition, and his idealism.

Through all these changes—there were also times when he spoke of the bar and of entering politics—Ary was a passionate disciple of the modern Dutch poets. They were his permanent love. He recited with fine feeling from the works of such men and women as Van Eeden, Kloos, Verwey, Henriette Roland Holst, and Van Collum. It was this devotion, more than that temporary aberration in the direction of painting, which raised him in high esteem with my Uncle Kees, whose taste in letters ran along the same lines. From the day that Kees heard the young man declaim from Madame Roland Holst's "Freedom Approaches" of the migratory birds which drift by in their flocks on calm October mornings, on their way to a goal hidden behind seas and mountains, to the green coasts whither they are drawn by nature's grace even as man slowly advances along the path of life to the point where he can see freedom's white banner rise in the offing—from that moment Ary was virtually a member of the family, or rather of that strange brotherhood which formed itself around my uncle, the libertarian painter.

Kees was about the only adult in town who held the moderns in respect and who made no secret of his admiration. In this, as in other respects, he was somewhat of a heretic and a rebel. For the literary Gorcum of my youth languished under the dictatorship of the instructor of Netherland language and literature at the Gymnasium, a certain Dr. Rinske Klasus Kuypers, long since gathered to his Frisian ancestors. He was the author of a grammar and a dictionary. This man laid it down that nothing worth reading had been produced in our mother tongue since 1880, which is precisely the year in which the Dutch literary renaissance got under way. His heroes were Beets, De Genestet, Da Costa, Bosboom-Toussaint, and Bilderdijk. It was, I imagine, to show his intellectual solidarity with these people's vanished epoch that our Dr. Kuypers wore a huge hat of the kind one sees on the heads of burghers in the paintings of Rembrandt and Frans Hals. The instructor of Netherland language was also addicted to the use of snuff.

Breaking away from Dr. Kuypers' influence and the outworn traditions he championed, many of the gymnasiasts and some others used to forgather in Kees' house after school hours and there in the so-called Sistine Chapel listen to Ary, and to a young lieutenant of artillery by the name of Hubert van Vredenburg, declaim from, discuss, and grow excited over the moderns. There, amidst easels and paint, all of us smoking pipes and occasionally indulging in a glass of beer, we talked to our hearts' content, certain that no spies could hear or informers carry tales to the authorities. There in Kees' house were the books we liked, those lamps that never go out, and the stock of authors, Dutch and foreign, that could not be had or seen at the public library, of which the aforementioned Dr. Kuypers was the honorary regent and effective despot.

The Sistine Chapel, so called, was a large room in the rear of my uncle's house. After his parents' death, Kees had the place remodeled. The walls and ceilings were torn out of several rooms on the first floor and a large glass-fronted studio was built in their place. This studio reached a height of some twenty-five feet and overlooked the river. It ran upward into the space where formerly the attic had been. The room in which my grandfather first heard the German boy's call for help during the storm in the autumn of 1907 had disappeared in the reconstruction. There was a separate entrance from the street to a stairway running straight up to the studio. The front part of the house upstairs, where the library and two bedrooms were located, as well as the whole downstairs and the medieval façade, had been left unchanged.

On the white plastered walls of the studio Kees had painted a series of murals representing events and incidents in the history of mankind which he deemed to have been of fundamental significance. They were the "Decisive Hours." One panel, for instance, showed the man Moses answering the call of the Great Anonymous from the burning bush. Another showed Jesus with his arm around the shoulder of the woman caught in adultery, facing a crowd of leering, ante-Nicene Calvinists. To any Gorcummer the faces of the woman's accusers were plainly recognizable: they were those of the dominies and the members of the local Consistory. In the next panel Saint Paul stood on a soapbox beside a scarlet banner, telling the Ephesian proletarians that in Christ there is neither bond nor slave.

Facing the large window, or rather the glass side of the room with its immense view of the river and the Castle of Loevesteyn at the confluence of the Meuse and the Rhine in the distance, were two pictures, one of the aged Galileo, surrounded by monks, staring horror-struck at the Inquisition's instruments of torture, and another showing Luther tacking his theses to the door of Wittenberg's Dom Kirche. Above the fireplace, directly opposite the window, sat William of Orange, the Father of our Fatherland, the rich, brilliant Prince, alone by the feeble flame of a candle

sewing his own ragged clothes in order to save a tailor's
bill so that more troops might be raised for Holland's
liberation. Next to that painting was Sully kneeling by the
bedside of Henri IV, his head close to the King's, carrying
on that whispered conversation which changed the destiny
of France and of Protestantism in Europe. Then came
Cromwell, pimpled face and all, in the act of ordering the
mace, symbol of royal power and prerogative, removed
from the table in the House of Commons. In the next panel
Jacques Danton was shown reading the Declaration of the
Rights of Man to an assembly of unkempt, pike-bearing
sansculottes. "The Last Barricade" in the Commune of
Paris, and Tolstoi in peasant garb, bent over a rough
wooden table, writing his letter to the Orthodox Synod,
completed that strange pictorial assortment of legendary
and historical events.

The room owed its nickname of Sistine Chapel to the
fact that like the famous shrine in the Vatican Palace, which
has Michelangelo's overwhelming fresco on its ceiling, the
studio's plafond was covered with an allegorical painting
called "Glory." An angel of alluring features and shape,
dressed in a flowing white gown, was shown flying off
toward the clouds with a beckoning gesture to a mass of
warriors and soldiers in the costumes of the different ages.
The men pressed forward, swords and banners in hand, in
pursuit of the angel. Some were on horseback, some were
running, others were falling down wounded or lay on the
ground with the pallor of death on their faces. But none
attained the elusive objective. It had taken Kees a full year,
lying on his back on top of a scaffold, to put that picture on
the ceiling. He insisted that it had ruined his eyes, but he
frequently lay gazing at it from one of the couches along
the walls of the room.

In that room Ary in one of his glorious rages called the
poet Bilderdijk, who was held up as a paragon of virtue at
school, a contemptible lackey of the Orange family, a
fraudulent free spirit who dedicated his works to the reigning Prince in order to hide his own and the ruler's inanity.
But it was not Bilderdijk alone who excited Ary's indig-

nation. From the security of the Sistine Chapel that boy waged a standing warfare with a substantial section of the human race. One day he announced his intention of going off to some far-off place, the Fiji Islands, or the Andes Mountains, or some other outlandish region, to get "a new perspective of man and society."

That was in his painting days. Nature was to be his sole teacher, as if Nature began only beyond the confines of our polders. If he could see the sun rise in some colorful jungle, or watch the dying day on a snow-capped mountain, he was sure to receive the inspiration for an enduring masterpiece. He was going after the untouched, the virginal, that which no human eye had ever seen, or rather what no master had ever expressed in colors before him: nature stripped of its false symbols: what the French painters had sometimes felt as a premonition and intuitively but had never quite succeeded in putting on canvas without allowing the color of their own subconscious spectacles to spoil, denature, and falsify the final effect. . . .

"But why go so far away?" Kees asked simply. "Why talk of sunsets in Patagonia? Why not start right here? See that rain coming down in a slanting drizzle on Sint Jan's steeple. Can you think of anything more miraculous? Why don't you make the sand on the river shore live as Josef Israels does? Go out there and paint us a field of snow, wet and woolly snow, with some crows sitting on a branch of a willow tree, or the swans on the frozen pond proclaiming the world's immense loneliness."

Oh, it wasn't that at all! It was the Dutch environment that was at fault. The Dutch atmosphere was once and for all, Ary felt, most uncongenial to his spirit. What he wanted really was to escape from Holland, "from that cage of bourgeois conventionality in which a million greengrocers, penny-catchers, sacristans, and other uninspiring idiots and deliberate fools sit gaping at each other over a million plates of mush and molasses." And above all be liberated from that "cage within a cage called Gorcum," and live undisturbed somewhere, anywhere at all, but in freedom, without any devil-worshipers around. Devil-worshipers was

Ary's pet name at the time for the fundamentalists because of their belief in brimstone and hellfire.

The vision of paradise on a deserted island did not last very long. But a utopian and dreamer of fantasies Ary remained all his life. One day, several years later, after reciting for us from Willem Gorter's marvelous epic "May," he suddenly announced his intention of founding a new society the basis of which would be a philosophy that recognized neither authority nor duty and that would ask for neither morality nor sanctions. Kees nodded his head approvingly as Ary went into a long detailed description of the mode and manner of setting his new society on its feet, but I could see by the faint smile on my uncle's lips that he was thinking of the old Fiji Island landscape.

"I once had a brainstorm like that myself," said Kees as Ary sank back in his chair half out of breath with the vehemence of his animadversion. "But I actually began carrying my scheme into effect," he added. "I told my father one day that I had my fill of civilization, that I wanted no more of it. I went out into the Dalem Veld, found a peasant's abandoned toolshed, a mere hut of straw it was, and took off all my clothes. I was going to live close to nature. I had bread and cheese for several days and I drank water from a near-by brook. I had just been reading a French philosopher of the neither-God-nor-master-school and I thought this an admirable slogan for one about to enter upon a life of complete individual liberty.

"Well," he went on, "it grew bitterly cold in the night. All the straw I packed around me failed to keep me warm. The rats were attracted by the cheese in my knapsack under my head. They came in droves and battalions, walking over me and fighting each other and me. I stuck it out nevertheless, although my teeth chattered with the cold and a hundred times I was on the verge of running home, sneaking into my room, and postponing the experiment till summer. I fell asleep finally and dreamed of my mother standing in the kitchen telling me to hand her a bottle of wine for some calf's liver she was frying. I woke up just as she asked me to slice a few sour apples while she made the dough for the apple dumplings.

"I rose very much discouraged and was sitting in the doorway of my hut sunning myself when I caught sight of Peer van der Zouwen, the rural gendarme. But he had seen me first, apparently. For presently he came up to the hut, ordered me to get dressed, and in spite of all my protestations and jeremiads he marched me to the lockup in Dalem village. The lockup was then located in the old tower that stands in the graveyard. 'If you want to play the wild Indian, you had better do it in the attic in your father's house,' said Peer. The charge he lodged against me was trespassing and indecent exposure, and the fine plus the magistrate's fee came to seven guilders, thirty-seven and a half cents. The seven cents and a half were for the stamps and seals affixed to the indictment. I never heard the end of that escapade," said Kees. "In fact some people still bring it up occasionally. Only last year when I signed my name to a voters' manifesto somebody went around and wrote the words 'dirty nudist' next to my name on the placards."

But Ary was not so easily put off. "You failed," he said, "and why did you fail? Let us analyze it. The existing social order opposed you and made you capitulate. That vile cop, whom we all know and who is the most intolerable scoundrel on the face of the earth and the worst-looking dog we have around here, was the instrument society used to destroy in you the vision of a free existence the moment you began to translate it into action. You outraged society's outrageous conventions and they made you conform. You should have roused others for your plan first and then you should have insisted on your rights. There is no law in this country forbidding a man to walk without clothes."

"Perhaps not," Kees half agreed, "but it has rather gone out of fashion, and besides Peer arrested me in the first place because I was trespassing on another man's land."

"The earth is the Lord's," Ary shot back. "That is what you should have told him."

"It would have led to violence," objected Kees.

"Violence, certainly," Ary assented. "Society uses violence, too. It is built on violence. It lives by violence. Violence is the only thing it understands and respects. Your gesture could have been the beginning of an insurrectionary movement. But you failed to use violence. You were meek. You were not even a passive resister. To get anywhere at all in this world, men must use violence, the utmost violence. They must be utterly ruthless, because destruction and annihilation are the only effective introduction to the great work of mankind.

"First man must learn to revolt against authority. When that revolt ripens in his mind, when he is finally ready to translate it into action, the greatest obstacles to a better world will have been removed. Then there can be hope again for the full development of man's capacities in science, in art, in industry, and in religion, too. After smashing the old we merely need to follow our impulses and intuitions. But first break to pieces what stands in the way, since it will never voluntarily remove itself. Meekness, that cringing spirit of subjects, that abominable Christian poison, is our worst enemy. . . ."

"I see that you have been reading Bakunin again," Kees observed dryly. "I smell the dynamite."

That was true enough. But a month later Ary would be just as likely, without disclosing what had brought about the change, to propound a totally reversed theory. Force was all at once no longer an argument. It was as foolish to be indignant with a murderer as it was to be indignant with his knife. The gentle forces were going to win the day. There was, after all, some good in the Christian approach if it meant to make an attempt to conquer evil by goodness. Reason alone was omnipotent. Men ought to be persuaded to do right by an appeal to their sentiments of justice and humanity. For the heart of man was naturally good and inclined to withstand evil. The lords of capitalism were to be asked to abdicate, or at least to mitigate the more glaring iniquities of the system. This had never been done, Ary maintained, and it ought to be tried. If he had time he would some day draw up the request. He felt sure many would accede to it. Then, gradually, all restraints would be removed.

Democracy was the least bad of all systems, but it was only a stopgap, a bridge to the ideal. The ideal was a society in which parliaments, states, and laws would be abolished. Without restraints of any kind, man's creative genius would at last be able to unfold to unparalleled and unimagined possibilities. Man would begin to climb the mountain of endeavor and reach its summit and then have nothing more above him but the heavens which—science would perhaps teach us how—in turn could be assaulted. We, his auditors, were to begin with giving up membership in clubs and churches and societies, for all these were fetters and implied some negation of individual liberty. We were to set the ball rolling toward the ideal.

Ary was twenty when he passed through what I would call the anarchistic phase. That period was enlivened by the writing of much poetry. His imagination had been kindled by the works of those animated thunderstorms, Kropotkin, Reclus, La Boétie, and strange to say, the writings of Richard Wagner. Mikhail Bakunin, we were told almost every day, supported by voluminous quotations, was the warrior with "*le diable au corps*," the greatest man that ever lived. On an alternate day the greatest might well be the Apostle Paul, who was given that position of pre-eminence in Ary's pantheon for turning the Roman Empire upside down, or again Castalion would carry off the honor for having resisted the dictatorship of John Calvin. It all depended on what our friend was reading at the moment.

One of the poems Ary wrote was entitled "A Hymn to Satan." In it the Devil was called the real inspirer of human freedom because he was the eternal opponent of authority in heaven and on earth. An acquaintance of ours, one Lodewijk van Nierop, who served as an apprentice in the printshop of the local Calvinist weekly, was persuaded to set the "hymn" in type. Fifty copies were run off the press one night in great secrecy. They were given to Kees for safekeeping. My uncle promptly burned them with the exception of the copy that was found among his papers after his death and which is still in my possession.

Kees valued Ary at his right worth. "Some day," he said, "that boy will be sorry for this flight of fantasy. There is no question that he has talent. But we have not yet arrived at the point here in Holland where admiration for an adversary's talents is not accounted a weakness. Ary Brandt is one of those spirits who is bound to meet with opposition in life. This pamphlet is liable to be held up to him as a matter of reproach. Let us therefore destroy it. For unless I miss my guess the boy will become one of the pillars of society, if not of the Stock Exchange."

But in this prognosis Kees was not altogether right. When I called on the Reverend Doctor Brandt in the summer of 1925 and asked him if he still wrote poetry from time to time, he shook his head. "You know," he added with a deep sigh, "I wasted a lot of my time with that stuff. There was so much that I could and should have done."

To this I nodded, not thinking at all, as he probably did, of the old hymn to Satan, but of the sensation he caused at the final examinations when he scandalized everyone present —instructors, curators, and the visiting Inspector of Gymnasia, Dr. Finkelstyn—with a verbal outburst that was long remembered and that cost him his diploma.

It came about this way. The instructor of history, Yssel Ponthieu, asked Ary a few questions on the constitution of the Kingdom of the Netherlands and the social atmosphere in the revolutionary year 1848, when that famous document became the highest law of the realm. Ary gave the names of the distinguished jurists who drew up the clauses— Thorbecke, Donker Curtius, De Kempenaar, Luzac, and a few others—and he added quite casually: "The times were quite stormy, but no wonder; that constitution itself was a denial of the principles of democracy."

Everybody in the room looked up sharply at this remark, but Yssel Ponthieu, with a rather sheepish, embarrassed smile, asked: "How so, a denial?"

Ary replied: "In order to be a voter, a citizen had to be a taxpayer!"

"That is not so foolish," came back the history instructor. "In fact it was an eminently just provision."

"Just?" shot back Ary. "If it was just, why did the people of Amsterdam rise in revolt against the provision?"

"Ridiculous," answered Ponthieu, "quite ridiculous."

"Why ridiculous, if I may ask?" queried Ary, who seemed to forget that it was he who was being examined and not Yssel Ponthieu.

"It was ridiculous to revolt in the first place," said Yssel Ponthieu, glancing nervously at the Curators, who were bending forward to catch every word. "Ridiculous, I say, because what did they gain by it after all? They merely had their damn-fool heads bashed in by the swords of the cavalry, didn't they?"

"You call that ridiculous?" Ary called back, and I could see by the deadly pallor of his face that he was terribly excited. Before anyone could stop him, he had blurted out: "Do you know, mijnheer, what is ridiculous? I will tell you what is ridiculous: that man, in whose mind originate the most exalted ideas, who is lord of creation, whose hands fashioned the most ingenious tools, nevertheless lives in stinking holes called slums, that he rides on a horse with his head stuck in a ridiculous bear cap and hops around like a kangaroo, the most ridiculous of all animals, and then beats down with a piece of steel on the necks of his brothers who demand their human rights until the blood streams down their faces and they are trampled by the horses' hoofs. And what for? For whom? For the landlord who gives him his slums! For the priest who feeds him poison and opiates! For the big industrialists who will some day drag him off to war to defend their interests! That is what I call ridiculous! I do not know anything more ridiculous in the whole world!"

He was already near the door when he shouted these last words, with the Rector pushing him by the shoulders with one hand and with the other, frantically pulling the bell cord for Muller, the custodian, to expel him from the building.

That was Ary's exit from the Gymnasium. He lost his

diploma that year and next year obtained it only by passing
the entrance examination to the university elsewhere. . . .

Thinking back to those years when our class was still an
unbroken entity, I can well imagine that a stranger observing its members at close range and hearing their conversation on certain occasions, might well have imagined that
if other schools in Holland were at all like ours, our country
should in the not distant future be peopled with a lively if
somewhat crazy assortment of atheists, new-lighters,
theosophists, devil-worshipers, anarchists, and other eccen-
trics and originals streaked with some queer twist or other.

No prognosis could be more amiss. Those young men of
whom I speak were in what the Germans call the *Flegel-
jahre* stage. They only talked daringly. Actually they were
as harmless as spring lambs. The revolution they talked
about signified no more than clenching their fists inside their
pockets. If they sometimes indulged in bold language or
speculated on far-reaching ideas it was not that they desired
to put on airs. They were in a vague and instinctive revolt
against their humdrum environment. Without anyone's
telling them they knew that the social and spiritual air they
breathed contained a poison destructive of all creative
energy. Heroism, daring, research, and initiative had been
the prerogative of their ancestors. For them nothing
remained, it seemed, but attempts to overcome the boredom
of existence. Life seemed composed of vicious circles from
which, they felt instinctively, it was possible to escape only
by an act, or rather by a succession of acts, of an intelligently
directed will. The direction was lacking and the will was
not cultivated by the educators. On the contrary, a free
intelligence was regarded with suspicion.

The boys therefore searched for themselves, gropingly
and awkwardly. A dozen times a year they were regaled
with eloquent dissertations and discourses on the greatness
of their country, the superior qualities of its statesmen,
philosophers, scientists, and strategists. But they grew
progressively aware that all this glory belonged to the past,
that nothing to speak of had happened in Holland since the
French Revolution. Names like Erasmus, William of

Orange, Grotius, Spinoza, Descartes, Calvin, Rembrandt, and De Witt were continually dinned into their ears along with panegyrics on freedom and democracy, but that idealization of the past was one of the strongest barriers against the free winds of the spirit that were blowing through the world. The history of Holland had become static. By a natural mental reflex these young people, therefore, projected their aspirations and hopes into an imagined world where they, too, would perform deeds of valor and show heroic initiative. They dreamed on until the vicissitudes of life overwhelmed them, smothered their idealism, and lassitude overcame their spirit until most of them were satisfied in the end, as Kees predicted, to become pillars of the Church and pillars of the Stock Exchange, or missionaries of an oil-and-rubber civilization in the Pacific wearing a ribbon of orange in the lapel of their dress coats as token of their complete tameness and innocuousness.

Out of school there was no association whatever between masters and boys. When Matthys Muller, the custodian, closed the door of the institution shortly after four in the afternoon, he also locked up cordiality and friendliness for the night. From that moment relations grew frosty and distant. To see an instructor talking to one of the gymnasiasts in the streets of Gorcum was so unusual an occurrence that it was bruited about as a sensation. Outside the school most of these gentlemen stood so much on their dignity and social pre-eminence that they rendered themselves quasi-inapproachable by an ice-cold and haughty demeanor. And not only did they assume this attitude toward their students. They were aloof and detached and only condescendingly polite toward the general run of citizens. With the officers of the garrison and a few dignitaries, such as the mayor, the revenue collector, the members of the provincial parliament, and the like, they formed a caste apart from the small burghers, the shopkeepers, artisans, and lower-school teachers. With the common people, the workers, servants, policemen, the lower-salaried class, they were, with some notable exceptions, often rude and coarse.

In some individuals this attitude of snobbish superbity

attained the ludicrous. One man, a certain Dr. van Elfrinkhof, who taught mathematics, was such an insufferable snob
that he had been given the nickname of "The Camel." He
walked with his head in the air, his nostrils dilated and his
eyebrows arched in a supercilious frown, scarcely deigning
to notice the soil on which he trod and acknowledging the
socially obligatory salutations accorded him in the streets
with a haughty stare and an almost imperceptible nod of
the head. I do not know who gave him that nickname, but
it was an apt comparison with that unlovely humpbacked
animal which according to the Arabs carries its head in a
scornful and arrogant manner because it happens to know
the only attribute of Allah not mentioned in the Koran.
Van Elfrinkhof moved with the same silent litheness, and
he also knew something; he knew more of mathematics
than the average human being. But that is all he knew.

The social exclusiveness of the instructors left the boys
very much to their own devices in the matter of acquiring
an education or a sense of discrimination in art, social
science, economics, and other subjects that did not figure
in the curriculum. It would never have entered the head of
any of these gentlemen to take us for a visit to the capital
city with its renowned Rijksmuseum, or to The Hague with
its important art galleries, or simply on a visit to one of
the neighboring villages to help us learn something about
the farms and the peasants, whose customs, habits, traditions, folklore, and dialects varied nearly every mile or so.
On the other hand for a student to venture into a public
lecture hall or meetinghouse to hear an out-of-town speaker
or to attend a concert by Percy Grainger, Madame Calvé,
Hans Kindler, Gerard Hekking, or Willem Mengelberg
was an undertaking fraught with embarrassing and often
serious consequences. If you happened to be spotted in the
audience on such an evening by one of the instructors, you
never heard the last of it. It simply wasn't done. You were
supposed to attend to your studies and to nothing else.

Only one man besides Snetlage, an instructor in the
classical languages, made a valiant unofficial attempt to
bring a breath of fresh air into the school's stuffy, almost

medieval atmosphere by lifting relations between himself and the students to a more human plane. This man was Corneille Henri Ney, a doctor of letters and a bachelor. Ney, who was of French descent as his name indicates, had originally studied for the ministry of the Walloon Church, the Huguenot branch of the Dutch State Church founded by Protestant refugees from France after the revocation of the Edict of Nantes. When I asked Dr. Ney why he had abandoned theology, he replied: "I found Greek mythology more interesting than those Judeo-Christian fables that I was supposed to take as dogmas. I couldn't stomach the unctuous stuff."

Sartorially he was the most advanced individual in Gorcum. In fact, he was the only one of the instructors who did not wear the long, black, tightly buttoned frock coat which made those gentlemen, as they stood together in the morning before classes began, look like a crew of under-taker's assistants waiting to snatch the corpse from a bereaved family. Ney, by contrast, affected the most lively, fancy suits, which he had tailored in The Hague. Usually he carried a flower in his buttonhole. There was something incongruous and laugh-provoking to see him there in the midst of his black-robed colleagues; a Beau Brummell in yellow-velvet waistcoat, purple tie, and gray flannel jacket with checkered trousers to match—or unmatch. The others looked at him with suspicious and disapproving glances out of the corner of their eyes and carefully avoided being seen walking in the streets in his company.

Dr. Ney's features were rather swarthy. Black hairs grew from his nose and ears in bushy bristles and he wore a mustache in the upturned style made famous by the late German Emperor. It was chiefly because of his fierce mustache, I presume, that a preceding generation of boys had dubbed him "Il Capo Banditto" because of his resemblance to one Musolino, the leader of the Calabrian Mafia whose picture appeared on the front page of a series of penny-dreadfuls which were very popular in Holland around that time. We of a younger generation simply called him "The Bandit" for short—but not to his face.

There was a mystery about the lady who occupied Dr. Ney's house with him. He said she was his niece, but sometimes he forgot himself and referred to her as his sister. Whatever the truth of the matter, she was a woman of extraordinary beauty and elegance, a French type with lustrous blue eyes and voluminous jet-black hair that she wore in a large knot that came down to her shoulders. Usually she wore dresses of black satin of a cut seldom seen in our little provincial town. The gowns accentuated the curves of her body and what the French call *la gorge*, just enough to arrest the eye and to make one swallow. She walked slowly and with dignity, always wore a bluish veil, and was the first to introduce the vogue of the picture hat, a daring innovation at the beginning of this century in a community where many of the rules and regulations of the Geneva of the sixteenth century were still in force. Beneath a black-velvet ribbon around her throat one saw a small square of olive-colored yet brilliant skin, and her feet were the smallest, most elfin things ever. Altogether a woman of voluptuous perfection, she was commonly referred to as Mademoiselle Ney.

After the Doctor's death she claimed his estate, as was just, but in the notarial act of succession, published in the local newspapers, the transfer of goods and funds was made in the name, behalf, and interest of Madame Jacqueline Anquetil, a circumstance that caused no little astonishment. When she inherited Dr. Ney's property, she wisely left the town and thus escaped annoyance and insult in the form of whispering and cutting remarks in the streets, a vicious habit in which many Gorcummers, both male and female, were past masters.

When teaching, Dr. Ney was in the habit of raising his bushy eyebrows to such a height as I have never seen it done by any other human being since. When he shook his head, which he did when someone made an error in translation, he actually wiggled his ears. This comical effect, we told him, would have been greater had he become a pulpiteer and practiced the gesture before a congregation. To such remarks he listened good-naturedly, repeating the performance as often as we asked for it. When he sat behind his desk facing us and looked over our compositions and he approved of what he read in the copybooks, he rolled his eyes to heaven and emitted a peculiar clicking sound with his tongue that was a personal and positively inimitable triumph of lingual dexterity. Thus amusement and earnestness alternated in Dr. Ney's classes as they did when Erasmus taught Greek to boys of our age at Cambridge.

It was Dr. Ney who put the idea in Ary Brandt's head of starting a debating club or perhaps an amateur theatrical society, promising to support the venture no matter what the old Rector or the Curators, some of them local pastors to whom the theater and all its works were anathema, would say about it. "You must simply be bold," said Ney, "and inform them that the society has been constituted and then invite them to come and hear you debate or see your performances as often as they like. But let there be no secrecy about the matter. In that case suspicions will be aroused and a decree of veto becomes unavoidable."

It fell to Jetze Sissingha and myself to inform the Rector of the project and to ask him for the use of one of the classrooms on Wednesday afternoons. He received us kindly enough, but on learning that we intended to stage plays by Hauptmann, Strindberg, Ibsen, and others, instead of confining ourselves to poetry recitals from the works of Bilderdijk and other national worthies, his face assumed an appalled look, as if he were staring the revolution straight in the eyes. At my mention of the name of Ibsen he exploded, *"Sit pudor!"* (Have some decency!) *"Ille piscator sordium!"* (That man is a fisher of dirty things!) *"Sit pudor! Sit pudor!"*

When I tremblingly ventured to remonstrate, he rose from his chair and stamped around the room, unable to find words to express his indignation. Then he suddenly shouted, but not in Latin this time, that we had better attend to our studies and to be gone out of his sight.

In spite of this unfavorable omen, the debating club and the theatrical society were duly launched, but neither lasted very long. The Curators or supervisors of the school, upon learning of the formation of the club, immediately stipulated that discussions of subjects relating to politics, religion, national history, or economics would not be tolerated, that on all other topics an attitude of the strictest objectivity was to be observed by the speakers, and finally that an accurate transcript of the proceedings was to be placed in the hands of the secretary of their body, a certain Reverend Dr. Blinkenberg, the Lutheran pastor. On these conditions we were allowed the use of one of the classrooms.

For a few months we carried on valiantly enough, confining ourselves to such burning questions of the day as: whether gas or electricity was the better for street lighting; whether Dutch or the German language was the older of the two; who was the greatest statesman of the hour, Wilhelm II or Edward VII, and other inanities of that sort. Not more than a dozen boys appeared, and in the end we transferred our deliberations on Wednesday afternoons to Uncle Kees' Sistine Chapel, where we could argue on whatever subject we pleased with reckless bias without paying the slightest heed to fools who imagined that everything on earth must be approached with impartiality.

The theatrical society was kept alive somewhat longer. But it went down, too, albeit more gloriously. It went out with a roar of battle in the streets and bulwarks of Gorcum under a physical attack led by a boy of whom Holland and the world were to hear more in the course of time—Anton Adriaan Mussert, future leader of the Dutch Nazi Bund who stabbed Holland in the back in 1940 when the army of "our German brothers" appeared at the gates.

I do not recollect ever having seen Mussert's father, nor do I know what trade or profession the man was engaged in. The late Hendrik Willem van Loon, who hailed from the northern end of our polder, wrote once that Mussert Senior was engaged in the river-dredging business. I have also heard it said that he was a miller. Whatever the case, judging by the kind of clothes the son wore and the superior brand of bicycle he rode, the father must have been reasonably well-to-do. The family lived in Werkendam, a large village on the opposite bank of the Merwede River about three miles downstream in the direction of the famous old city of Dordt. From Werkendam came a score of boys and girls on their bicycles as far as the village of Sleeuwijk, which lay directly opposite Gorcum, and thence by steamboat ferry across the river to attend our town's various educational institutions, such as the Normal School, the High School, the Lyceum, and the Gymnasium. There were sixteen schools in all and the population was twelve thousand.

Young Mussert was a pupil of the High School. He had reddish hair, a freckled face, and was rather stockily built. On photographs taken of him in later life, which show him in the role of Führer of the Storm Troopers strutting the goose step before Hitler and Seyss-Inquart, his bodily length and slenderness astonished me. That was not the squat and dumpy Mussert I had known. It may be, of course, that he suddenly shot up after reaching maturity. This happens sometimes. It may also be that he added a few inches to his stature by wearing boots specially built to give him a more commanding appearance. Another Duce wore that kind of shoes when he hung like a slaughtered pig in the Piazza Loretto of Milan.

"Toon" Mussert ate his noonday meal at the house of an uncle of his who kept a wine and liquor shop on one of the busiest thoroughfares of our town. This uncle, Veenman by name, a former instructor of physical culture in the army, had been discharged for reasons of health. I think he had tuberculosis. I recall him well as one of the most dashing and popular noncommissioned officers attached to the permanent staff of instructors of the garrison. He was one of those who drilled and limbered up the conscripts when they came raw and awkward from the rural regions in the autumn and before they were taught the manipulation of firearms. I passed the drill grounds two or three times every day on my way to and from school and often saw Sergeant Major Veenman putting a batch of recruits through their exercises. He was an excellent instructor. But he was also somewhat of a bon vivant. This I also know from firsthand observations.

The noncommissioned officers had clubrooms in the rear of the King William barracks. Over the top of the trees of a few intervening gardens, I could look straight into these rooms from the window of the cubicle on the third floor of our house where I did my home work in the evening. I frequently borrowed Uncle Kees' telescope, ostensibly to observe the stars in their courses, but in reality to have a better look into the noncommissioned officers' messhall, especially on nights when these gentlemen held a dance or staged some other jollification. On such occasions I learned, among other things, that Sergeant Major Veenman was a formidable trencherman and also that it was he who brought the prettiest girls in town to the military celebrations. Of course I should not have looked, and had my mother suspected that I could be tempted to spy on the doings of people who, as she thought, lived "without God or His commandments," I doubt not that she would have moved me to some other part of the house. To avoid that, I never breathed a word about the nocturnal spectacle before my window.

Ary Brandt sometimes came up on some excuse or other and we took turns with the telescope in identifying persons in the dance hall and watching their antics. We kept count of the schooners of beer the waiters carried over to the tables of different defenders of the realm, and particularly admired the gallant way in which Sergeant Major Veenman escorted his lady to the floor each time he drained a stein. This girl, a lithe, feline creature with golden hair and a taste for good clothes, was well known to us, by sight at least. She was nineteen or twenty at the time, that is to say, fully twenty years younger than the Sergeant Major. She is of some importance in the history of Holland, since but for her, Sergeant Major Veenman's nephew, Anton, would not have gone to the Polytechnic University of Delft, would never have become an engineer in the government department of rivers and canals, and never Führer of the Dutch Nazis. For the Sergeant Major married this girl and then died a year or so after his wedding, and the nephew succeeded his uncle in the lady's affections.

Ary Brandt knew Anton Mussert from crossing on the

same ferry with him when homeward-bound after school. Sometimes we accompanied our friends to the boat and lingered in the small park outside the Water Poort chatting and watching the strollers, among whom were our sweethearts. In that park Ary met the girl who became his wife, and I too sometimes spoke to the one who has been my companion all the days of our years.

Although a deep social and intellectual cleavage separated gymnasiasts and high-schoolers, Toon Mussert and his comrades sometimes joined us in the park while waiting for the six o'clock paddle steamer to come in. I distinctly remember the first time I came face to face with him. He sauntered up pushing his bicycle with his hands and, addressing himself to Ary, remarked: "Say, Brandt, you'll never guess what I saw today." And although Ary looked at him coldly without saying a word in reply, Mussert went on as if he did not notice the scarcely concealed hostility of our entire group.

He got himself into trouble with one of our fellows named Frederik Goethals when he started to tell a nasty story. "Do you know Marie van der Zalm?" he asked.

"The only Van der Zalm I know," replied Goethals, "is the crippled old man who runs an oil-cake booth at the cattle market on Mondays."

"Yes, that's her father," assented Mussert. "Did you ever notice a young girl with him, seventeen or eighteen? That's Marie. Good-looking, isn't she? How do you like her?"

"I thought she was a maid of Dr. Mendoza's," replied Goethals. "I'm sure I recognized her the other day when I had the Doctor look at my eyes. I'm sure it was that girl who opened the door. . . ."

"What of it?" Mussert shrugged his shoulders. "Maid or princess, they're all the same when they take their clothes off."

"You saw another naked woman, did you?" asked Goethals.

"Yes, that's what I started to tell you," went on Mussert. "Marie charges one florin, but for another quarter she strips off everything."

"How do you know?" Goethals asked.

"How do I know? Why, man, I just came from there, I've been to see her more often than I've crossed on that ferry."

"In your imagination, no doubt, lying in bed," interjected Jetze Sissingha.

Mussert threw Jetze a glance of hatred. "If you don't believe me, ask Zeger van Rietvelt," he said, referring to another of our schoolfellows. "There goes Zeger now. I saw him come out of the alley where the Van der Zalms live."

"Old man Van der Zalm is a respectable man," said Goethals. "What are you trying to concoct? He's a cripple, but he's a good man. I know him."

"A respectable man, is he?" snickered Toon Mussert. "I tell you what he does. He watches outside the door while his daughter amuses herself and earns some money."

"Earns money from you, huh?" asked Goethals again with an incredulous sneer.

"From me and from others," said Mussert. "She sees everybody who comes. It's easy to get into her house. But you have to go by the rear, mind you, along the ramparts. She doesn't want the neighbors to know."

"She doesn't, eh? But you're telling everybody about it like an impresario. What's your game?"

"Well, I just wanted to let you fellows know in case you want to give her a try. That's all. Believe me, she's worth the trouble."

"You're pimping for her, are you?" asked Goethals in a rigid tone of voice.

"Take that back, Goethals," said Mussert, "or you will be sorry!"

"I take nothing back," said Frederik. "You're a liar and a souteneur. No, you're not even a real procurer. You only have a pimp's ambition, that's all. I call you a sneak, and a dirty bastard—what are you going to do about it? If you want a fight, put your bicycle down, I'm ready. . . ."

But Mussert would not fight. "I can wait, Goethals," he hissed, twisting his face in a crooked smile. "I'll wait, but I'll get you."

And "get" Goethals he did. He crippled him for life a few months later. Ary Brandt he killed outright. But that was in 1943, when Mussert's chief job was to denounce Dutch citizens to the Gestapo.

As the first act of their revenge Mussert and his gang mobbed our annual theatrical performance, held in a hall in the rear of a popular tavern known as Gambrinus. Having yielded to my mother's insistence, I did not have a part in the production of the play, which was Rostand's *Cyrano de Bergerac* in the Dutch translation by Henri Borel. From the moment I entered the hall to sit in the audience I had a distinct feeling that something was amiss. Since we made no charge for admission, the auditorium was filled long before the appointed hour with a heterogeneous crowd of young workers, shop apprentices, soldiers and their girls, and a sprinkling of adults, the latter mostly parents or relatives and friends of the actors and of the members of the club which sponsored the performance.

In four or five places in the hall, significantly seated in compact blocks, were boys from the top classes of the High School. It was a noisy and tumultuous crowd from the beginning. They stamped their feet, upset chairs and benches, and sent up catcalls to the stage even before the curtain rose. When the small orchestra we had engaged to liven up the occasion struck up the old students' song *"Gaudeamus igitur,"* half the audience broke into a vulgar ditty, completely drowning out the music. Then the curtain rose, but no sooner had our Roxana and Cyrano uttered their first words than pandemonium broke loose. The actors received such a bombardment of carrots, cabbages, and miscellaneous refuse from the day's vegetable market that they were forced to duck back into the wings.

Jetze Sissingha, who acted as impresario and general manager, stepped before the footlights and asked for order. His appeal was the signal for a second volley, but this time a shower of rotten eggs and paper bags stuffed with flour

burst upon the stage. He motioned to the stagehand in the
wings to turn on the lights. As the tumult continued and
Jetze called again for silence, a huge turnip struck him
squarely in the face. That was too much for our hot-
tempered Frisian friend. With a leap he cleared the prompt-
er's box, bounded off the stage into the auditorium, and
made straight for the person who had thrown the missile.
He knocked the youth over a couple of chairs and then
pummeled him with his fists. That youth was Toon Mussert.
Toon screamed blue murder, and in a flash the entire hall
was turned into a battlefield. Someone must have run out
for the police, for presently a gendarme made his appearance. When the man called loudly for order, the gangsters,
by preconcerted signal, began to sing the national anthem.
They sang one stanza after the other (there are nineteen
in all, I think), and the audience slowly dispersed.

Then followed a period during which individual gymnasiasts were the victims of molestation and attack by members of the gang at whose head Toon Mussert roamed about
in the town and the environs. What these youths lacked in
courage was easily made up by the vast superiority of numbers. They seemed to be able to muster a mob at a moment's
notice when it came to pouncing on one of our fellows riding quietly home on his bicycle to one of the outlying communes or when he happened to pass through a little-frequented street. One day it was Jetze Sissingha, who was
forced to dismount from his bicycle by a sapling thrown
across the road, whereupon a dozen boys, with Mussert in
command, came out of their ambush, tore his schoolbooks to
shreds and punctured the tires of his wheels. Another time
Alfons Boogaert, the gentlest of our classmates, who had no
part at all in the quarrel, was set upon and had a bottle of ink
poured over his head and clothes. A Jewish student, David
Dalmaden, could scarcely leave his house in the evening
without being trailed by the gang and subjected to all sorts
of indignities.

The epidemic of hooliganism reached its climax one afternoon in the park outside the Water Poort when a group of
us standing around chatting with our girl friends were sud-

dcnly treated to a hail of stones coming from the direction
of the earthen ramparts near by. First we simply moved out
of range, but when the shower continued and some of us
were hit, we decided to make an end of the nuisance once
and for all.

We raced up the sloping walls of the bastion right in the
face of the hail of stones. Our attackers broke and fled.
With some we came to grips, and after giving them a thrashing dumped them into those huge stone pots along the
river's edge in which fishermen dye their nets. Toon Mussert
escaped us. He had disappeared while we were busy ducking
two of the captured assailants in the saffron-colored liquid.
We were soon again attacked by reinforcements Mussert had
drummed up in the interval. As we turned to repel the fresh
assault, Frederik Goethals was seen to fall. Nobody paid
any attention to him until we returned victoriously from a
futile pursuit of the gang.

When we came back to the spot where Goethals was
lying, he was found to be unconscious. A thin flow of blood
trickled from his forehead. It was not until our friend was
carried home and a physician had been called that we learned
that he had been shot with a 22-caliber bullet. The police
investigation which followed brought to light that Mussert
during the lull in the fighting had fetched a small rifle and
some cartridges. The actual firing had been done by another
boy to whom Mussert had loaned the rifle. This boy pretended that he had fired the shot merely to frighten us off.
He was nevertheless sent to a reformatory. Mussert escaped punishment then as he again escaped punishment in
1938 when after having shot down a man in cold blood in
Amsterdam's Jewish quarter, the Dutch Government took
the strange view that "a man of Mussert's political importance was entitled to carry a revolver"—and use it! Frederik
Goethals, after hovering between life and death for weeks,
recovered sufficiently in the course of time to be able to
walk after a fashion. But he was completely paralyzed on the
left side, as the bullet could not be extracted from his head.

After that incident, which effectively sobered everybody

concerned, we did not renew these childish and somewhat presumptuous but well-intentioned attempts to raise the cultural level of the Gorcum population. The proletariat began to stir itself and at long last mustered up enough courage to form a branch of the socialist movement in Gorcum. We followed with eager interest the lectures and courses by Marxist teachers and propagandists, who now began to visit our town regularly. These men attracted the workers where all the churches had failed, because they spoke their language and dealt with subjects that were of immediate concern to them: jobs and wages and economic relationships, the inevitability of slums and of war, constantly more murderous and inhuman in character in a society based on that unbridled and unscrupulous scramble for markets and profits known as private enterprise. Except for Ary Brandt, who went over bag and baggage, we did not join the new movement, although most of us had reached or passed the age of eighteen, which was the only requisite for membership. We remained loyal to my Uncle Kees, who was instrumental in bringing to our town such men and women as Bartholemew de Ligt, Enka, Hugenholtz, Clara Wichman, De Jong, and others who called themselves Religious Socialists.

The years drifted by almost imperceptibly. Summer vacations came and went, leaving memories of visits to relatives in Frisia and Flanders. Sometimes I accompanied Kees on his sketching and painting trips. Endless walks they were along the shores of rivers, canals, and the North Sea, through ripening wheat fields under torrid skies, not blue in color but mauve suffused with an almost violet glow against the contrasting green of the countryside. It was the pagan month of August when Great Pan ventured as far as our boreal regions, and his flute could be heard with "the lily-soft voice" of the cicadas and in the song of birds.

Drizzle in the evening or chilling clouds of mist at dawn were signals that the short feast of summer was nearing its end and that the homeward journey lay not far ahead. Fires were lit on the hearths to draw the moisture from the rooms in the rural inns where Kees and I lodged. In the night I lay listening to the gurgling of the gutters and to the rain playing its nostalgic music upon the windows and roofs of those still houses. Or Kees would be in one of his talkative moods and discourse half the night on every conceivable subject under the sun. But then would come the day at last when you found yourself suddenly, unaccountably almost, back in Gorcum, walking through the familiar streets, meeting familiar faces and sights, with strange regrets tugging at your heartstrings over the fleeting passage of summer. The yellow leaves, falling about your feet in the parks, seemed so many letters written by death itself.

There was the old cat of the baker's sitting on the threshold and the hunchbacked child of another neighbor painfully limping after a hoop; Tony the town idiot shuffling by, mumbling his incoherent monologue; and down the street in the distance the bell-ringer going to his work, recognized even from far off by his shabby cloak, green with age. Then, out over the road that led over the bulwarks and fortifications, to hear the sentries in front of the powder magazines call from a distance their perfunctory warnings against smoking and to see the moisture-dripping black tarpaulins over the breechlocks of the big guns that pointed their muzzles menacingly at the inoffensive villages across the river. And then back into the town again through the back streets where, in their cages hanging before the façades of the fishermen's cottages, sat the feathered prisoners, the pigeons, cuckoos, magpies, and finches, the friends of the poor, unable to sing the Lord's song in a strange land, blinking disconsolately at the raindrops and at the passers-by —all the humble witnesses of our days, steeped in life's sad monotony and resigned sottishness. In the gloom of the narrow alleys where most of our people lived you felt as if you would like to take them all in your arms and rock and hush and heal them.

And in the distance, ever present, more felt than heard, the subdued, sustained murmuring tremor of the river running past the town, moaning and sighing its thousand-year-old lament of the world's pain. . . .

The annual levy for the artillery regiment came into town during the latter part of September. Not till they had been confined to barracks for a couple of weeks and put through a strenuous course of limbering-up exercises were the recruits judged fit and presentable enough to be let loose in the streets. Many of them, who hailed from the rural regions, wore leather shoes for the first time in their lives when they entered the army. I remember several whose dialect was difficult to understand. They gaped and marveled at the inconsiderable buildings, shops, and monuments of our town as if they beheld the architectural and cultural wonders of a metropolis. Others, more sophisticated and nimble-witted, sons of Holland's greater cities, could scarcely conceal their disdain for Gorcum's pettiness and backwardness. To them we were the yokels. Very often the first venture of the new soldiers outside the drill grounds and the barrack square was into the studios of the local photographers. There, in their brand-new uniforms with brass buttons, short saber in hand and shako resting on a small table, they struck that stiff martial pose "for God, Queen, and Fatherland" which may be seen in a thousand reproductions, with that identical inscription on the frames, above the mantelpieces of farmhouses and dwellings throughout the realm.

Some years there were acquaintances among the lads. Other boys brought letters from their pastors asking my father to guard the innocents against the temptations of "big-city life." These were virtually adopted in our home, where they spent the evenings and the Sundays when free of military duty. The recruits were, on the whole, grave and self-respecting lads imbued with the conservative, lawabiding Dutch spirit. Several, I recall, insisted on keeping their headgear near at hand when sitting down to table. Not that they, like the Jews, put on their hats while praying. When saying grace before and after meals they merely conformed to an old custom that required a man to hide his face in or behind his hat when addressing the Almighty. The only other place in the world where I have seen this done was among the Huguenot peasants in the Cévennes.

The presence in our midst of a garrison of two thousand men, including the permanent staff of officers and noncommissioned officers, little affected the even tenor of our ways. Only when the reservists came back under arms for ten days' supplementary training was the communal life really upset. Then the fat was in the fire and sizzling aplenty. Their arrival doubled and trebled the strength of the military force. The streets were crowded with hilarious *landweer-* and *landstorm-* men who had often grown too stout or too lean for their uniforms. The landstormers were over forty and some had grown impressive prophetic beards. The notion of discipline entertained by these veterans was not of the best. Their behavior was not unlike that of the Canadian and Australian troops after the Armistice of 1918 in the towns and villages of France, Flanders, and England, of which I need say no more.

Our men marched off in the morning to the ramparts and the outlying forts, but returned to town in the evening. After supper all the saloons, bars, taprooms, taverns, dance halls, and other establishments of that stripe did a roaring business. It was said that the goings-on at night were a disgrace to civilization and especially disastrous to the morals of females. To the truth of this allegation I can testify from personal observation, having seen dozens of couples climb the three hundred winding stone steps in the tubelike shaft inside Sint Jan's tower to the first gallery and the spacious clock room, where the bell-ringer by the light of a hurricane lamp supervised accommodation and charged ten cents admission. Of course, these amorous expeditions into the upper regions were unknown to and remained unsuspected by elders, dominies, city fathers, and such moral supervisors. At least I can hardly believe that they shut their eyes or even winked at the scandal. Most local mothers followed the sage advice of Saint Jerome, who wrote that on occasions of public rejoicing or of a troop of soldiers being quartered in a town no virgin should be allowed to wander a hand's breadth from the parental doorway.

The upheaval in the community produced by the defenders of the realm came to an end after ten days and ten nights when the military band and the recruits marched their older comrades in arms to the railway station. There, before entraining for home, the veterans were addressed by the colonel commanding the regiment, who in a little speech under the flag thanked them for their services, for their exemplary behavior, and for their loyalty to the House of Orange. The whistle blew, the band struck up *"Liebchen adee, scheiden tut weh,"* "Farewell lover, parting is sad," and the country was safe again for a year.

Thanksgiving passed and the light withdrew still further. Everything grew dim. The fronts of the houses turned gray and the streets went black. The lamps were lit in school at three o'clock in the afternoon, and the spirits of men darkened as the year wore on. It was often as if courage and good cheer had left us with the summer's light. The gloom deepened until one morning the hoarfrost glistened on the paving stones and the air was crisp and sharp and the old men said: There is snow on the way.

Solemn hour! What a thrill ran through the class at the sight of the first flakes fluttering past the window. Then your mood changed with the color of the sky, which went from that of ashes to a ruddy, lurid, sulphurous ocher. You turned your head from the work on hand to the millions of white tufts and wisps of wool swirling down in incalculable legions. When you looked again, it seemed as if the snow had taken advantage of your momentary inattention to install herself as a universal queen and had transformed the world: the roofs were other roofs, the ironwork fence was another fence, the trees were other trees; leaden-gray Sint Jan was unrecognizable in a coat of ermine with hat and collar and pockets of silver.

Then the books on the desk were forgotten, and all that was in them. Your thoughts floated out through the windowpanes into a white dreamland. The instructor standing by the window, forgetting the Homer he was teaching, would mutter that there must be three or four inches by now, his own voice rousing him from his reveries. At last came the long-awaited invitation to approach the windows. "See how the telegraph wires are bent in long arches, as for a prince's triumphal entry! Will they break? Look, the belfry of the Catholic chapel looks like a woman with a fur cap pulled over her ears!"

Now the noises in the streets grew muffled and distant. The bugles of the soldiers returning to the barracks from the fortifications sounded as if they had silencers forced down their raucous copper throats. Carts and carriages rolled by no longer shaking the walls or making the glass tinkle in the lamps, but hushed, lightly, inaudibly, as if bales of cotton had been spread out for them to glide and slide over. There was no more echo or reverberation anywhere. Over the town brooded a singing silence in which only the carillon tinkled sweetly like a music box. But sparrows fluttered on the window sills, chirping in alarm that their granary had suddenly been lost to sight.

When you stepped outside, it was almost an intoxication to feel on your cheeks the furtive, delicate sting of a thousand small white bees. You couldn't get enough of the sight of the old town in its new garb. For hours my brothers and I stood at the window at home gazing at the deserted street and the shops covered with a strangely mobile cloak that gleamed and scintillated and actually seemed to move in the light of the lone gas lamp on the corner, itself powdered with a myriad of tiny crystals.

The snow did not stay long, not that first snow. With the showers and drizzle that followed the former melancholy returned. Until spring the sun's rays were feeble and wan on the rare occasions that they succeeded in breaking through the low clouds. On winter days life slipped back coldly into the shadows after two or three o'clock in the afternoon. The old women sat by the chimney spinning wool or knitting socks and shirts, but the stoves gave out no more warmth than a hot stone. Hunger drove crows and even sea gulls into the town. They flew in wide circles over the Linge, a small river that cuts Gorcum into two equal parts, or they sat forlornly on the naked branches of the elms in the church square.

In the evening men frequently gathered in the stables that stood in two long rows on either side of a canal not far from our home. For most dairy farmers brought their cattle into town during the winter months. No stables or permanent buildings of any description existed within a circumference of several miles outside the city. Gorcum was a fortress, and no obstruction whatever was permitted to stand between a hypothetical enemy and the two or three hundred old breech-loading cannon that dotted the earthen redoubts and bastions, which circle the town in a triple ring broken only by the five gates.

Truck farmers and dairy farmers, therefore, whose holdings lay in the vicinity of Gorcum lived inside the gates and stabled their beasts there. This circumstance, dictated by stern though somewhat antiquated military considerations, was a boon to many townsmen who sought the comforting warmth of the stables in the evening. Those stables were the clubs of the humble, who went there to play cards, or more often, to talk politics and religion by the light of a lantern placed on the lid of a feedbin or, for greater security amid all that hay and straw, hung from one of the time-blackened beams overhead.

The local symphony orchestra, the Clarion, officially known as the Society of the Free Blowers of the Town of Gorcum, for years held its rehearsals in a cow stable owned by a farmer named Paul Smit, five of whose sons were members of the band. Smit Senior, who was not a musician, acted as treasurer and carried the gold-fringed, medal-bedecked green-velvet banner of the society in festive processions like those on the occasion of the Sovereign's birthday. Many times my schoolfellows and I visited there on so-called repetition night. While the frost stabbed with needlelike sharpness outside and the driven snow could be heard swishing against the windowpanes, the snug warmth of the animals made the stable a pleasant retreat. The "Free Blowers" sat on benches made of planks laid over supporting milk vats in three or four semicircles on the threshing floor between two rows of stalls. The cows and horses, their heads protruding over the red-brick troughs, watched with no less fascination than we the movements of the conductor, a certain Bertus Evertsen, a cake-baker by trade. This man's extraordinary agility and passion in the manipulation of the conductor's baton had earned him the nickname of "Beethoven Bis." He accepted the title as something wholly self-evident and deserved, as an ambassador accepts a decoration.

In order to live up to his exalted reputation, he affected an old-fashioned frock coat of the kind Beethoven is shown wearing in the painting depicting him strolling in Schönbrunn park with Goethe. Like the immortal composer, our Beethoven Bis walked through the streets with his hands hidden under the tails of his frock coat, his thought-burdened head lowered and his face pressed into deep frowns as if he were in constant creative meditation. He went bareheaded, his long leonine hair waving in the wind. Thus he succeeded in resembling the pictures of the creator of the *Eroica*. Our Mijnheer Evertsen was also an Elder in the church, but a rather indifferent attendant at services. For this he excused himself by saying that he was unable to bear the preludes and fugues of the organist, one Frans Pommard, who as a critic writing under the pseudonym of "Orpheus" fully returned the compliment by mercilessly deriding the Clarion's summer concerts.

The rehearsals in Paul Smit's cow stable invariably ended with Mrs. Smit and her six daughters serving coffee and cake. Both the "Free Blowers" and the audience shared in these delicacies, all having earned an equal reward. After refreshments the musicians resumed their seats and gave as a finale a musical poem of Beethoven Bis' own composition. Its title was "Doomsday." The last strophes of this chef-d'œuvre were in the form of a rollicking march symbolizing the gathering of the nations of the earth on Resurrection morning.

It was an ingenious and highly imaginative piece of work. You could plainly distinguish the approach of each nation into the awful presence by the playing of a few bars of their national anthems. The French blew the "Marseillaise," the Germans *"Die Wacht am Rhein,"* the British "God Save the King," and so on. They all answered the summons except the Belgians, who had been omitted by the composer for patriotic reasons, inasmuch as the words of their national anthem contain an insult to the reigning House of Orange.[1] In the end the hymns of all the nations were drowned out in one terrific blast of strings and brass, accompanied by the roar and rattle of drums, cymbals, bells, timpani, and bombardons. It was the "Wilhelmus," our own national hymn. Its

[1] *"La mitraille a écrasé l'Orange de l'arbre de la liberté."*—"Our guns have shot away the Orange from the tree of liberty!"

majestic strophes, in that thundering finale, were supposed to drive the Devil to flight, as well it might, and usher in the era of perpetual peace.

His composition, Beethoven Bis said, was an apocalyptic overture. But it came off without a hitch. The audience joined in singing the chorus, while the horses, alarmed no doubt by Evertsen's paroxysms and his fantastic windmill gestures, stamped nervously on the wooden floor, the cows rose in amazement from chewing their cuds and stared at the conductor with wide-open eyes, while the pigs, farther back in the stable, squealed in what might have been peals of pure aesthetic pleasure. It was indeed a fine piece, and it could easily be performed by anyone having a set of old pots and pans at hand.

The feast of Saint Nicholas on December 6, with its brightly decorated shops and the children's processions through the streets, provided a brief respite from the monotony of the long winter months. But Christmas Day did not. With us the commemoration of the Saviour's birth was by no means a joyous celebration, or the occasion for mirth, conviviality, good cheer, and pleasant social gatherings, as it is in all other countries of Christendom, and in latter years, I understand, in many places in Holland too. In my youth we clung to the old Calvinist interpretation of Christmas as handed down, I presume, from that gloomiest of men, John Calvin himself. Christmas was a purely ecclesiastical function, a solemn observance of the most awesome mystery of the ages: the Incarnation of God Himself.

Others may look upon the birth in Bethlehem as a turning-point in human history, as the dawn of a new era of grace and freedom, and thus make it the occasion of rejoicing. Not so our spiritual leaders. There are some out-of-the-way places in the highlands of Scotland and in the Cévennes in France, among kirkmen and Huguenots of the old stamp, where the same mournful and funereal atmosphere prevails around

Christmas. But I think we were unique in this respect,
that even the singing of carols was considered tanta-
mount to blasphemy, that festive candles and gaily
decorated fir trees were deemed pagan abominations,
while light talk or a specially elaborate meal on that
day was a snare of Satan.

I do not recall the year—it may have been 1911,
but it may also have been a year earlier or a year later
—when an incident occurred that makes the memory
of an old-fashioned Calvinist Christmas linger in my
mind with dread and amusement. It was bitter cold in
the Great Church that morning. Worshipers pulled the
collars of their overcoats up around their chins and
sat with their hands in their pockets. Women wrapped
their shawls tightly around their shoulders, for the
vast nave and transept were unheated, except for
little wooden boxes open on one side to hold a small
earthen pot with charcoal. The heat escaping through
five holes in the top of the box, or *stoof*, as it was
called, was supposed to keep your feet warm.

These boxes were carried around in huge stacks by
the ushers before the service. You could get one for
the price of ten cents. Many men covered their heads
with skullcaps such as the Jews wear in their synagogues, or they simply kept their hats on. That morning I had a muffler wrapped around my face and still
my teeth chattered with the cold. When the congregation sang, their breath steamed up in faint white
clouds toward the golden chandeliers.

The preacher that morning was a certain Dr. van
Hoorn, a man of small stature with dark eyes and
a coal-black beard. He was a representative of the
ultraorthodox or confessional faction. Nobody in our
family ever went to hear him. But that Christmas
morning we made an exception.

For it so happened that on Christmas Eve, the
organist Frans Pommard, alias Orpheus, had sent
word to my Uncle Kees that he was too ill to fulfill
his duties at the service on the morrow. Kees, happy

over the opportunity to play the great organ, now sat in the loft peering down through the green-baize curtains on the congregation of about two thousand souls and on the pulpit, which stood fifteen feet high, a sculptured wooden tower, with its back to one of the pillars in the middle of the nave.

The organ, a towering structure, rested on two marble columns and stood in a niche on the west side of the church on the site where in pre-Reformation days had been the high altar. It reached upward a full hundred and twenty-five feet. Although quite old, it still had a superb tone. Its viola di gamba and its vox humana especially were renowned throughout the land and indeed in all Europe, having been deemed worthy of praise by four master organists as far apart in time as Constantine Huygens, Pieter Sweelinck, Widor, and Albert Schweitzer. All four had played on it.

It had three keyboards, one free-pedal, thirty-eight so-called "speaking voices," and forty-eight stops. The wind was provided by a man treading over a huge pedal consisting of twelve parallel beams. By stepping on those beams air was blown into the bellows. These beam pedals were located in a large inner room above the Consistory Chambers, that is, outside the church proper. A narrow passage between the pipes led from the organist's seat to the pedal room.

Uncle Kees took my brother and myself with him into the loft that morning. He chuckled softly as the minister in his opening prayer blessed the Almighty for having called "but one from a house and two from a city" to form with the other elect of all the ages "Thine own Israel in all eternity." But that was only the beginning. In his sermon Dr. van Hoorn soon struck an even more pessimistic note. Christmas, he said, signified the descent of God into the tomb of human flesh, "that charnel house of corruption and dead bones." He called it an inconceivable humiliation for the Divine Majesty to have left His glory in

Heaven behind and to have entered the vile cesspool of time by clothing Himself with the mantle of our sordid humanity. He dwelt almost sadistically on our depravity, our utter worthlessness, the blackness of our hearts, tainted as we were from birth with original sin. We were worms, we were gall, we were abject, contemptible, and black as the night with sin.

Kees listened spellbound as the minister grew more dismal every minute. Christmas was God's descent into Hell, into torture unimaginable, eternity voluntarily submitting to the limitation of time. The assumption of the human estate was so at variance with the divine essence that it amounted to God's self-immolation. The dominie groaned and the men and women of the congregation bowed their heads in awful awareness of guilt for God's distress.

As the sermon progressed—sermons usually lasted a full two hours—Kees grew more and more restless. He scratched his head, pulled his hair back and forth onto his face, giving himself alternately a ludicrous and a sinister appearance. Then again he tugged at his mustache and goatee in a manner betraying extreme nervous tension and mental agitation. He could scarcely sit still for a minute. Now he rose from his seat to take a few steps in the narrow space in front of the organ bench only to sit down again and, with a rapid gesture, spreading apart the short curtains above the balustrade and cupping his head in his hands, to resume his fixed staring at the pulpit.

"Man, man," he muttered, shaking his head, "are these the good tidings, the simple glad message, that?" And turning to my brother and myself, he whispered fiercely: "That man smothers the hope of the world in the dustbin of theology!"

We sang a doleful psalm by way of interlude and the sermon, which had already lasted an hour and forty minutes, now moved toward its climax. It ended in so deep a note of despair that across the span of years I still feel a recurrence of the anguish I then experienced. It was quite well possible, nay, it was more than likely, the Doctor threw out by way of a parting shot that of his entire congregation not a single soul would enter the Kingdom of Heaven. Many were called, but few were chosen. The number and the identity of the elect was God's own secret, guarded from before the beginning of time, which we should not even try to unravel, for that would be pride and presumption. Man's eternal fate was settled, he said, and nothing, not good works or contrition, not piety or merit, not the most ardent prayers, could change by as much as one iota the immutability of the divine decree.

Kees shook with indignation as the minister concluded. He seated himself on the organ bench and began leafing through a volume of Bach's postludes. But after one glance he slammed the book shut.

For a moment I feared that he would not play any postlude at all and would walk off in a huff. I had known him to do rash things before in a fit of exasperation or impatience. Down below in the church Dr. van Hoorn could be seen lifting his hands for the benediction. Kees looked away from the scene and suddenly threw off his jacket, kicked off his shoes, and pulled out all the stops on the organ. From the nave, reverberating against the vaulted ceiling, came the unctuous voice of the Doctor. When he had finished speaking there followed a moment of intense silence.

Presently the minister put on his velvet cap and, holding up the skirts of his Geneva gown, began the descent of the spiral pulpit stair. Six of the Elders, dressed in frock coats, stood waiting for him at the foot of the steps. They formed a small procession, the Elders walking in pairs and the Pastor bringing up the rear. They went in the direction of the Consistory Chambers, the entrance to which lay through a door situated directly beneath the organ.

"Is he down?" asked Kees, who had just pulled the bell cord to give the signal to the organ attendant to begin working the bellows. He sat facing the keyboard with his back to the nave and could therefore not see what went on below.

"Yes," I said, "they are walking this way."

Kees waited one instant longer while we heard the air pour into the old instrument. His face wes set and grim and he looked extremely pale. He was biting his mustache and I noticed that his chin trembled as my mother's chin trembled when she was overcome with emotion. Then, throwing his head back and opening his mouth as if he were going to shout, he brought his fingers down on the keyboard.

Hallelujah! Hallelujah! Hallelujah! Hallelujah! The organ roared the tremendous finale of Händel's chorus from *The Messiah*. And again with an abrupt crashing effect, as if a million voices burst into song: Hallelujah! Hallelujah! Hallelujah! The music swelled and rolled with the boom of thunder against the vaulted dome, returning again and again with the hallelujah blast of praise like breakers bursting on the seashore.

It was a storm of music that Kees unleashed, a tornado of melody. Heaven and earth, the voices of men and angels, seemed joined in a hymn of praise to a God who did not doom and damn, but who so loved, loved, loved the world . . . Kees played on. Mountains leaped with joy. Icebergs melted. The hills and the seas clapped their hands in gladness.

The perspiration was rolling in big drops off his fine face. His eyes were blurred with tears. But his hands moved over the keyboard with speed and force. His stockinged feet flew over the pedal as if their owner were dashing in haste on a desperate errand. . . .

Now the vox humana softly intoned the tender, plaintive recital that comes just before the end. It was like the still small voice that followed the whirlwind of Elijah's vision in the wilderness. Kees beckoned to me with his head. I stepped nearer. "More air!" he called out. "Tell Leendert to give me more air!"

I ran back quickly behind the pipe cases into the bellows chamber, where the attendant, Leendert Bols, was stamping down the beams like a madman, transported by the music, waving his arms in the air.

"More air!" I shouted. "He wants more air!"

"Hallelujah!" Leendert shouted back. "Hallelujah!" The man grabbed me by the arm and together we fairly broke into a trot on the pedal beams.

Once more the organ's notes were swelling into that crescendo of hallelujahs which seems to reach forth to the end of time. Then the anthem came to a close.

But Kees was not through yet. He pushed in a few stops, and now the organ sang out sweetly what is the Dutch people's most-beloved evangelical song: "The Name above every Name, the Name of Jesus!" which is sung in Holland to a tune very similar to "Home, Sweet Home."

We sang it with all our hearts, Leendert, my brother, and I, and below in the church the congregation, on its way out, could be heard joining the chorus. Kees had triumphed.

His face was bathed in sweat. He wiped his forehead. I noticed that his handkerchief was wringing wet. In the subzero temperature the steam rose from his body. Leendert Bols came out of the bellows chamber and stood gazing at my uncle as if he beheld a phantom.

Kees had finished putting on his shoes and now he threw his Sunday cloak over his shoulders. He did not say a word as we clattered down the stone steps of the narrow staircase that ran from the organ loft into the nave. But as he flung open the iron door at the foot of the stairs we stood face to face with Dr. van Hoorn and the Elders. Crowding behind them were hundreds of members of the congregation, curiously craning their necks to witness the encounter between the Doctor and the organist.

"You?" exclaimed the Pastor even before we had closed the door behind us. "You? How did you get up there? Since when are you the organist? If I had known . . ." He did not finish the sentence, for Kees interrupted him by explaining the circumstance of Frans Pommard's illness.

"But why did you do that, play that?" Dr. van Hoorn in turn interrupted angrily.

"That," said Kees, "that was a protest against your sermon!"

"You have no right to protest!" fairly shouted the minister.

"I did protest, nevertheless," said Kees, "I protested because you dishonored man. You . . ." He got no further.

"*Ketter!*" screamed the minister, and his fanatical black eyes darted flames of wrath. "Heretic, madman, anarchist, that you are! Go away from God's house! Never," he yelled, "never, do you hear, will you play that tune again! Never will you . . ."

Kees threw his head back and burst into laughter. And then, bending forward, for he towered over the raging Pastor, my uncle said quietly: "You are wrong again, Doctor! I shall be playing that hymn, only much better, I trust, up there in Heaven on the day when you and millions and millions of the elect come marching in!"

With that he swept his hand from his cloak in a gesture that embraced the whole world.

Chapter III

THE LITTLE FATHER

UNDER the terms of a pious bequest by a local humanist who flourished in the seventeenth century but whose name I have forgotten, "two boys of indigent parents of exemplary moral character" were annually chosen by the Curators, after examination into their aptitude for study, to enter the Gymnasium as so-called pupils of the town. The identity of the two boys who received the scholarships was supposed to be kept secret. But in a small town there are no secrets. Everybody understood quite well that the pork butcher Boogaert, who lived on the edge of one of the most squalid quarters of Gorcum, could not afford the several hundred florins required for tuition fees and books. Moreover, his son's educational origin, so to speak, gave him away. The boy came to us from one of those elementary schools known in official language as "popular schools," but which in everyday parlance were often designated as *armenscholen*, or schools for the poor. In these institutions there was no charge for tuition. They were frequented by the offspring of the clog-wearing proletariat. It was a rare occurrence that one of them made his way into the Gymnasium. To begin with, he could not compete for the entrance examination without first having had some extracurricular or preparatory instruction. For instance, the French language was not taught at the "schools for the poor," yet that subject was included in the entrance examinations. Unlike David Dalmaden, the other "pupil of the town" of our year, who came through with flying colors, Alfons Boogaert, the butcher's son, made the grade by only a narrow margin. He was extremely nervous in facing the examiners and was almost rejected. In fact the Rector had already sent the usher to the waiting-room, to summon the unsuccessful candidate for the purpose of communicating to him the heartbreaking news when a commotion occurred.

The principal of the "school for the poor" of which Boogaert had been a pupil had accompanied his protégé into the waiting-room. He was sitting there in conversation with my father when he heard the usher call out Boogaert's name. Suspecting an unfavorable significance in that summons, the man jumped from his chair and asked to be taken to the Curators assembled in their room.

This principal, Mr. Jan van Kremer, was known in the community as "the political schoolmaster." It meant that he raised his voice, quite literally, at various political meetings in the interest of every sort of forward-looking cause. He was, in fact, a socialist. His hair matched his political color and he had a tongue that was not only sharp as a barb but dipped in vitriol. On his insistence he was admitted to the Curators and presently was talking to these gentlemen in so loud a voice that every word could be heard in the waiting-room, although the door was closed and there was a hall between that room and the Curators' chamber.

Mr. van Kremer spoke of his pupil's genuine ability, his thirst for knowledge, and his humble spirit. He pleaded that the boy be given a chance, at least for a year, at the expiration of which the Curators could, if they saw fit, refuse to let him continue. In the case of a town pupil this would mean leaving the school. He spoke long and earnestly, and his argument won the day. The collegium of Curators, which was made up of one count, two pastors, a banker with a German name, and one lawyer, after some further deliberation admitted the Boogaert boy conditionally. That his rejection would have been a gross mistake became evident almost as soon as school opened. From the beginning he was the brightest scholar of all, and for years stood at the top of our class.

Alfons Boogaert was not only a zealous student. He was

a boy of a temper as sweet as his manners were winning. His conduct was without a speck. I do not think I exaggerate when I say that he was that rare and blessed creature, a Christian soul by nature. What was remarkable about him was not how many of his fellows loved him or how much they loved him but that everybody seemed to love him with the very best kind of love of which they were capable. It was like loving goodness itself. His own lively, ready, transparent affection for others, too, seemed the very spirit of love. He was the only Roman Catholic in the school; and he was to end as a priest and martyr of that faith in the course of the imperialistic war in Asia in 1941-45.

Alfons Boogaert, or Fons as he was affectionately called, was slenderly built and of medium height. His hair was fair, faintly orange, and usually clipped very short. His spring-like blue eyes were easily the most arresting part of his features. They were deep and serene as a pool of water. There was a touch of green in them giving them a wondrous transparency. The color seemed to change with the light and heightened the mystery in their depths. When he walked Boogaert hunched his shoulders as if he were shivering with the cold, which was sometimes indeed the case. He held his arms close to his body and habitually kept his hands in his trousers pockets.

The strangest peculiarity about this boy was the fact that he had a premonition, as long ago as those years in Gorcum, of the manner in which he would some day be called upon to bear witness for his faith. How he knew I do not pretend to be able to explain. But we often talked about the future while walking after school or during recess, for he never took part in games or social diversions of any kind. He was as one set apart from the beginning. And this not because he was tainted with a streak of misanthropy, that his mind was morbid, or that he was given to some kind of precocious sacerdotal aloofness. The reason lay elsewhere: his family, although middle-class, was desperately poor. When I invited him one day during our first year to join in kicking a ball around in the square in an idle period, he said to me, aside: "I can't do it, because I can't afford to risk my shoes."

When I glanced questioningly from his face to his shoes and back again, he added with a smile: "They are not mine alone, you see. My mother wears them also when she goes to early mass. It's the same with my jacket. My little brothers have to wear it after me. It has to last a long time yet, because my father is ill and very little money is coming in."

"Is your father very sick?" I asked, trying to divert the conversation from the subject of his family's poverty.

"Yes," said Alfons, "he has tuberculosis of the lungs. He's very low. The doctor has given him up. The doctor says he can't live till Christmas."

"But that's terrible, Fons," I said, aghast, thinking of the tragedy the butcher's death would bring to his family of five children. When I looked sideways at Alfons, I saw to my amazement that he was smiling. He caught my look of surprise and said with calm certainty: "But Father is not going to die, you needn't worry. I'm not afraid in the least. He will recover."

"But the doctor . . . I thought you just said . . . What will save him, then? Is your mother perhaps thinking of taking him to Lourdes?"

"For going to Lourdes we haven't the money," replied Alfons. "My mother and I are praying for his recovery night and day and we have the assurance that our prayers will be heard."

"Assurance?" I blurted out, overcome with astonishment. "How? What do you mean?"

"Ah, Pieter," he said softly, "that's something I can't explain. It's an inner certitude, it is something that comes from the outside into our consciousness." There was a strange light in his eyes as he spoke and I quickly left off questioning him, having grown not a little disturbed myself.

Many mornings when I was up and about early to take a look at the river at dawn or watch the sun rise above the hill-like fortifications of our town, I would see Mrs. Boogaert and Alfons going to the chapel of the Immaculate Conception, she wearing his shoes and he a pair of clogs.

"There they go," my Uncle Kees would say if he happened to be out, for I had told him about the circumstances in the Boogaert family, "there they go with their faith that moves mountains! Isn't it a marvel with what spiritual strength that Church knows how to inspire its humblest children! Mother and son! To those people religion is not a matter for speculation or discussion, but a reality which they question no more than the crust of bread they eat. You may be sure of it," went on Kees, "this Boogaert Senior is going to recover and will yet slaughter many a pig and that boy of his is going to convert the heathen by the score and maybe some Protestants into the bargain. With such a faith as they have a man could jump over a house or break down a dike."

And what's more, the elder Boogaert did recover! He was still living, and apparently in good health, in March 1940, the last time I visited the Netherlands.

During the father's illness Alfons and his mother managed the butcher shop, that is to say, after school hours the boy installed himself behind the counter, sliced roasts, chops, and livers, and wrapped the viands in squares of newspaper, a bundle of which was stuck on a hook in the corner of the shop. The rush hour, so to speak, was from five until about seven. On Saturday afternoons Fons made the deliveries to the doors of the customers. The slaughtering was done by one of his father's local colleagues who came over from his own shop once a week to perform that ghastly act of charity. On the evening of that day Alfons scoured the place, for the slaughtering was done on the floor of the shop itself, with the shutters closed.

When I dropped in occasionally to consult Fons Boogaert on some detail or other of the next day's agenda, I would find him sitting under the shop's lone gas lamp. Frequently it was so cold that he had put on his overcoat and had his wooden shoes stuffed with straw. His books were spread out on newspapers on the hack block. When a customer came in and ordered some sausages or chops, Fons would quickly slip on his father's white linen butcher's smock and wait on the man or woman with a politeness that made you think he was addressing a member of the nobility instead of a poverty-stricken proletarian from the poisonous, sunless alleys near which the Boogaert shop was located. And all the time he would ply his customers with solicitous questions about their health and their work and their family relations. If there was occasion to do so, he counted out the change very carefully and wished them a good appetite and blessings without end.

"You can't imagine," he would say, turning to me as soon as the customer was gone, "you can't imagine what fine people live in this neighborhood of ours. Take that man who just went out, you saw him, he works at the shipyard outside the Chancellory Gate. He has four children, a sickly wife, his mother-in-law is staying with him, and all these people live in one room and never have quite enough to eat, yet he has a temper as gentle as any I've ever seen, though he's an unbeliever."

"He's an unbeliever?"

"Yes, an atheist. He told me so himself. I wonder what will become of all those lovely children!"

"Maybe you ought to show them the light a little, Fons," I suggested half-seriously.

"Well, I do give them pictures, you know."

"What pictures?"

"Pictures of the Virgin Mary and of the saints, with simple prayers printed on them."

"What good is that? It's bread and milk they need."

He looked at me with wide-open eyes of astonishment, as if he did not understand.

"That I cannot give them," he replied. "I'm sorry. I wish I had the money to buy those things for them. Yes, that would be a pleasure indeed, plenty of food and sunshine right here in this quarter of the town, cleanliness, whiteness, freshness, and simplicity, just to make a few people happy, just to put things right a bit, just to make things easy, just to straighten out tangled lives. It makes me rage at times because I myself am so helpless. It's so unfalteringly ugly around here, Pieter—life, I mean. Is that wrong, do you think?"

"Is what wrong?"

"That I become so angry, so indignant, so boiling and

seething mad about it all, about what goes on here in this awful neighborhood."

"What could be wrong about that?"

"Oh, but it is wrong to revolt, to be rebellious, and that's what I am at times, a rebel. Long brooding over these wrongs I'm afraid may plant in me some pagan and erroneous ideas. Poverty does make people cynical."

"Revolt," I said bluntly, "is the citizen's chief duty when conditions become unbearable. Unless people grow angry, very angry even, so angry that they smash things up, conditions will never fundamentally change. From time to time the upper classes feel a pang of conscience and become suddenly concerned about the poor and patch things up a little, smooth things over, remove the ugliest sores; but most of the time they are content to keep that side of the picture of civilization out of their sight, or ignore it altogether. A radical cleanup will not come until there is a universal burst of anger and the social outcasts themselves turn everything upside down."

But such were hardly the ideas, one could easily tell, to which Fons listened gladly. He looked ill at ease whenever at his father's shop or in school questions of social reconstruction were brought up. He would grow silent and, if he could, he would shift the conversation as quickly as possible to other matters that were of more interest to him: spiritual and ecclesiastical things, such as grace and the Real Presence, and the tragic breach in Christendom, which was his tactful and sensitive phrase for the Protestant Reformation. He would speak readily enough of the possibilities—no, of the certainty—he felt of that breach being healed some day so that the spiritual unity of our Europe would be restored in the image of one fold and one shepherd. That was his great hope.

On that subject we talked often, for sectarians as we all were at school, we felt vaguely that in that fatal breach made by Luther lay the tragedy of our European fatherland. We agreed that nothing contributed so much to its disunity as the multiplicity of discordant sects in our country drowning in the jar of their vehement disputes the still small voice of sympathy between all good men. I would not subscribe to that view today, believing as I do now that it is wrong to inject into realms of pure intelligence the spirit of compromise, which should be restricted to practical concerns. Whatever unity there is in the Church today is that of inertia, when unity is to be achieved only by action and passion. Men are at one only when they all passionately desire some high object. They are not, and cannot be, at one when they try to maintain a unity by compromise. To me disputes and controversy and sectarianism are signs of life, that the spirit still bloweth where it listeth.

Fons was never so happy—because it showed him that we too thought seriously about his great hope for unification—as when I presented him on his birthday, on behalf of the boys who gathered at the Sistine Chapel, with the three volumes of Thureau-Dangin's famous *Catholic Renaissance in England*, a work of the greatest value dealing precisely with the spiritual storm unleashed by the Tractarian movement which drove Manning, Newman, Ward, and many others from Protestantism into the Church of Rome.

At nine o'clock in the evening he would close up to go home, into that gloomy apartment in the rear of the shop where the family was gathered, to recite the rosary with his brothers and sisters, not without courteously inviting me in and being overjoyed when I accepted. There, in the fireless living-room, lay his father in a deep cupboard-like bed in the wall, a ghostlike figure whose large hollow eyes never left his son's lips as he recited the prayers. "Hail, Mary, full of grace . . ." Fons recited that invocation with an intensity of feeling that produced a perceptible spiritual tension.

After prayers he returned to the shop to study some more, or to talk. There, his mother, having put the children to bed, would sometimes join us. As I remember her she was a woman of good common sense and deep piety. Although not erudite in any manner or form, she was a woman who knew her book, as they said in Calvinist circles. In fact, in our milieu where Biblical imagery was in daily use, she would

probably have been called a Mother in Israel. She was calm
and restrained in her manner, talking or listening readily,
without affectation, yet always, as in her son's case, as if
some one great interest possessed the depths of her mind
and other things were but momentary distractions of the
surface. She possessed a virtue that is scarcely believed by
Protestants to exist in modern Roman Catholicism: she had
faith. She had some kind of certainty that life was not an
aimless mechanical process. She did not merely follow a
cult. We of the Protestant sects believed, and believed
honestly, that ecstasy, mysticism, deep, inner piety, had
long ago been replaced in the Roman communion by a mere
automatic performance of ritual, by observances similar to
primitive taboos, fetichism, and other Tibetan prayer-
wheel performances. It took Mrs. Boogaert's simple words
to drive that notion out of my head. Her faith rose far
above all dogmatic conceptions and ecclesiastical limitations.
She believed in the sense of life. In her case that belief
saved existence from senselessness. Without such a belief, I
realized, no religion can exist. For where else can religion
find its justification if not in its power to instill into men
trust, confidence in the sense of life? From that belief this
simple woman, the mother of a remarkable son, derived her
will to do good and a heart that beat for her fellow men.

Those people, the Boogaert family, almost paupers themselves, were always worried and concerned about the circumstances of others. They actually shared from their own
meager resources with neighbors still less fortunate. No
beggar, male or female, and there were plenty of both in
Gorcum, was ever sent away empty-handed from their
doorstep. It was known through our friend David Dalmaden, who had straightened out the butcher's books once
or twice during his illness, that Boogaert Senior, incapable
of refusing credit, allowed some of his customers' bills to
run up to a point where his own solvency was seriously endangered. The man simply couldn't say no to the starvelings
when they came to his shop, although he had to scrape and
sweat himself for every penny he earned. The girls, Fons'
sisters, were always knitting socks and undergarments in

their spare time, to be given away to the most needy in the neighborhood.

All this went on in secret, of course, without any ostentation or flourish. That abomination, charity for publicity's sake, had not yet been invented. Secret, also, or at least never mentioned between us, were Fons' visits to sick people with whom he went to chat in his cheerful, happy way after school hours. Only two or three of us, his schoolfellows, knew the reason why he hurried home after four o'clock when school closed and when others often lingered and dawdled in the streets, or accompanied friends to trains and boats.

It was from these visits, I seem to recall, that he acquired the nickname of *de pater*, the father, the Latin word *pater* being the title of Roman parish priests in the Northern Netherlands. Fons didn't mind in the least. He smiled shyly when one of us, in referring to some incident would say: "Didn't that happen in your parish?" or, "Isn't he or she one of your parishioners, eh, Pater Boogaert?"

Once Fons' ministrations accidentally came to public notice with the result that the whole town talked about him. It happened this way: Not far from his father's house, in a hovel that was nothing less than a pigsty, lived a woman, or rather a horrible, filthy hag, commonly known as Jans de Harrel (*harrel* is an ancient Dutch word for harlot). She was incredibly old, and suffered from a disease which had caused her legs and feet to be inflated to the size and shape of sacks of cement. Her face was like the beak of a bird of prey, wrinkled almost beyond human recognition. Being extremely deaf in addition, she imagined that everybody else suffered from the same disability and therefore shouted whatever she had to say—and that was plenty— at the top of a hoarse, croaking voice. No truer likeness of a witch, as shown in the old prints, was ever seen. She carried a staff, and moved about with the greatest difficulty, emitting blasphemies, curses, and the vilest conceivable language at every painful step of the way. She lived by begging from house to house, and people quickly gave her a penny or some stale bread in order to be rid of her. The bread she carried in a sack slung around her neck.

She was in the habit of stopping everyone in the street. High or low, rich or poor, it made no difference whatever to Jans, and her voice, railing and cursing at God and the world, could sometimes be heard a block away in our quiet streets. She was a public character, a familiar sight, a fixture of the streets like Toni the Idiot and Oppy the Innocent, two little old men who slobbered in their beards while talking gibberish.

One day this Jans de Harrel disappeared from view. It wasn't noticed at once, of course, for nobody really bothered about her. Very old persons who remembered her as a girl or a young woman used to say that her present abject condition was simply the wage of sin and that she was doomed to the worst anyway. Yet after a time people began to ask questions: What has happened to the Harrel? Have you seen her lately? Is she dead? In the end someone from the synodal poorhouse went to investigate and found her lying on a sack of straw on the floor of her hovel. Or it may have been the rent-collector who found her, I do not recall. Some food, bread and cold coffee, stood beside her on a board. In another corner of the room lay three small pigs in a wooden box.

The police were brought in and, naturally, a crowd gathered outside. It was proposed to move her to the public clinic, but mention of that place made Jans scream blue murder. She wasn't sick at all, she yelled. She had a right to stay in her own house. With vehement curses she defied the officer to touch her or go near her darlings, by which she meant the little pigs in the corner. Indeed, she rose from her bed and brandishing her staff, drove the invaders away. As the policemen and the others withdrew to take counsel Jans appeared in the doorway and shouted that her good young man, the one who looked after her, would protect her rights. He wouldn't abandon her. She was in good hands.

That good young man, it turned out, was our Fons. He had been going to that hovel every day for weeks and weeks, giving her food, sweeping the floor, cleaning up, and shaking up her straw bed. In the end it was he who prevailed on her to allow herself to be taken to the infirmary, where she died shortly after, with Fons kneeling by her bedside and holding her ugly withered hand.

Fons was severely reprimanded by the authorities for having kept old Harrel's condition a secret. Uncle Alexander commented on the incident in the *Weekly Gazette*. But our *Conrector* Dr. Snetlage thereafter would stare at Alfons in a curious sympathetic way and whisper to Ary or to me: "What an extraordinary boy!" Kees said bluntly: "We have a saint in Gorcum. We ought to feel glad and treat him with the greatest consideration."

There were other incidents that marked our little Father as a man of destiny.

Mother Boogaert watched over her boy, and especially over his religious education as if it were the only thing in the world that mattered, which was indeed the truth in her case. To hear from Fons that he and his mother read the *Lives of the Saints* together, or some other edifying book, seeing them go to mass together at break of day, and on Sundays seeing her eyes follow him lovingly and intently as he performed the duties of an altar boy, might well have brought to mind the noble companionship of the young Augustine and Monica, if it were not for the fact—*toutes autres proportions guardées*—that unlike the Bishop of Hippo, our schoolfellow had never dabbled in heresy, had never known doubt, had never been spiritually harassed as the author of the *Confessions* was so fiercely by the deep melancholy, the self-accusations, and the sense of sin that proceeded from the bitter discordance of his personality. Boogaert's faith was of the fullest, and all the firmer for the lack of any conflict that might have shaken it.

Fons Boogaert possessed an inner harmony, and the more passionate emotions virtually ceased to exist for him. That boy's faith, or his mother's, had transformed the most intolerable misery into the profoundest and most enduring sense of happiness. In the depths of his mind there seemed to be no room for anger or carnal desire. He never felt compelled, like some of us, in order to subdue the flesh, to fast or to walk with peas in our shoes. Cupidity and hatred were alien to his spirit. In the social question he had no deeper insight than a spontaneous pity and love for his fellow men. He knew nothing about patriotic devotion, about race or nationality; the whole world was his parish. He was an ideal priest.

At times the absence of a normal or rather a common psychological reaction in Fons made you feel that you were in the presence of something or somebody almost other-worldly. Because his family came originally from Bruges and in that city, as we know, the great tradition of mysticism clung to the very atmosphere, I thought of him sometimes as a kinsman of those teachers with whose lives and thoughts our country and the world have been blessed. Like them, Ruysbroeck, Thomas à Kempis, Agricola, Gerhard Groote, our Fons seemed to understand the highest spontaneously with his heart, where others sought to seize it through intellectual insight and meditation. Like them, he seemed to be in such a perpetual state of receptiveness and grace that the divine infiltration occurred almost naturally, without struggle or effort or resistance or questioning, in the way a dewdrop penetrates the calyx of a flower.

I know that such persons are rare, and rarest of all perhaps in Holland, where people are, by common repute at least, sober-minded, rationalistically inclined, and eminently practical. But in Boogaert's veins there flowed the dark and mysterious blood of Flanders, which is capable of strange exaltations. Fortunately he was too preoccupied at home and in school for his mystic inclinations to turn into a means or a method for the acquisition of those extraordinary spiritual experiences that lead to constantly more intense ecstasies, states of exaltation and visionary conditions the indulgence in which or submission to which may well provide the subject with keen psychological and even sensuous delight, but which, I believe, have nothing in common with genuine piety or love of God. The belief that God will reveal Himself directly to us because of some special merit or perception of our own incurs the danger of conjuring up phantoms created by our own egoism. Perhaps, and I like to believe that it was so, the daily companionship of more sober-minded, skeptical, not to say agnostic class-

mates helped to save Boogaert from falling into some of
those pathological aberrations which make certain Latin
saints so unpalatable and abhorrent to Protestants, and to
men of common sense in general.

When in later life I watched an attempt at saint-making
in full process in the person of Theresa Neumann, the Bavarian woman on whose hands and feet the divine stigmata
were said to appear every Friday at the hour when Jesus
is commonly held to have expired on the cross, I thought a
great deal of Fons Boogaert. I waited many times with
other curiosity-seekers and pilgrims in the woman's house
for the miracle to occur. The parish priest, a ruddy-faced,
red-necked Franconian peasant with a face like a West-
phalian ham, had taken charge of the woman's case—
against the advice of his bishop, let it be said in fairness.
I saw that man excite her and spur her on when a spell of
moaning and twisting was upon her until the business became not only pathetic but downright sordid and nauseat-
ing. The priest calmly attributed the nonappearance of the
stigmata when I was about to the presence of "an unbeliever" and pointed a pudgy finger directly at me.

There were moments when Boogaert's eyes, too, lit up
with a curious light, when his cheeks began to glow un-
naturally and his breath came in quick gasps. They were
rare, to be sure, but these manifestations lasted long
enough to make his friends realize that the danger line had
been reached. Then a deliberately jocular remark, or even
a harsh or crude interjection by Ary Brandt or one of the
others, would break the unhealthy spell and bring him back
to earth.

"Fons, now please don't start having visions like that
hallucinated Soubirous girl in Lourdes, or hear the angels
talk like Joan of Arc. It isn't done in the twentieth century,
you know. Rather recite us something from Gezelle"[1]—who
was Boogaert's favorite poet—"and we will hear an authentic voice."

With all his intelligence and quick perception Fons was

[1] Guido Gezelle, poet, mystic, and priest, was one of the fathers of the
Flemish Nationalist Movement.

not of a casuistical and prying disposition. To the contrary,
he was the most unthinking, the most unphilosophical, of
men I ever met. He believed whatever he was told by the
priests, or what he read in books approved by them. No
miracle in the *Acta Sanctorum* was too far-fetched for him.
He swallowed it without questioning. Naturally, we chided
and teased him at times for his simple-minded credulity.
Our favorite subject was the reliability of Fons' idol, the
truth-loving renowned Doctor of the Church, Saint Augustine, who declares in one of his sermons that in Africa he
not merely heard rumors, but saw, saw with his own eyes,
conversed with and studied the morals and social institutions of, a race of headless men who have one single eye
placed in the center of their breasts.

I do not mean that we made light of Boogaert's convictions. We held our companion in high respect and were not
a little proud of him because of the brilliance of his mind
and his natural disregard of snubs and slurs on the part of
certain instructors, who held his lowly social origin against
him. Some of these gentlemen, when they spoke to Fons,
something they could not very well avoid, would avert their
eyes. The Camel made this a habit. Others, Yssel Ponthieu
for one, more than once openly insulted our comrade by
contemptuous reference to the quarter of the town in which
he lived or to his father's humble trade.

When that happened, the class grew menacingly silent.
Except for Zeger van Rietvelt, a young aristocrat in our
class, who never let an opportunity pass to show his disdain
of the common people, and who would laugh uproariously
at Ponthieu's sallies, the rest of us kept straight faces. Sometimes we burned with indignation. I recall one incident that
might have been fraught with serious consequences.

Yssel Ponthieu, the history instructor, standing by one of
the high windows in the classroom one day, asked Fons to
discuss certain incidents in the reign of Queen Elizabeth of
England. There was nothing unusual in this request; it was
asked in the ordinary course of procedure and Boogaert
promptly complied. But instead of repeating verbatim the
text of the history book, which quoted in the original Eng-

lish the angry expletives and coarse sailors' oaths employed
by the Virgin Queen in conversation with her privy councilors
and prelates, Fons merely remarked that Elizabeth often
used intemperate and even scurrilous language. He got no
farther. I do not know what came over Ponthieu at that
moment; he may have felt that Fons in avoiding quoting the
actual words of the text implied a criticism of the book, of
which our instructor himself was the author. I do not know
what else could have brought on that access of fury. Whatever the cause, the man wheeled around sharply and blazing
with rage, snarled at our friend: "Fellow, you should be
with your father making sausages, instead of wasting my
time and your own in this school!"

Fons blanched as if he had been struck in the face. He
looked down upon his desk and I saw tears well into his eyes.
For an instant there was a painful silence and I felt my heart
sicken. Suddenly Brandt spoke up. Looking in the direction
of Yssel Ponthieu, Ary, who had turned deadly pale, said in
a voice that trembled with suppressed emotion: "That was
a most unfair remark to make, sir!"

Ponthieu, who stood smoking a cigar while gazing out
of the window at the clock tower of Sint Jan in the distance,
turned around as if he had heard a thunderclap. He advanced a few steps in Ary's direction, his fists clenched and
his bloodshot eyes protruding from their sockets. "Who
asked you for an opinion?" he fairly screamed. "Who do
you think you are anyway?" And then he broke into a flood
of vituperations: "Rascal, good-for-nothing, country yokel,
big-mouth! Get out of my sight, and don't dare come back
without a written apology from your father!"

Ary gathered up his books, rose from his seat, and walked
slowly to the door. He deliberately fumbled with the knob,
at the same time looking around the classroom, letting his
eyes travel over the faces of his speechless classmates. He
did not utter a word, but I felt so clearly the meaning of that
mute appeal that my heart hammered in my throat and my
knees trembled. "Come what may," I said to myself, rising
to my feet, "I cannot let him down." Except for Fons and
Zeger van Rietvelt, all the others followed. Jetze Sissingha

was the last to leave his seat. As he walked out, the history instructor, still quaking with anger, but now clearly somewhat disquieted, too, by the turn events were taking, stopped him with the words: "Why must *you* go?"

"A question of principle, mijnheer!" replied Jetze, with that monumental calm of his, and walked on.

Principle or no, there we were: out in the hall, a badly frightened group of boys. Nobody spoke until Ary asked: "Was I wrong? If you fellows say I was, I will go back and apologize to him right now. He called me a rascal and a big-mouth. Maybe I am. But this badgering and snubbing of a fellow because he is a Roman Catholic or because his father does not belong to the Liberal Club has lasted long enough. I can't bear it any longer. Sure, I'm impertinent and brash. But Ponthieu was contemptibly unfair. Maybe it's none of my business. I spoke impulsively, I know, but not to have obeyed that impulse would have seemed almost unnatural, like a self-inflicted dumbness. I felt that I would have choked if I had not spoken out just now."

While Ary was still speaking, Yssel Ponthieu emerged from the classroom, marched by with long determined strides without a glance in our direction, and disappeared into the Rector's chamber at the end of the hall. "He's gone to report to God Almighty," said Jetze dryly, and added, quoting from Domitian: "The Senate deliberates; the turbot will be served with a prickly sauce."

Presently the old gentleman himself came out of his room; Ponthieu remained inside. He told us that we were all suspended while he thought the matter over. He intimated that he considered our conduct deplorable, rash, impertinent, unbecoming, frivolous, dangerous, and stupid. But he did not rave or thunder, or even raise his voice. As a matter of fact he patted some of us gently on the back and advised us to go home quietly and wait there till he would notify us through the Custos of his decision.

Things did not turn out as badly as we feared. Nobody was expelled, nor was any one of us called on to apologize. It was Yssel Ponthieu instead who landed on the carpet. For the incident was taken up by Jetze Sissingha's father, a distinguished scholar and pastor who happened to be Scriba of the Synod of the Dutch Reformed Church for the Province of Gelderland. Dr. Sissingha did not approach the authorities in Gorcum at all, neither the Rector, the Town Council, nor the Curators. He went to The Hague and spoke to the Prime Minister.

This statesman, the leader of the Calvinist or the so-called Anti-Revolutionary party, had been carried to power by a coalition of all the orthodox groups, Roman Catholics included, whom he had found "branching from the same root of faith." This phenomenal discovery of the Prime Minister's stood us in good stead. For it involved a struggle against the state or neutral school's predominant position, which derived the basis of its rationalist approach to education from the epoch of the French Revolution. The Government, in order to satisfy its Calvinist and Catholic supporters, sought to enlarge and widen the scope of denominational learning and was on the lookout for an opportunity to strike a blow against the neutral or secular school system, of which all our instructors, of course, were ardent advocates.

At any rate, the Prime Minister came personally to Gorcum. He was not the kind of man to let even one of the little ones of his coalition fold be pushed around or discriminated against by so-called liberals. He may have had some other business in our town as well, I do not know, but he did call at the Gymnasium. I saw him walking through the streets in the noon hour on his way to a hotel where the local branch of the Anti-Revolutionary party, of which my father was the secretary, offered him a *déjeuner d'honneur*. He wore a top hat and took short, careful steps, almost like a woman, as he picked his way over the sharp-edged cobblestones. As Brandt and I stood gazing at him from the steps of the newspaper office in the company of the editor and some others, our caps deferentially in our hands, we saw a local advocate and politician who accompanied the Prime Minister whisper to him.

The great man listened attentively to his companion and then suddenly, as if he had made up his mind, he turned his face toward us and lifted his hat in a wide sweep. A broad smile illuminated the usual grim countenance of "The Tremendous One," as he was popularly known.

My heart gave a leap, and I think we all gasped. Uncle Kees, who had taken up a position on the stoop of a house a few yards down the street with some other burghers to see "the God-given leader," and who had observed the Prime Minister's gesture, walked over to us and said: "There are not going to be any expulsions, I'll wager. But as to Yssel Ponthieu, I'm not so sure he won't get his behind nicely toasted presently."

What took place in the Rector's room I do not know, of course. For a time there were rumors floating about town that some rather harsh words had been spoken there. All I remember is that the day following the Prime Minister's visit to Gorcum we were summoned back to school and no reference was made by anyone to the Boogaert incident. One of the consequences was, though, that Yssel Ponthieu for weeks thereafter did not once address the class by word of mouth. He conducted all his dealings with us in writing. He did not depart from this foolish practice until the annual examinations, when he was under the eyes of the Curators. The next semester he seemed to have forgotten the incident and behaved like a normal human being.

Alfons Boogaert unexpectedly left the Gymnasium in the middle of the examinations for admission to the last term. On the morning of that particular day we were still discussing plans for the coming year. During the noon-hour recess he and I walked home together and there seemed not a cloud on the horizon as he spoke with his usual cheerfulness. A quarter of an hour after we reassembled at two o'clock to resume the examinations everything was changed. When I happened to glance up from my work for an instant I noticed that Fons appeared distressed about something, or rather ill at ease. He looked perturbed. He was fidgeting with papers and books on his table. I saw him wipe the perspiration off his forehead and glance around the room in a sort of helpless, disconcerted way. In his eyes, which met mine in a fleeting glance, there was a look of either surprise or alarm, I could not tell which. I signaled to Ary with a nod of the head in our friend's direction. We knew perfectly well that the task before us could not give Fons any difficulty, for it was a simple translation from the Latin and Fons was beyond question the best Latinist of the class. What could it be? Ary shrugged his shoulders as if to say he could not fathom the cause of our friend's obvious disquietude and went back to work. I did the same, but glancing up again later I saw to my amazement that Fons had put his pen down and had closed the book.

A moment later he walked out of the classroom resolved never to set foot in the school again. He did not quit in a huff or in a sudden fit of temper, as could perhaps have been expected from a boy with so tempestuous a character as Ary Brandt, who did indeed quit the school a year later under circumstances already related. Nor was it that a sudden animosity had sprung up between him and one of the instructors. Fons went out deliberately and with quiet dignity. He rose from his chair and informed the astonished Rector and two of the Curators who were present to supervise the examinations that he could not remain because he suddenly realized that he did not belong. The Rector was too taken aback to reply. He fumbled with the clay pipe he was smoking and broke the stem from sheer nervousness. We who overheard Alfons were no less astounded. In the days that followed there was a good deal of censure in the town on the subject of the pork butcher's son who had, as it was said, virtually thrown his scholarship back into the faces of the authorities. People thought it an impertinence and a piece of ingratitude blamable from every point of view. But on reflection and on Fons' explanation becoming known, we came to see the justification for his act and the validity of his attitude. He had acted out of principle, and we were forced to admit that he could not have acted otherwise.

What had happened? That morning we were examined in the *Allegoriae Homericae*. This book deals, among other things, with the ideas of certain Stoics who transformed the myths of Hercules into an allegory of virtue. Whatever the

hostile earth produces of terror and horror is conquered by
Hercules. He is always victorious, and he grows in stature
through trials and adversity and manifold catastrophes.
Because of his irrepressible courage he is everywhere regarded with the honors and the admiration due to a god.
The whole world speaks of him as of a hero with divine
attributes. He penetrates into the realm of shades, seizes
the awful guardian of the nether world and brings him up
captive to heaven. With that deed he becomes the man who
has at last solved the great enigma, the riddle of the universe. He has cast aside the burden under which all mankind had groaned since time immemorial. He has opened,
for the harassed and perplexed human race, the road that
leads back from the kingdom of the shades. He has broken
death's shackles. He has overcome hell in order to reach
heaven.

The road from the earth to the stars is not an easy one,
not even for Hercules, who has been exposed from his
earliest youth to terrifying dangers. But he is descended
from Jupiter himself, he has been born a god, he is the son
of the eternal father of the gods. And he, who has walked
on the waters of the sea, who has conquered fate, who has
interrupted the convolutions of the wheel of destiny and
broken the curse of the *decretum horribile*, the horrible
decree of antiquity, who has outfaced death itself and who
has returned from hell, may well say: Now there is nothing
more to fear in heaven and earth and in all the universe.
Through his hand and his works peace on earth has come
at last. The world can hold him no longer and gives him back
to heaven. Although he is a god and the son of a god and
without equal, and even though the world lies at his feet and
he is lord of all, yet he meets his fate with resignation.
When he knows that he is about to die, not a murmur or a
plaint comes from his lips.

On this subject ran the morning's examination. None of
us, as I recall, had any difficulty with it, and the event came
off without a hitch. The written part of the examination was
to follow in the afternoon. It should be borne in mind that
our sole concern lay with the language, with its technical

composition, not with the thought content. At least, I do not think any of us, Fons then no more than the others, gave the allegorical considerations on Hercules a second thought. The classics are full of miraculous stories, beautiful no doubt, but surely not to be taken more seriously than myths engagingly and excellently told. Whether Fons came to see the morning's work in a different light during his short absence in the recess, I do not know.

In the afternoon we took the written part of the examination. We were asked to translate certain passages from Seneca's drama *Hercules Oetaeus*. In that somber and majestic epic the mythological hero is described as the Son of God who appears on earth in human form in order to suffer for mankind. He accepts death voluntarily in order to be elevated to a place on the right hand of God the Father. Although he is fully entitled to remain in heaven, he gives up his glory and the company of the immortal gods. On earth he walks a road of bitterest sorrows. In this way he wins his way back to the stars. He humbles himself by assuming the role of a menial servant so that there may be peace on earth. During his sojourn among the mortals, he retains his divine character, and while on earth he takes the place of the highest God, whom he calls Father. As a human being, however, he is subject to the laws of all flesh and therefore must taste death and be buried.

Gladly he makes the sacrifice of his life. Although abandoned by all his friends, he suffers in silence and endures the most outrageous treatment without a word of complaint. When he calls for water, his prayer is not answered. He speaks encouragingly to his unhappy mother, the witness of his suffering, and calls out to her: "Thy son liveth!" Hearing the voice of his heavenly Father, the divine Son groans in death's anguish: "Take Thou my spirit in Thy hands!" Nature enters into the divine tragedy as God causes darkness to fall on the earth amidst the rumble of thunder. At last the Son exclaims: *"Consummatum est"*—"It is finished!" and thus renders up the ghost with the exact words put in the mouth of the dying Jesus by the writer of the Fourth Gospel. All things in heaven and earth are henceforth subject to Hercules. He has triumphed over the powers of evil and he ascends to heaven as a god.

Seneca's drama did not necessarily have a direct influence on the writers of Jesus's passion, but it forms so striking a parallel with the story of the Nazarene's last hours as recorded in the Christian Gospels that the existence of a community of ideas between the Evangelists and the Stoics on the subject of a suffering, dying, and ascending Son of God is unmistakable. The two accounts bear so many similarities and correspond in so many inner particulars that the possibility of their common source and origin cannot be lightly dismissed.

We had never before read this portion of *Hercules Furiosus*, and Fons Boogaert, after glancing over it rapidly and then looking more carefully at some of the details, was too shocked to continue the translation, as anyone would have been who all his life has believed that Christianity represents a particular and exclusive revelation and suddenly makes the discovery that his religion, like all others, is subject to the laws that govern all living things, that it is a product of growth and synthesis. Alfons could not bring himself to write down something which seemed to him to border on blasphemy or denial of Christ's exclusive divinity.

He had on previous occasions spoken to us in confidence of his difficulties as he found himself being pulled between the practices of the Christian faith and the daily study of Greek and Roman pagan mythology, poetry, and religious views. He remarked once that after attending early mass, the reading of certain Latin poets an hour or so later seemed almost a desecration, an undoing of the state of grace in which he had entered through confession and communion and by witnessing the ever-recurrent miracle of the Eucharist on the altar.

He thought the simultaneous teaching of Christian virtues and pagan doctrines an inconsistency fraught with extreme danger, in that it might lead persons not firmly rooted in the Christian faith to lose respect for things sacred and holy. We agreed with him, but we argued back, as usual, that he looked upon the matter in far too serious a light, that none of us took the Greek myths for more than charming fables and pleasant nonsense, that they were read only for the sake of their literary qualities and were to be forgotten as soon as we left school.

The very men Fons admired so much, we reminded him, Saint Augustine, Thomas à Kempis, Aquinas, and others, Fathers and Doctors of the Church, hadn't they acquainted themselves with classic learning before they gave the world their immortal works? But Fons, never easily swayed, was immovable on matters touching the faith. He maintained that the mixing of the two could lead to nothing but confusion, that not everyone had the moral and spiritual strength of the men we named, and that it was an unpardonable irresponsibility on the part of the Ministry of Education to permit an indiscriminate reading of the classics, instead of a careful selection for young people whose minds were not yet fully formed.

Although the Rector and the Curators were thrown into a quandary when Fons left the classroom so abruptly, his fellow students, who knew him intimately and were acquainted with his views, quickly grasped the reason for his departure. We felt vaguely that a great crisis had occurred in our friend's life. We could not imagine what would become of him now that he had deliberately flung away the chance of continuing the six years' course to its conclusion and therewith the possibility of capturing a university scholarship. There was only one more year to follow. But he was out, gone, never to return. For we knew that his gesture was a final one, the result of a sudden but irrevocable decision.

What would be his next step? He had never told us definitely, in so many words, that he intended to become a priest, although that was tacitly understood. Where, to whom, would he turn?

No sooner was the business of the day terminated than Ary proposed to visit the Boogaert home. He and I set out together, but on the way we met our friend in the street. He was accompanied by his mother. Instead of a depressed and worried Fons, we found him smiling and cheerful. He told

us he was on his way to the parish priest, a certain Father
Arts, and that he, Fons, would like to meet with us in the
evening. We proposed Uncle Kees' studio as a place of
rendezvous, but Mrs. Boogaert insisted we come to her
home.

It was there we learned that Fons was preparing to leave
Gorcum, to enter what is known as a little seminary, as
distinguished from a grand seminary, located at Roesselaere
in Flanders, near Bruges, the very place where his idol,
Guido Gezelle, the poet-priest, had once been an instructor.
The local priest, Father Arts, a kindly and wise old man,
had listened to the story of Fons' withdrawal from the
examination and had given it as his opinion that under the
circumstances the young man could not continue to study at
a secular institution without endangering his faith.

But if that were so, I remember our asking Mrs. Boogaert,
why had Fons gone to the Gymnasium at all, why hadn't he
been sent to some Catholic preparatory school in the first
place? It had always been understood, we said, that Fons
was to be a priest. In a Catholic institution he would, moreover, have been spared the eternal quibbling and the snubs
and humiliations that had come his way in the Gymnasium.
She answered that such an institution did not exist in or near
Gorcum, and that before recommending her son for study
at the little seminary, Father Arts had wanted to be certain
in his own mind of the genuineness of Fons' divine voca-
tion. He had watched the boy carefully for years, and while
taking note of Fons' own persistency in believing that he
was called to holy orders, the parish priest had made up his
mind fully only that very day. For years the priest had
deliberately put obstacles in our friend's way. The long
stretch at the Gymnasium had been itself a trial, something
in the nature of a spiritual test-tube experiment to try out
and prove the soundness of Fons' belief that he was truly
called to the priesthood. The incident with the translation
from Seneca had clinched the matter. Fons had done the
right thing. He had shown by his resolute action that his
fervor was not of the flighty and frothy kind, but a genuine,
enduring manifestation of the divine will.

And so the little Pater left us. "There'll be no more pondering for dear old Fons," said Ary. "He's gone where inquiry is a sin." Jetze, David, and I were at the railroad station a month later when Fons' mother and the members of his family bade him adieu. I do not think his mother ever saw him back. From Roesselaere, after a year or so, he went to Louvain and from there, upon his ordination, he left for the Far East as a missionary. I was to see him once again, but only by chance and for a few hours. That was in the City of Rome in 1927, where he was on a visit to his ecclesiastical superiors and where I happened to be waiting at the Albergo d'Inghilterra to be called to the Palazzo Chigi for an audience with the then chief of the Italian Government, Benito Mussolini. From that visit to the Eternal City Fons Boogaert went to his death.

Chapter IV

THE STRANGERS IN OUR GATE

BESIDES Alfons Boogaert there was another so-called pupil of the town in our class. His name was David Dalmaden. There is a city called Almaden in Spain located in the foothills of the Sierra Morena, about halfway as the crow flies between Córdoba and Talavera, where a fierce battle was fought in the beginning of the recent civil war. It was from this city that our schoolmate took his name. For David Dalmaden was a Jew whose ancestors had settled in the Netherlands with tens of thousands of their race after their expulsion by Ferdinand and Isabella. David's father had in his possession a parchment scroll on which was inscribed in Hebrew characters a list of the names of his forebears from the fateful year 1492 onward. The first Joaquin d'Almaden to come to Holland had been a physician, but his descendant Baruch, the father of my fellow student, was not a professional man. He was a merchant; he manufactured, repaired, and sold umbrellas. If I call Baruch Dalmaden a merchant, it is because he was a member of the Honorable Guild of Merchants and not because he was some Maecenas or mighty man of commerce. Of those famous Dutch merchant princes about whom one reads in history books that their ships sailed the seven seas and conquered half the world, there were few left in my youth and certainly none in Gorcum. Dalmaden was a poor man. How many umbrellas can one sell in a community of twelve thousand souls where there are at least two rivals producing the same commodity? Had Baruch Dalmaden not been a

member of the Guild, he might well have been called a ped-
dler. Some people in our town and in the villages around
knew him only as the Umbrella Jew, in the same manner that
another citizen with the difficult Spanish name of Jeshurun
Pereira Cuja was commonly called, not in any way mali-
ciously, *de schapenjood,* or the Sheep Jew, because he was
the chief purveyor of sheep to the weekly market.

The Dalmadens lived five doors from my paternal home
in an old, not insubstantial house that had known better
days. It had been built or inhabited in the seventeenth century, as a plaque in the façade indicated, by no less a personage than Jan van der Heyden, the inventor of the fire
engine. In the spacious hall with its white marble floor,
Dalmaden Senior had his shop and manufactory. A short,
polished oaken stairway, flanked by a set of finely wrought
iron banisters, led from the left side of the shop to a door
in a deep sculptured archway which gave access to a large,
high room. On the ceiling of this room appeared the painted
figures of the four Archangels in the act of blowing long
golden mail-coach horns. Their rosy cheeks were puffed up
with the exertion and their eyes protruded slightly from their
sockets as if they suffered from a touch of Basedow's disease. By those familiar with the heavenly economy these
winged shapes were said to be occupied in raising the dead
in anticipation of the Last Judgment. The judge, a young
man with curly locks and pointed blond beard, dressed in a
judicial robe with neatly ironed ruff and tabs, was depicted in
the middle of the ceiling just above the chandelier, seated on
a silver chair which rested on the fleecy clouds. His half-
open mouth and slightly lifted eyebrows gave him an expression of critical expectancy, or perhaps annoyance over the
delay in bringing the defendants forward. The features of
one of the seraphim—I think it was Raphael—bore a striking resemblance to Jan van der Heyden himself as preserved in the portrait of that friend of the human race in the
Rijksmuseum of Amsterdam.

If the worthy Jan personally commissioned the artist to
immortalize him as an Archangel it was perhaps as well that
the citizens of Gorcum knew nothing about it. The sin of

pride stood very near the top in the Calvinist docket. The
angelic quartet and the judge with the pronounced Flemish
features were the work of one José de Beuckelaere, one of
Rubens' epigones who took delight in presenting the human
form in ample proportions and in flaming colors of lusty
good health. Under different circumstances the painting
might well have served as a recommendation for some popular brand of muscle-building pap.

All this I knew from my Uncle Kees, who had once been
allowed to inspect the ceiling in his younger days when he
was painting some murals in his own father's house. Kees
wanted to discover old Master de Beuckelaere's secret of
making the paint stick to the plaster in our damp climate.
When the orthodox Jewish family of the Dalmadens moved
into the house, the graven images were duly covered over
with strips of white canvas, so that only a tuft of Gabriel's
flaxen hair and a portion of Uriel's uncommonly large feet
were showing. It was in that room that Baruch Dalmaden
kept his accounts and his books. It was called the "bureau."
That man had more books, I should say, than any other
private citizen in Gorcum, except my Uncle Kees. But
whereas Kees had purchased his here and there in his wanderings, Dalmaden's came to him by inheritance. Some, I
was told, had been brought from Spain hundreds of years
before. Books lined the three walls of the large room solidly
from top to bottom. Even above and beneath the windows
on the fourth wall were rows of huge, ponderous tomes
whose weight made the shelves sag in long curves.

I did not enter that room until I was sixteen, and then
only for a brief instant. It happened on the day when the
Jews celebrated their New Year. At school that day I
asked the Reformed Pastor, a certain Dr. Dekker who
taught Hebrew in the two highest classes, to tell me the
equivalent of the words "Happy New Year" in the language
of the Old Testament. The Doctor replied that the Jews
did not always greet each other with that salutation customary among us, but that they rather employed a formula
that had come into use among them after they were driven
out of their homeland by the Emperor Hadrian. The expres-

sion, he said, was: "Next year in Jerusalem," or in Hebrew, *"La-shana ha-ba b' Yerushelaim."* I repeated these words to myself all the way home.

When I passed Mr. Dalmaden's house and noticed that the shop was closed for the holy day, I knocked at the window of the bureau and walked over to the door. Presently one of his sons opened it and asked me to step inside if I wished to speak to his father. I was led into the large room next to the shop, where I found the elder Dalmaden seated at the table. As he looked up at me over his spectacles, I said: *"La-shana ha-ba b' Yerushelaim."* If I merely say that he was startled I would not be saying enough. He seemed completely overwhelmed and for a moment he did not reply. Looking at him closely, I noticed two big tears roll down his face into his graying beard. At last he said, "Now I have surely been repaid. Your mother has often asked me: 'How can I repay you?' Tell her that I have been repaid *volkomen*, quite fully." I did not understand what he was talking about, nor did I ask what he meant, being too much upset by the sight of those tears. I had not intended to cause the old man any pain. On the contrary, I had intended my little compliment as a surprise and to be agreeable to him. So I walked quickly out of the house and went home. I told my mother at once of the strange incident. While I was speaking to her I saw that her eyes, too, filled with tears.

"Well, now," said I, overcome with astonishment, "what is the matter? Why are you so upset? It was only for fun. I just wanted to surprise Mr. Dalmaden with a few words in his own language. What's wrong in that? Did I insult him? I don't understand it at all."

"No," said my mother, "you didn't insult him. You reminded him of something that happened sixteen years ago." And then she told me for the first time how on the day I was born, a frightfully cold day in February when the Merwede froze over solidly between dawn and dusk so that my father, who had crossed by ferry in the morning, walked back over the ice at night, how on that day toward eleven o'clock in the morning she was suddenly seized with great pain.

The nurse was not yet in attendance, having been engaged for a few weeks later. The only other person in the house was a young maid, who lost her nerve completely at the sight of my mother's distress. The girl ran out panic-stricken, saying that she would fetch the doctor. The first person she met in the street was our neighbor Baruch Dalmaden, to whom she cried out that my mother was in great trouble. "She is dying! Please run for the doctor!"

Mr. Dalmaden said to the girl: "You run for the doctor yourself! You have younger legs than I!" At the same time he hurried into our house, alarmed in spite of his outward calm, knowing that my mother was alone, for he had seen my father leave the house in the morning. He ran up the stairs and remained with my mother till the accoucheur, Doctor Mendoza, finally arrived. But by that time I was born. The carillon in the clock tower of Sint Jan—our house stood quite near the Great Church—was just playing the hourly tune before striking the noon hour. The tune it played was that of the old hymn: "There is a voice, there is a noise of shouting in Jerusalem."

I wasn't doing any shouting yet, my mother said in telling me of the events of that day. For an hour or so after my birth it was feared that I would not live, and my mother, too, was in grave danger. "But *wonder boven wonder*," she said, "miracle upon miracle, we both came through and we both owe our lives to Baruch Dalmaden." Then I knew why the old Jew was so strangely silent when I stammered my greeting in Hebrew that afternoon. And a good many other mysteries were solved, too. I realized, for instance, why my father commissioned me each year on the anniversary of my own birthday to take a box of cigars to Mr. Dalmaden. The circumstances of my birth were never mentioned between Mr. Dalmaden and myself, but whenever we met, which was almost daily, it seemed to me that a faint, intimate smile hovered on the old man's lips.

He was on the tall side, our umbrella merchant, and well preserved for his age, for he must have been in the sixties when I moved out of Holland and he was still going the rounds then. By this I mean that two or three times a week he drove out in a two-wheeled vehicle of the kind known as a tilbury to the neighboring villages in the Provinces of Gelderland, South Holland, and Brabant at whose juncture the town of Gorcum is situated.

One of his sons drove the horse while Baruch Dalmaden himself sat deep in the hooded carriage protected against the weather by a broad curtain of leather, stretched across the interior of the vehicle behind the driver's seat so that only his venerable head was visible. I think he dozed a little on those trips, but he may also have read, for he never failed to take one or more books along on those trips. His stock of umbrellas and other merchandise was kept in a large black box slung across the rear of the tilbury.

Around six or seven in the evening he returned. On approaching the town's ramparts, Dalmaden Junior, the driver of the two-wheeler, would put a bugle to his mouth and blow a few bars. This served as a warning to Mrs. Dalmaden that her husband and son were nearing home and that it was time for her to put supper on the table. The Dalmadens were not alone in giving such musical announcement of their approach. All the local merchants, grocers, crockery-sellers, druggists, hucksters, brush and broom manufacturers, and the rest who went out with horse and cart to peddle their wares in the farming communities in the vicinity employed that method of notifying by long distance, so to speak, their respective households of their appetite. Each tradesman had a different signal, and the boys of our town could distinguish as easily between the horn blasts of the merchants as children nowadays can tell the automobiles of their neighbors apart by the sound of the klaxons. My brother Jozinus had an extraordinarily keen ear for those bugle notes. He did not need to wait for the end of Dalmaden Junior's long blast followed by seven short notes in different pitch to know which of the merchants was proclaiming his nearness. At the first sound my brother would say: "That's Mr. Dalmaden. He's coming in by the Chancellory Gate" (or the Dalem Gate, or the Arkel Gate, whatever the case might be). "I'm going to run and get a ride in." And off he went. Sometimes he stabled their horse for the Dalmadens, for he loved animals. The old man, tired and exhausted, and his son, glad to be relieved of the chore, would then go home to their evening meal.

Dalmaden's youngest son, David, was my classmate. He was a late-comer in the merchant's family, there was a difference of some eight years between him and the brother before him. He was a quiet, studious lad of uncommon physical appearance. Unlike the others in our class, he had dark hair, an olive-colored skin, a prominent nose, and startlingly luminous black eyes. He was as tall as his father and had the same high forehead. His nature was gentle and sensitive, in sharp contrast to Ary Brandt's passionate and imperious character, yet the two were fast friends to the tragic and heroic end of their lives.

After four hundred years David was the first in his family to take up the profession which the first Joaquin d'Almaden had practiced on his arrival in the Netherlands: he became a physician. But like his distant ancestor, David Dalmaden too was eventually forced to take up the wanderer's staff. In 1942, when the Nazis introduced the Nuremberg Laws in Holland, they drove him out and transported him to Poland along with his wife and children and thousands of other Dutch Jews.

Did he, like Alfons Boogaert, have a premonition of what was to come? There was an undeniable streak of gloom in that Jewish boy. Did he obscurely see, "as in a glass darkly," the advent of that "time of troubles" which was to cost his life and the lives of countless numbers of his people, that he appeared so sad and that he was so constantly turned within himself? Who can tell? The Jews are an old people. They have seen everything and have forgotten nothing. Can it not be that they have developed some sixth sense in the course of their long and melancholy sojourn in the Christian West, a hypersensitivity or an intuition that warns them of dire things to come?

At first I attributed David Dalmaden's reticence to unhappiness deriving from an awareness of being a stranger in our midst, of being of a different psychological make-up than the rest of us. With youthful zeal I nourished the notion

that if he could only be brought to the light of Christianity
all would be well with him. This feeling I shared with my
parents, especially my mother. She had an immense sympathy
for the Jews in general and prayed for the time when they
would abandon their stubbornness of heart and accept
Christ. To her the Jewish people were still the Chosen Race
from whom salvation had come and through whom in some
mysterious foreordained manner would come the ultimate
redemption of the world. Once the people of Israel should
be brought to the profession of Jesus' divinity, the proph-
ecies concerning a millennium of justice and peace on
earth would finally go into fulfillment. That was her hope,
unlike the feeling of many of our townspeople who held the
Jews in contempt for having willfully forfeited their privileged, in fact their key, position, if I may call it so, in the
divine scheme of things by their collective crime of executing
the Son of God. For this affront to the Divine Majesty, our
people believed, as do many millions in America to this day,
the Jews must bear the consequences till the end of time, or
at least until such an hour as they will freely acknowledge
their error and in repentance accept Him whom they scorned
and crucified.

In order to hasten that day, in nearly every Dutch town
with a considerable Jewish community there was a branch of
the so-called Hebrew Missionary Society, whose aim was to
convert Jews. For several years, I must confess, David
Dalmaden and his spiritual condition were my own special
concern and preoccupation. I was sorry for him and I
imagined that by talking patiently and explaining, chiefly
by pointing to texts in the Old Testament which seem to
refer to the person of Jesus and to events in His life and
passion, I could bring my classmate around. Even if he
should profess Christianity in secret, I felt, and no longer
spit in disgust at the mention of Jesus' name or in passing
a Christian place of worship (which I had been told was the
secret practice of Jews), I would be well satisfied. Curiously
enough, there was competition, and strong competition it
was, for the soul of David Dalmaden. Alfons Boogaert, too,
had his missionary eye on our friend. I learned of this when

Fons confided to me one day that whenever he heard the Jewish boy speak in the classroom, he uttered a silent prayer for his conversion, and also that he burned special candles of intercession in David's behalf before the statue of the Virgin in the local chapel of the Catholics. For a time this was a source of deep distress to me, because I feared, and had good reason to fear, not so much the candles as the efficacy of Boogaert's prayers. One who had by prayer counteracted the deadly ravages of tuberculosis was not to be underestimated when he set his heart on converting a Jew.

My interest in Dalmaden's spiritual condition ceased, or rather took an entirely different direction, when I witnessed what happened to Jews who were received into the Christian faith. To this degradation and humiliation I could not wish any human being to consent, least of all a friend. Distinctly I recall but three occasions when a Jew and his family made the transfer into our religious community. When that occurred the activists of the local Hebrew Missionary Society were all in a dither. They made an enormous fuss about the converts, leading them around from one home to the other to be entertained and to be stared at as if they were human freaks, like the tamed Borneo headhunters who were occasionally exhibited at country fairs.

In each new home where the Jewish neophytes were introduced they were expected to say a few words of "testimony" on the circumstances that had led to their repudiation of Judaism. For instance, they might tell of a chance reading of the New Testament and of suddenly being overcome with a sense of guilt and contrition over what, according to the book in which they were browsing, had taken place in Jerusalem two thousand years before. Or if they had already mastered something of the peculiar parlance in which religious experiences were then, and perhaps still are, discussed in fundamentalist milieus, they would harp on the mysteries of the operation of the Holy Spirit who overnight (like a thief in the night, was the way to say it) had wrought the miracle in their souls and made them entirely different beings from what they were before. Such reference to the spontaneous regenerative powers of the Holy Spirit was accepted as satisfactory proof of the genuineness of their conversion. Long-drawn-out struggles with the Spirit were not relished by our dominies and Elders. Conversion had to be a lightning-like affair, à la Saint Paul on the road to Damascus, in order to meet with the full approval of the ecclesiastical authorities. On hearing the "testimony," the Elders would gravely nod their heads and the Pastor, if he was present, would seize on the occasion to dilate a little on the unaccountable and diverse manners in which a soul might be snatched from perdition and have assurance of justification through the secret *testimonium Spiritus Sancti*. The more dramatic, sudden, and blitzlike the light had burst upon a given Jew, the sounder proof it was of a real conversion.

Since Calvinists in any given community, not only in Holland but in the Swiss cantons and in France and Scotland as well, generally constitute a closely knit "household of faith," so that one can almost speak of one big family whereof the various members have no secrets from each other, urge their children to intermarry, patronize each other's business to the exclusion of dealing with persons belonging to other denominations and creeds, we were in and out of each other's homes in Gorcum as if we were all blood relatives. In this way you saw and heard the neo-Christians making their debut not just once, but at least half a dozen times. One Sunday evening they would be visiting Elder So-and-so's house, the next Lord's Day after evening service they would be at another brother's place, and so on till they had practically gone the rounds. And on each occasion you were expected to listen to their story.

The performance never varied. It almost sounded like a lesson they had learned by heart and were now repeating automatically. Boring as the recital became, I must admit that I listened with the liveliest interest, especially when the converted man or his wife would relate what hateful misuse, annoyance, and petty persecutions they were subjected to by the members of the synagogue with which they had just broken.

How those Jews teased and harassed and bruised each other! The women turned up their noses and sniffed in disgust at the converts whom they passed in the streets or encountered in the shops, or they made untoward and obnoxious noises in their presence, as if they suddenly had to clear their throats or had swallowed something vile. The men, we heard it said, would go out of their way to molest and injure the neophytes in their business affairs, speak evil of them, denounce them behind their backs as unreliable customers, counterfeiters, sharpers, word-breakers, quoting the old Dutch adage that it is for the sake of the fat that the cat licks the candlestick, thus making more mischief by pouring doubt and suspicion on the sincerity of the converts' motives in joining the Christian Church. It was a most shocking mixture of backbiting, slander, and insult, but it was amusing to hear, I must say, especially when a converted Jew would mimic his adversary's gestures and speech or, wrinkling his nose, would dish up some calumnies or soft-buzzing slander of his own about a former coreligionist who was making his life miserable.

And there was trouble, too, occasionally with these newly baptized and newly confirmed Israelites. You had to mind your tongue in talking with them, especially on the subject of their conversion. That was a delicate matter, a subject full of pitfalls and snares in which you had to proceed cautiously and warily, as my youngest brother discovered to his sorrow when a boy with whom he went to Commercial High School visited our home in the company of his father. The boy, Bernard Pimentel, said to my brother on leaving: "Now I am a Hollander just as much as you, Jozinus!"

"A Hollander?" asked the surprised Jozinus. "How do you make that out?"

"Well, I was baptized today and I was born in this country."

"When a man is born in a chicken coop, does that make him a chicken?" asked Jozinus. "Ten thousand baptisms can't change your nose, Bernard, believe me! Take a look at yourself in the mirror when you get home and see for yourself whether you're a Dutchman or a Jew!"

Then there was the devil to pay! That was the very kind of language against which we had been repeatedly warned. We had been admonished—no, we had been implored to go out of our way to be kind and helpful to Bernard Pimentel as to all other Jewish boys whose parents had taken the decisive step, in order to make them feel that, to all intents and purposes, they were indeed of the very household of Calvinism. And now my brother had spoilt it all in the case of the Pimentels by his inconsiderate and flippant remarks. How would Bernard's parents feel when they learned of it? Wouldn't they sense that, in spite of their sacrifice and their courage—for it took courage to brave the other Jews in town—they were still where they had been before, that they were at best only tolerated in the company of people who secretly harbored suspicions against them and who in spite of appearances still entertained arrières-pensées?

My brother was severely punished. Among other things, he was compelled for weeks on end to sit in a pew all by himself during Sunday church services. It was the pew which was in olden days reserved for those who were under the Synod's ban of penitence. The seat was located behind a pillar against which the pulpit leaned, so that the occupant could not see the officiating minister, nor be seen by him. My brother utilized the time of his solitary proscription by carving his full name, the date, town, canton, province, kingdom, continent, and hemisphere of his birth in the oaken desk, where, I trust, it may be seen to this day. We fully expected Mr. Dalmaden, when he learned of the incident with Bernard Pimentel, to be offended with my brother, and no longer permit him to stable the horse or do other chores around the stable in which he delighted so much. But in that surmise we were wrong. Mr. Dalmaden liked Jozinus even better after that.

Nor did David Dalmaden, my schoolmate, show the least rancor or bitterness. He knew full well, of course, about those testimonial tours of the Jewish converts and that our home was a sort of clearinghouse for missionary activity. When I mentioned casually that such and such a Jew had come over, or that another Jewish person had about made up his mind to join the church, he would smile and shrug his shoulders, or he would say: "Oh, I can stand the loss! Never worry!" That was all. He acted as if it did not concern him in the least. Once he said: "We Jews are a strange people; we are nowhere at home, not even in the church. Those converts won't be happy!"

He made this remark one day when he, Ary, Jetze, and I accompanied my Uncle Kees on a hiking and sketching trip during the summer vacation.

Kees turned to David and said: "That's quite true. You are a strange people; you are Orientals, nomads, but not by choice or by inclination. You have a permanent home, but you have lost it, and I expect you will not be at ease and calmed down until you have got it back."

David was silent then, but on one of the following days when we were marooned in a rural inn on account of the pouring rains, he remarked, standing at the window: "When I enter one of these farmhouses, it is always as if there is a secret load resting on me, something disquieting and distressing. Every time we come to a new house I have the same feeling."

We had all noticed that wherever we put up for the night, a simple hostelry generally, or some hospitable farmhouse, David underwent a complete transformation. He would all of a sudden grow unaccountably quiet, he would stop talking, hold himself aloof and stare before him, his face taking on a wearied expression and his eyes losing their customary vivacity. One might have suspected that he was bored or felt ill at ease—yes, sometimes one got the impression that it was out of arrogance or from a secret sense of superiority or contempt for the humble people whose house we had entered that he acted so unsociably.

He spoke in monosyllables, answered "yes" and "no" to questions, and it was obvious, at least so we, his companions, thought, that he lacked both a sense of anticipation and one of cordiality. For he did not, as we did, look around eagerly and inquiringly in our new surroundings; there came no exclamations of surprise or pleasure from him. He behaved as if he had been there before, as if every object was familiar to him and as if the people we met were the selfsame persons from whom we had parted in the morning at our previous lodging-place. His behavior in fact exasperated us at times, because it infected the others and dampened our good spirits. Ary remarked upon it to Uncle Kees, but Kees, after a sidelong glance at David, shrugged his shoulders and said: "It's the contrast, I suppose, between this cheerful house and the mournful situation at the Dalmaden home which produces these spells of melancholy."

But that was not the secret, as Ary was quick to point out. The trouble had another source, for mournful and bleak as the situation in the Dalmaden home unquestionably was, David was known to lapse into those fits of dejection only when he was out with us and then only when he came in contact with strangers. And that morning, as he stood by the window in the large house where we were held captive by the rainstorm, we had the answer.

Suddenly he said: "Look, all those farms and roads and trees and meadows lie there as steady and fixed and settled as if they were anchored down. . . . The farmer calls his pastor father and the pastor calls the farmer his child. The farmers speak of their country, their Queen, their laws, their markets, their religion. It all hangs together like pearls on the same string from one end of the country to the other and from ancient times onward into eternity. Even the cows and the horses and the sheep and the chickens are an integral and inseparable part of the whole, and all of them, men and beasts, live in self-evident happiness. But I, I feel as if I am not a part, as if I do not belong. I am an outsider, a passer-by who comes today and is gone tomorrow without leaving trace or memory.

"When I go out with my father in vacation time and watch him deal with the countryfolk, I am upset, disconcerted. I stand by in a kitchen or a living-room and see how they watch my father. They are silent when we enter. Their faces grow tense. They stare at us. When they speak to my father, it's in an unwonted, unnatural tone of voice. They may talk nonchalantly. But it's an affectation. They don't mean it. I catch the forced, dissembling note in their voices.

That is not the way they speak with their children or their neighbors. With us Jews they are on the alert. It is as if they would protect themselves against my father's facility of speech, or his volubility—call it what you like. In town it's not so bad, it's less noticeable, I mean; people seem less on their guard because we Jews are a familiar sight, and they know us. But out in these rural places, among the farmers, it's different. We do not talk and act and think as they do. There is something in our nature that raises a barrier between us and others. There is a wall between us, a wall, invisible but real. I don't know whether it's a wall of hypocrisy or of what secret animosity. But it is like an abyss yawning at my feet. I am aware of it all the time, even at night. In my dreams I fly away from it into some unknown land . . . as far away as I can, and it still haunts me. . . ."

Now what could one say to that? David had spoken rapidly in a monotone, without looking around, his eyes staring dully out of the window while we, the four of us, stood or sat around the room where the breakfast dishes still lay on the table. All at once we sensed the significance of the peculiar way in which the proprietor of the farm, a big jovial fellow, an old acquaintance of Uncle Kees, had looked at David while he was in the room and talking with us a few minutes before. The moment that man came in, David had fallen silent.

Ary sensed the depth of the Jewish boy's distress. "It's a question of our contemptible Dutch parochial, village-pump mentality, David," he said quickly. "What else? We distrust and hate the stranger, as all barbarians do. We are only half civilized, didn't you know that?"

"But is David a stranger here, then?" I asked. "His people have been in Holland five hundred years. There are people in Gorcum who are much more strangers than the Dalmaden family. What of all the Huguenot families—the Bridés, Gaulards, Fortiers, Du Quesnes, Sembats, Froments, Le Grands—and the descendants of Waldensian and Savoyard refugees—the Peverellis, Antoniolis, Ravellis, Sinos, and Sizos—do you ever think of them as strangers, does anybody, do they themselves?"

"What are you talking about?" interjected Jetze, looking up from lacing his boots. "The Jews are a sect. They constitute a religious community of which the members are Dutch by nationality and Hebrew by religion. That's all there is to it."

"If that be true," Ary objected, "why should Jews feel themselves strangers in our midst and why should we, we might as well admit it honestly, look upon them surreptitiously as strangers, too? If Jetze is right there is really not enough difference between us to worry about, for we are also of Dutch nationality and quasi-Hebrew in religion as well. Christianity is a Hebraic cult, isn't it?"

"Not quite," Kees shook his head.

"Well, in that case," spoke up Jetze again, "tell me, if a Jew abandons his religion, does he cease to be a Jew?"

"No," everyone agreed. "He remains a Jew even if he should become an atheist."

"Can a Jew ever cease to be a Jew?" I asked.

"Personally and individually he cannot, at least not in the eyes of the world," David spoke up. "His children's children may cease to be Jews if they intermarry. The process of intermarriage extended over several successive generations may thin the blood sufficiently to cause distinctive Jewish peculiarities, psychological and physical, to disappear."

"If that is so," suggested Ary to David, "it is not merely a question of religion and nationality with the Jews, but also one of race and blood, is it?"

"Yes, it is that," assented David. "If it were no more, nothing deeper than adherence to a set of religious rules and laws of nationality, we Jews would have disappeared long ago. We would have blended with the peoples among whom we are dispersed. But we clung to our religion because it clung to us. A Jew's religion is part of his make-up. It's something in his blood. I mean it is not something superimposed or acquired from the outside, as it is with some so-called Christian nations. His religion is the Jew's expression of what's in him. It is the true inwardness of the man. It's his instinct and his life's directive. For the last two thousand years our religion has been our instrument for national survival. Before that we had other instruments, we had a country and a state. If we should ever give up our religion, we would cease to be. We would become an anemic people and die. We are at present a people temporarily cut adrift, you might say."

"Temporarily?" asked Ary. "Do you call two thousand years a temporary state of affairs?"

"The length of time does not enter into the question at all," replied Dalmaden. "Even if we were deprived of our country ten times longer, we would still be a people. But we are not entirely cut off, you see; we carry our country with us in our hearts. It's all here." He pointed to his breast. "It lives in every Jew's heart, unconsciously sometimes, often reduced to a mere spark."

"That's what Heine said," remarked Kees, "but is carrying a pious memory sufficient for survival?"

"No, it isn't," replied David. "The memory will grow pale in course of time; that's why we must sooner or later substitute the reality for the symbol. We must get a country—a physical, material country!"

"America will be your people's country," said Jetze. "Nineteen thousand Jews passed through the port of Rotterdam last year on their way to America from Russia. I just read about it in the newspaper."

"Jews are well received in America," David agreed. "My eldest brother went there and found work as soon as he stepped ashore. He's now building a home of his own. But then Jews were also well received in Spain once, and in Poland, and in the Venetian Republic, and in Algiers; and it all ended disastrously nevertheless. Not only did the Jews come to be regarded as undesirables there in the course of time; they did not manage to build up an autonomous position which might have served as a means for maintaining themselves in spite of attacks. They did not manage because that is precisely what they were not allowed to do. National states do not look with favor on the idea of a state within the state; and for cultural plurality we're not yet ripe in Europe."

"America will be different," Ary reassured him.

"Why should it?" asked Dalmaden, shrugging his shoulders.

"David is right," said Kees, who had lived in France during the anti-Jewish excesses connected with the Dreyfus Affair. "One cannot speak about any country with certainty. If a horrible thing like the Dreyfus Affair can occur in France, what can the Jews expect from other nations who have not even reached the position France occupied a hundred years ago? In America everything is still topsy-turvy. It's a nation in the making. The country is in a fever of building and industrial expansion. Everybody is welcome, no question asked, except Can you work? But once the period of foundation-laying is over and things grow more settled, the inhabitants of the New World will begin to look at each other and will make the discovery that there are a good many Jews among them.

"They have begun to look around them already, it seems. Do you know that in some American universities there is a restriction on the number of Jewish students, as there is in Hungary and Rumania and other backward European regions? Such things do not augur well, do they? In America the test simply hasn't come yet. It will not come for a long time perhaps. It all depends on the rate and rhythm of industrial expansion. At present Americans go on blindly and unconcernedly as if there will never be an end to that pleasant process.

"But there is a limit indeed, and the laws governing life and technical evolution will not stop short at the coast of New England. Capitalist democracies are hospitable so long as there is abundance and prosperity and new frontiers to conquer. But once markets begin to fail and bellies begin to pinch, democracies of that kind behave quite humanly, or rather quite doggishly. They begin to look across the borders at their neighbors' goods or they scan the faces of those who are theoretically entitled to share in the remaining benefits. In other words, they become nationalistic.

"At such moments the Jew does not stand a very good chance. He is too easily recognized and designated as the other one, the non-belonger, the nonconformist, the alien intruder. And then the ubiquitous demagogue can easily persuade the frustrated, disillusioned, unreasoning masses that by eliminating the Jew there will be more room at the trough for them. The Jews have had many harrowing experiences in the course of their dispersion," continued Kees, "but the worst experience may well come in so icily materialistic a country as America—I mean where the humanist traditions have had no time to take root among the people. For the moment things seem to go well enough, judging by reports of travelers and investigators. Everything is colossal, enormous, breath-taking over there, a roaring frontier camp, and every returning observer bubbles over with optimism. But we should not forget what an authentic American, William James, said of his own country, that "the bigger the unit you deal with, the hollower, the more brutal, the more mendacious is the life displayed." When I read the history of labor relations in America, the harshness, the resort to violence, the massacre of workers at Ludlow, the sweatshops of New York, the abysmal squalor of the mining villages, the inhumanity of it all, I fear that the Jews will not have an easy time of it in that paradise."

"True," agreed Jetze, and he added bluntly. "But why should the Jews then not give up their peculiarities, whatever they are? Wouldn't that spare them a lot of suffering? Give up their religion, their folkways, and all that distinguishes them from other peoples, intermarry as much as possible and thus lose their awful identity and avert attention from themselves? Isn't that a solution? Didn't you say yourself just now, David, that that is the only way the Jew may disappear in the long run?"

"Should the Jew disappear, then? Is that desirable? Is extinction a program for any people? Have the Jews gone through hell all these centuries to preserve their identity only to abandon everything now?" asked Kees.

"For his own sake, yes, the Jew should disappear. David admitted as much," came back Jetze.

"Jews will not give up their civilization unless they can aspire to something higher and better in return." David shook his head. "If all the peoples of the earth, for instance, were to advance to a higher moral level, if they came to regard the human race as one, as one family, with no degrees of superiority or inferiority existing between the various members but just degrees of excellence and each member of the family entitled to the same respect and treatment, the same rights to worship God in his own way—not merely by praying and singing in a peculiar manner, for that is not the essence of religion, but to work out social and economic and human problems in his own way, according to his own instinct, according to his own inner aspiration . . ."

"If all became Jews, in other words," Kees called out laughingly and nodding his head.

"Yes," agreed David, "if the ideals of Judaism were accepted by all and everywhere . . ."

"That's Biblical," said Ary. "That's fundamentally the view of the prophets. That's all that is worth preserving in the Christian tradition, prophetic Judaism."

"You mean socialism," said Kees. "Ho! The rain has stopped!" he exclaimed the next moment as he looked out the window. "Packs on! Forward march and no looking back!" A few moments later we were on the road and singing, *"De regen die maakt dat je grooter wordt—grooter wordt!"*—"The rain makes that you grow a lot, grow a lot, grow a lot taller!"

It was seldom, even in the summer vacation, that David Dalmaden could find the leisure to accompany us on those expeditions, which not infrequently kept us away from Gorcum for days on end. He had his customers to consider. Not that David was engaged in any business venture, but from the age of sixteen or seventeen he acted as tutor for children preparing their entrance examination for high school or normal school or who, for some reason or other, had fallen behind in their studies. In addition he kept the accounts of several small businessmen in town who had no time, inclination, or aptitude to attend to the matter themselves, or simply could not spare the money to engage an accountant. The Jewish boy did the work just as well, and he was much cheaper. David's earnings went toward the upkeep of his family. It cannot have been a great deal, a few florins a week at the most, but every bit helped. Baruch Dalmaden had a hard time making both ends meet, and David was really the only one of his children who made a serious effort to increase the family earnings. Later, when he had become a physician, he was the sole provider.

Mr. Dalmaden's other six children were not indolent or ne'er-do-wells, but they were all hampered in their earning capacity in some way. The eldest son had gone off to Amsterdam, and from there emigrated to America after marrying a non-Jewish girl, a circumstance which had caused his strictly orthodox father to break off relations with him. To Baruch Dalmaden his eldest son was dead, and his name was never mentioned in the family. The eldest daughter, a mature woman when I knew her, was mentally ill. She was usually to be seen sitting at the window of a room on the second story of their house, playing with rag dolls and other children's toys. Two other daughters, Esther and Rebecca, ran a small modiste shop in their father's home. They had learned the trade in Brussels, and spoke French together. They were inseparable, but they had very few customers. Then came the son who drove the tilbury, then Tobias, then David.

Tobias, who was eight years older than David, was a young man of unprepossessing physical appearance. He was tall and thin, a scarecrow of a man. He lacked his father's grace of manners and our friend David's gentle, melodious voice. One of his shoulders hung loosely, noticeably lower than the other, causing his left arm to swing with a curious unrhythmical motion from a large awkward frame. Besides, he limped badly as the result of an injury to his hip sustained in childhood. His broad red face tended to the ridiculous. On first making his acquaintance people had to force themselves to look him in the face so as not to hurt his sensibilities by following a natural impulse in keeping their gaze averted. His eyes, deep-set within red and prominent cheekbones, were of a peculiar hazel color. With his upturned nose and coarse wide nostrils he made you think, especially when he was agitated and breathing fast, of one of those grotesque masks worn by youngsters on Carnival nights. When he smiled his lips curled downward and upward in a crooked leer revealing a set of yellow, irregularly placed teeth and thick gums.

For all that, Tobias was the most genial person in our neighborhood, always greeting everybody with kind words and always willing and eager to lend a helping hand. His physical strength was phenomenal. And strange to say, in spite of that hideous exterior he had a peculiar attraction for children. Adults might pass him by in the streets without a word or with merely a cursory, half-fearful glance. Children, on the other hand, ran to him gladly the moment they caught sight of him. He would often sit on the steps of the Great Church in the small park opposite his home and watch them at play.

He was their unappointed guardian at such moments. He wiped noses, dried tears, kept the peace, and invented new games when the old grew tedious. Many times I heard my youngest brother Jozinus plead with my mother to be allowed to go out "only for a little while" after supper and being refused for fear he might get into mischief until he would assure her in a challenging triumphant tone: "But Tobias will be there!" That generally settled it. Then my mother felt reassured and permission was given. On the steps of that church, I too first heard from him familiar fairy tales and other wondrous stories.

Where did he get all that enthralling lore which nobody else knew? I think the answer lay in the fact that Tobias, in spite of his extreme poverty, his social awkwardness, his repellent appearance, and lack of schooling, was a natural scholar who loved knowledge for its own sake. His capacity for learning was enormous. All that David was required to learn at school Tobias mastered by merely glancing through his brother's textbooks at odd moments, and this included Latin and Greek and French, English and German. When David had any difficulty, he had only to consult his brother. Tobias knew all the answers. Besides, he was an omnivorous reader. That boy—I should say young man, for he was already in his twenties when David attended the Gymnasium

—had read virtually every book in town: those in the public library, the thousands of volumes in Dr. Mendoza's collection and Kees' vast stock, as well as those in his own father's "bureau" and even those dry-as-dust tomes reposing on the shelves of the Reformed Consistory, which no one had disturbed for ages. He read everything he could lay his hands on.

My Uncle Kees was extremely fond of Tobias. The dominies in our community regarded him with a certain mysterious awe because of his erudite knowledge of the Hebrew language and Jewish lore and philosophy, a branch of learning in which they, like so many of their colleagues in the Christian ministry, were miserably deficient. His greatest friend, however, was Doctor Mendoza, our family physician. Night after night those two sat in the Doctor's study talking, talking without end. From our garden at the rear of the house, which was separated from the Doctor's property by a narrow stream, the two men could be observed through the shrubbery and the tree branches on warm summer evenings, when the doors and windows of the study were left open. My brothers and I would steal near and watch them.

At that distance we could not make out a word they said, of course. We could only see them and we noticed with interest that in their discussions they wore skullcaps. Knowing that when Jews spoke of religious matters they covered their heads, I sometimes indulged in a little anti-Semitic agitation, if I may call it that, by opening the organ in our own living-room and playing some particularly militant Christian hymn, like "Stand up, stand up for Jesus!" One of my brothers would then move up stealthily as far as the bridge separating the two properties to watch the effect of the "goyish" music on the two Jews. He reported that they didn't even look up, or they merely shut the window to keep out the noise that interfered with their eternal discussions.

"What do they talk about so much?" I asked David once.

"Oh, they study."

"It's a religion with them, it seems."

"It's more than that," replied David. "Study is a sacrament."

As an adolescent, Tobias Dalmaden had been apprenticed to a book-and-stationery shop, but he had soon lost the sympathy of the proprietor. Not because of any unwillingness or incapacity to work. He was dismissed because it was discovered that he frightened customers away. It was said that a lady had stepped back startled by the grinning face of the young man who had run to open the door for her. The proprietor of the shop told him that night: "Tobias, my boy, you have a horrible face, a face to scare people. I can't keep you any longer."

That had been a hard blow to Tobias, who had his heart set on working in a bookshop or in a library. But who would employ him after that? In the resulting gossip the incident of the startled lady was magnified out of all proportions. She had not merely been taken aback, but had screamed, she had been carried off in a dead faint. She had been shocked into illness. All kinds of stories went the rounds. Out in the rural regions the rumor circulated that the redheaded son of the Umbrella Jew had the evil eye. Silly stuff, of course, and old wives' trash, but Tobias suffered under it, nevertheless.

For that reason he never accompanied his father on those peddling trips in the countryside. Before anyone else, the old man, with his keen insight into the dark and mysterious mind of our peasants and farmers, had sensed the evil portent of those half-curious, half-fearful glances directed at Tobias by the countryfolk dawdling among the booths and stalls that lined our street on market days. Baruch Dalmaden wasn't taking any chances of having the young man accused of casting a spell on the crops or a baby, or causing some expensive Holstein milch cow to miscarry. Tobias was therefore ordered to stay home, and he too understood.

Still, it was Tobias who had introduced into his father's business the one single attraction which all the other merchants lacked and which had not a little enhanced the elder Dalmaden's repute in the countryside as a trustworthy and

God-fearing citizen. The boy was very skillful with his hands. He was always making things: a doll's house for the girls, a hilariously funny Jack-in-the-box, a birdcage, tops, hoops, and other toys, sleighs in wintertime, and I don't know what else. He had once turned out a perfect reproduction of a Swiss cuckoo clock. Every family in our neighborhood owned some object or other from the Dalmaden boy's workshop. In one house it was a salad bowl with fork and spoon carved from solid oak, in another a walking-stick of rosewood fitted with a fancy handle from the umbrella shop, or a picture frame, an inkstand, a coat rack, articles and knickknacks of that sort. To my mother he presented a jewel box which is in my possession to this very day. Originally it was just an ordinary box, probably an empty cigar box. But Tobias had overlaid the outside with strips of red velvet. Over that he had glued a thin layer of plywood in which he had carved an exquisitely symmetrical design of snowflake crystals, through which the red velvet gleamed. Inside, the box was lined with blue silk fringed with white ribbon cord; and in the lid he had placed a small mirror. It was all so intricately and finely wrought that my mother remarked that even if it was useless to her as a box for jewels, since she did not own any, it was nevertheless a jewel of a box.

But Tobias' masterpiece was something of far less trifling character. It was a reproduction in miniature of the temple of Yahveh in old Jerusalem. To anyone who had once seen it this was a piece of art never to be forgotten. Tobias worked on it for three years, night and day, with never-flagging patience and study. When it was finished at last, it brought honor not only to the maker, but to our town of Gorcum as well. The ensemble of the temple, the sanctuary proper, the courts, the gardens, the booths, the colonnades and arcades, the schools, the treasure building, the stables for the sacrificial animals, and King David's royal fortress-like residence on the right, took up a space of about three square feet.

In executing the plan he had followed the specifications given in the Book of Kings, but on a reduced scale, of course. Yet not a single detail had been neglected or left out. When Tobias removed the roof of the sanctuary proper and placed a small lighted candle in the space before the veil that marked off the holy of holies, and then replaced the roof, you could see the interior through the stately pillars gleaming with the splendor of golden walls and jeweled archways, just as Solomon had ordained it. Before the altar of the sacrifice stood the tiny figures of a host of priests in white garb, and at the top of the broad steps leading from the Court of the Gentiles was the choir of the Levites with uplifted hands. When a button was pressed the entire congregation, worshipers and priests, prostrated itself and then rose. It was truly a marvel to behold.

When Tobias' temple was placed on exhibition in one of the rooms of the Reformed Consistory, people flocked from far and wide to see the wonder. One of the dominies gave an explanatory lecture and, Bible in hand, praised the exactitude and precision of Tobias' work. Some renowned Biblical scholars from Utrecht and Amsterdam, I remember, made a special trip to Gorcum to see with their own eyes the most accurate reproduction ever made of Solomon's temple. I recall this circumstance particularly well because my father sent me, much to my disgust, to accompany one of these learned gentlemen, who lodged at our house for the occasion. It took the professor five long hours by my watch and chain to verify every detail and make notations in a fat notebook. He later wrote a glowing article about it in that famous religious journal, *The Friend of the Family*.

After the exhibition, Tobias enclosed the model in a box and his father took it along on his trips in the country. The box stood beneath the seat on the old tilbury. When Mr. Dalmaden was invited into a farmhouse and had done a satisfactory amount of business (the son who drove the carriage sold handkerchiefs, shawls, lace curtains, and other useful articles on the side), the box with the "Holy City" was brought into the parlor by way of bonus and the farmers called in the hired help and the children to look at "the original House of God."

Later, when several farmers to whom Mr. Dalmaden

showed the "City of God," as the model came to be known, had expressed regret that one could not hear the particular psalm the Levites sang, Tobias introduced the machinery of an old music box in the hollow beneath the sanctuary, so that by turning a small crank the supreme moment of adoration in the temple halls was made more realistic and impressive by the tinkling of that number from Valerius' ancient miscellany which is known in Anglo-Saxon countries as the "Netherlands Hymn." In Dutch that anthem begins, appropriately enough, with the words "Now stand before the Lord's face." Tobias' "City of God" opened doors as nothing else could, and went a long way toward making a living for the Dalmaden clan.

Tobias himself made light of his success. It was nothing, he said, just a question of precision and patience. Anybody willing to spend the time could have done it. There was really nothing original or creative in the thing. Now, if he had the opportunity, he would rather try something else. He had something in mind, some vague projects.

What, for instance?

"Oh, I suppose I'd like to be a poet," he told Uncle Kees, who had presented him with a set of tools for wood sculpture. "Not a poet who writes verses or a book, but one who shows man what he is."

"You mean hold up a mirror to man, as is done in the theater?"

"Yes, something like that. But not quite that either," replied Tobias. "None of that nonsense about 'Do you love me still?' and 'It's fate that keeps us apart.' There's enough of that already in the books. I would rather show man how he has come through ages of darkness and ignorance and struggle, how he has come as far as he has with nothing but evil forces around him, and how great he really is. I would want to show him as he took up the fight against the Devil and was victorious, so that those who came afterward dared to breathe and laugh and do as they thought fit.

"That was a great day in history when someone at last dared to look the Devil in the face. Who was the first? Where did it happen? I don't know. But I can see them,

great crowds of men shaking with superstition and magic
and stepping into the sunlight. They must have stood awestruck, blinded for a moment, hardly seeing anything at all
at first. I feel that I was right amongst them, that I have
made the whole journey with them through darkness,
through fear, blindness, and superstition. I would want to
show the moment men became aware of each other, and the
moment that one of them becomes aware of himself, and
the battles they waged, one against all and all against one.
Show the man who in losing everything still won everything."

"Work away!" said Kees. "Get your hands on those tools.
I feel that you've heard the call Samuel heard in the night."

The first product to come from Tobias' attic studio after
months of experimentation was the statue of a naked man of
the prehistoric Cro-Magnon type looking down with an
expression of half-elation, half-surprise at the five fingers of
his upturned hand. The work of art was put on show in the
window of Miss de Ruyter's bookshop. In order to divert
attention somewhat from the statue, for Tobias foresaw the
possibility of some of our strait-laced brethren taking
offense at the biological details, he simultaneously put on
exhibition a model of the town of Gorcum.

In the fabrication of this model, which required even more
patience and precision than the "City of God," for the simple
reason that not only scholars but every street urchin could
check the verisimilitude of its most minute details, Tobias
had the assistance of his brother David. They must have
worked on it for years, what with measuring and verifying
the length, width, height of bridges, towers, public buildings, streets, and canals and reducing it all to the scale of
tiny wooden structures. But then it was perfect. Everything
in Gorcum was there: every house and hovel with the exact
number of windows and doors, the color of the roofs and the
façades, every fountain, pump, lamp-post, tree, windmill,
church, school, the ramparts, moats, military installations,
and even the shipyard outside the walls. One saw the town
at a glance as I was to see it in later years from airplanes.
Crowds milled in front of Miss de Ruyter's shop to get a

look at their homes in miniature. But they also saw the statue of polished mahogany in the background.

One of the local gazettes gave a favorable notice of the exhibition, complimented Tobias, and urged him to continue his interesting experiments. But the following week the opposition paper came out with a virulent assault, asking how a woman of Miss de Ruyter's honorable standing in the community could permit that indecent, execrable, immoral, vile monstrosity now on view in her establishment to remain an hour longer.

That would perhaps have ended the debate had not Ary Brandt, Jetze, and David Dalmaden, instigated by my Uncle Kees, paid a visit to the editorial offices with a view to inquiring further into the outraged critic's views. They found a young man well known to us all as a former student at the Gymnasium who had been expelled, sitting behind a desk with a cigarette dangling from his mouth. Assuming a superior air, he gave his callers to understand that he was willing to write a favorable article, for the statue wasn't half-bad, he admitted, if—he made a gesture of rubbing his index finger over his thumb.

"But then the notice you printed wasn't your honest opinion?" asked Ary.

"What can one do?" the editor replied. "They praised it across the street—in the other newspaper office. We have to show our independence, don't we?"

"Do we?" asked Ary. "Is that the way you work? If that's the case, I'll show you a little independence, too." With that he emptied the fellow's inkstand on his desk, tore the calendar from the wall, kicked the chairs around, and finally turned the desk upside down. Jetze and David dragged him away before he could lay hands on the editor, who had retreated trembling into a corner.

Two nights later someone pitched a brick through Miss de Ruyter's shop window. There was a fight in the shop and the police carried the statue to the hoosegow in the crypt of Sint Jan's tower. Tobias was shocked almost out of his wits. He never did another stroke of wood sculpturing.

His irate father ordered him to occupy himself with something less troublesome and more remunerative.

Shortly after, Tobias entered into a deal with a local painter named Karel Kou to peddle from door to door both in Gorcum and in the outlaying communes the pictures of snow-capped mountains and roaring waterfalls which Kou had never seen but which he copied from Swiss picture post cards. That partnership was automatically dissolved by the disappearance of Kou, who went off without paying Tobias his share of the proceeds of the venture. Thereafter Tobias hung around the cattle market waiting for a chance to drive some farmer's beasts home.

This was utterly heartbreaking work. Not only did it involve walking and running many painful miles behind a bucking and stampeding drove of cattle, but rarely did a farmer pay the crippled Tobias the sum agreed upon. Arrived at their destination, and having stabled or penned up the animals, the farmer would dismiss Tobias with a pat on the back and a few dimes: "Here lad, here's something for your trouble!" The man would say it quite jovially, and with an expansive gesture as if he were handing out a bounty, and look surprised when Tobias politely pointed out that the sum agreed on was much larger. Hearing that, the farmer would grow indignant and abusive, and Tobias could thank his lucky stars if he got off with no more than words. "Be off, you rascal, before I set the dogs on you or give you a thrashing, you devil's spawn!" I don't know how often I heard of such experiences from David.

And then, one day, the inevitable happened: Tobias rebelled. He turned on one of those men who habitually took advantage of his simplicity and his goodwill. The incident took place at the close of the horse market on the day after All Souls. Tobias left Gorcum shortly after three in the afternoon leading four horses. The owner of the animals walked behind leading four more. They had eight miles to go along the military highway to a village called Meerkerk. From six o'clock on it was pitch-dark and raining steadily. The horses were restive all the way, made nervous, no doubt, by the farmer's drunken shouts and the way he made his metal-shod stick rattle on the cobblestones. The animals reared and shied at passing carts, jerking at the lines so that several times Tobias was thrown off his feet.

When they finally reached Meerkerk through the long poplar lane which branches off from the main road, the boy was exhausted with fatigue and staggering with pain. The farmer handed him a twenty-five-cent piece. Too weary and miserable to put up an argument, Tobias pocketed the money and started the long tramp homeward. Yet after a mile or so his resentment grew. Perhaps it was the pain in his legs which made him realize that the imposition had been too great. He resolved to turn back and ask the farmer for what was due him. He reached the farm just at the moment when the man was closing the stable doors. Tobias held out the quarter-florin piece and said: "You promised to give me a florin for my work. There are still seventy-five cents coming to me."

For answer the farmer laughed and slapped his thighs: "Ha! A fine time to come and ask for more money! Why didn't you make your complaint a while back when we were settling accounts? I paid you all I'm going to pay you. I paid you in full. I don't owe you a cent." Tobias argued for a while but the farmer remained stubborn and finally grew abusive. "I paid you every cent I agreed to pay you back at the market,' he said. "And don't think now I'm going to stand any longer for your Jew tricks. Get off my property this moment, you hear!"

With that he made a pass at Tobias with the lantern he carried in his hand. But Tobias seized hold of the lantern and tore it from the man's grasp. He put the light on the ground at his feet, and when the man sought to retrieve it, the boy grabbed the man's coat, pinned his arms to his body, and held him in an iron embrace that cracked the farmer's ribs. When Tobias released him at last, the farmer fell to the ground panting for breath. Then Tobias did the thing he should not have done; he reached into the farmer's pocket, extracted the man's purse, and took from it the seventy-five cents still owing to him.

A week later the Cantonal Court in Gorcum sentenced Tobias to three months at hard labor on the charge of theft. When he returned to Gorcum after completion of that sentence, he was a doubly marked man, physically marked and a moral outcast. He was the shame of the family, the black sheep of the Jewish community at whom everybody pointed an accusing finger.

His chance to find work was gone for good. People now had a new reason for shunning him. They could turn their backs on him in holy indignation and give a moral reason for their ostracism. He did a few chores for neighbors now and then. His brother David told me shortly after his release from jail that he was engaged by an officer of the garrison as a sort of valet and gardener. But the officer, a newcomer in the town, was soon told about the mistake he had made with Tobias. He promptly got rid of the "ex-convict." His excuse was that Tobias had not put a sufficiently brilliant polish on his riding-boots.

Tobias' life was virtually useless after that. We saw him drag himself through the streets, leaning over bridges, watching the ships go by, loitering in the squares, or standing by in the fish market when the day's salmon catch was auctioned off. He was always alone. Still he did not complain or grow bitter against fate. I spoke to him quite frequently, and although the incident with the farmer in Meerkerk and its consequences were ever present in his mind and subconsciously conditioned his every gesture and action, he did not humiliate himself by self-pity. He merely said that life was difficult, and once remarked that the leisure he had gave him an opportunity to see more than others noticed and that therefore his manhood seemed to him senseless, evil, and unjust.

In the twilight I often saw him sitting on the steps of his father's house, bent forward, his hands held around that big, unshapely head of his as if to protect himself against the world's blows. In that head were all the traces of all the injuries and insults he had experienced. Toward the end Tobias no longer looked at the world the way it is—a bird flies, a cloud drifts by, a flower springs to bloom—he saw everything mirrored in the dark sea of his unwept tears. He looked at the world with mistrust and the world answered him with silence.

All he could get now was odd jobs that came his way from his father's neighbors. One householder gave him a few days cleaning up a garden, shearing the lawns, spreading a fresh layer of gravel on the paths, trimming hedges and trees, or just freshening up the whitewash on walls and outhouses. Occasionally he could be seen lugging crates of bottles for the taproom keeper on the corner; and on winter evenings when there was a *bal masqué* or some other celebration for the soldiers and their girls at the tavern of the Black Knight, he helped with dishes and glasses there, and mopped the floor when the revelers had left. For my father he did some masonry work, building a low wall of granite at the end of our garden where a swift-running brook kept undermining its shores, causing miniature landslides and endangering the supports of the wooden bridge that led to Dr. Mendoza's property. Tobias became the neighborhood's handy man. In that way, by being steadily occupied with some chore or other, he seemed to regain something of his former cheerfulness.

If he seldom ventured far from home in the evening it was that he might be on hand should Dr. Mendoza require his services. For the Doctor frequently employed Tobias to drive his coach at night on emergency calls in the rural regions. Rather than summon his regular coachman, who lived in a relatively distant part of our town, the Doctor, upon receiving a late call, would simply ask Tobias to harness the horses. On many a cold night when the frost doubled the intensity of sound in the streets, we heard the Doctor's carriage round the corner and rattle off toward the Chancellory Gate, the only exit from walled-in Gorcum leading in the direction of Schelluinen, Giesendam, Noordeloos, Goudriaan, and other villages and hamlets. It took a good driver to keep to those narrow roads on the dike tops when the night was pitch-black and a northwester was blowing. But Tobias was such a driver. More than once, too, Tobias rowed the Doctor across the river, for the ferry service was suspended after nine in the evening.

It was on one of those trips on the Merwede that the final tragedy occurred. One dull gray evening in November

a call came for our Doctor from a medical colleague in the
village of Almkerk, which lies about an hour's walk inland
from the opposite or southern shore of the Merwede River
in the Province of Brabant. The young wife of a farmer
named Terboven had been in labor for the better part of
two days and her strength was now spent. The rural physician who attended her sent word by the last ferry for
Dr. Mendoza to come, seeing no other issue but death for
both mother and child unless a Caesarian operation could
be performed. He dared not venture on so radical a course
without expert advice and assistance. Would our Doctor
please come, and hurry, for a consultation.

Dr. Mendoza immediately walked over to the Dalmadens' to look for Tobias. On the way back to his own
house to fetch his instrument case he chanced to meet my
father, who was returning from a stroll in the small park
by the Great Church. They stopped to talk for a moment
under a gas lamp. The Doctor told my father of the circumstances that called him away to Almkerk at so late an
hour.

"Would you operate in a farmhouse like that?" asked
my father in surprise.

"No," the old Doctor said, "I wouldn't operate there,
or anywhere else. I've never operated in all my life."

"Yet you've never lost one child or a mother."

"Clean hands, my dear friend, clean hands—that's the
one and only secret."

As he was speaking he was joined by Tobias, and a few
minutes later the two were at the river's edge. They
launched a rowboat, and presently were pulling for the
other shore, a good mile distant. The sky had been overcast
all day, there was no moon, and a Stygian darkness lay on
the water. But the river was calm. In crossing over to
Sleeuwijk they had the advantage of the current, for that
village lies about half a mile downstream. They had no
trouble whatever and were across in a little over half an
hour. At the ferry house in Sleeuwijk they found Terboven
waiting with a horse and gig, and in that conveyance they
covered the rest of the journey to Almkerk. The child was

duly delivered, sometime after midnight. But the Doctor stayed another hour or so at the farmhouse in consultation with his rural colleague.

By two o'clock in the morning Dr. Mendoza and Tobias were back at the ferryhouse in Sleeuwijk. The weather was still good then, though a fine drizzle was falling. They stepped into the boat and both rowed hard, for now the going was upstream. In sight of Gorcum's shore lights, a sudden gust of wind coming from around the bend at Loevesteyn Castle, where the Rhine and the Meuse merge to form our Merwede River, blew them off their course. At the same moment a rain squall blotted out the lights on both shores and doused the lantern they carried in the boat.

The boat was swung violently around by the current and they were sent spinning helplessly downstream at terrific speed. They could not see each other in that inky blackness. Their shouts were scarcely audible above the roar of wind and water. The rain came down in torrents. The wind, instead of blowing in a steady, sustained fashion, came in short, irregular, blustering blasts, buffeting their craft now from one side and in the next instant knocking it back from the other side with redoubled force. It's easily said now that they might have ridden out the storm by keeping the rudder steadily set with the current. In that case they might perhaps, sooner or later, have been driven ashore at some point where the river makes one of its many curves. But how keep on the water, let alone steer a straight course, when the wind veers around as unpredictably as it did that night, twice or three times within five minutes or less, and when it makes your boat twirl around like a crazy weathervane? Experienced rivermen might possibly have been able to extricate themselves from that raging whirlpool, but the Doctor and Tobias lacked the skill.

Tobias dropped the oars to hold the rudder, the Doctor crouched in the forward part of the boat. In an hour they were swept far beyond Gorcum. At one moment they skirted the foot of the dike at Hardinxvelt and saw the lights of that village, which lies fully three miles below our town. They seized the oars again and pulled with all their strength. But their efforts were in vain; they were sucked back into the middle of the roaring stream. Time and again they were deluged by giant rollers that broke over the side of the boat. The Doctor tried to bail the water out with his hands, but that was as hopeless an undertaking as trying to row into the jaws of the storm.

Suddenly the wind shifted again, charging and whistling over the surface like some unseen, crouching animal. Their boat was caught lengthwise and lifted high on a rolling wave. Tobias quickly threw the rudder over in order to cut into the next breaker, but it was too late. Under the impact of the wave the boat capsized and they were both thrown into the water. They went under, and a moment later were close together clinging desperately to the side of the upturned boat. The waves dashed over their heads. Tobias shouted to the Doctor to hold fast while he himself clambered on top of the keel. As he lay full length on the craft's bottom, he reached out for Doctor Mendoza's hand and dragged the gasping old man to his side.

Then came the most dreadful event. The boat lay deep in the water and could scarcely hold Tobias alone. When a second man's weight was added it began to sink. Noticing the boat sinking, Tobias slid back into the water, leaving the Doctor on the boat's back.

"There's no room for us both," he yelled at the Doctor. "It's the anchor that's dragging us down. I'll dive underneath and loosen it."

"No," screamed the Doctor. "Let's both cling to the side. That's our only hope."

He started to move closer to the edge preparatory to slipping back into the water. Tobias became aware of the old man's intentions and shouted at him: "If you move another inch, I'll knock you unconscious. You've got to be saved. It doesn't matter about me."

"Perhaps we'll be washed up in another minute. Wait, I think I see lights," Doctor Mendoza called back.

"I don't see any lights," answered Tobias. "Lie still and hang on. I'm going to cut the anchor."

"With those words," the Doctor said later, "Tobias

dived under the boat. He seems to have cut the rope, too, for the craft rose perceptibly. Lying there," the Doctor continued, "face down, holding fast to the slippery bottom, I looked up and saw the first streaks of dawn. Land was just ahead of me and it seemed I was racing for it with the speed of an express train. In another minute the boat was carried upon it and crunched into the sand. I stood to my waist in the water, looking for Tobias, but he was gone."

Such were the circumstances at the Dalmaden home. One son had cut himself off from the community of Israel and had become an unavowed but perpetual source of sorrow to his parents. Another son, an outcast from society, had perished. With that there was the eternal scraping and fretting for the daily bread and to keep up that appearance of middle-class gentility which the bourgeois, Jew or Gentile, seems to prize as the highest good. The struggle of the Dalmadens would have been a lost cause but for David, on whose future was centered the hope of all the members of his family. For the father was declining rapidly and with him his earning power.

No wonder then, that David went around with careworn face and pale cheeks from overwork and sleepless nights divided between study and adjusting accounts for the local merchants. With his deep sense of responsibility, David was in constant agony over his future. What if he should fall ill or have an accident or die? What should then become of his parents? And how, in the name of heaven, was he ever to fulfill their dream of seeing him a physician? Where was the money to come from for his tuition and expenses at the university, and later as an ill-paid intern in some large city hospital? Those weren't easy problems to solve.

On top of that was the rapidly worsening condition of his eldest sister Judith, the one who sat by the upstairs window playing with dolls and waving at passers-by with a little white handkerchief. It grew daily more evident that she could not remain with her family indefinitely. In fact, Dutch law specifically forbids the harboring of the insane in a private home. And that Judith was insane nobody doubted for a moment. Dr. Mendoza had warned the Dalmadens that Judith's hallucinations, in spite of the absence of any noticeable outward change in her physical appearance, indicated a progressive deterioration.

But precisely because she was ill and helpless and at the same time retained the sweetness and gentleness of a little girl, her parents' affection for her seemed to have deepened. They would not hear of sending her to some institution far away where she would be shut up in a room with barred windows, one patient among many, and perhaps be treated in an impersonal and cynical way by paid attendants. Rather than that, they would keep her near, in spite of the disorder her presence caused in the household, and the constant attention she required. And Judith might well have stayed on at home had she not, as Dr. Mendoza had foreseen, begun to hurt herself and to become dangerous to others.

Three or four times she broke the window behind which she sat by simply pushing her hand through the glass, cutting herself severely. And then one day, after one of those long spells of sunless, doleful March weather particularly depressing to sensitive souls, as Mr. Dalmaden returned toward evening from one of his trips in the country, just at the moment that he alighted from the tilbury in front of his house, it happened. As the old man walked up to the door and the carriage drove off toward the stable, the window above was shattered by heavy blows and Judith was seen trying to force her body through the broken glass.

She seemed about to jump to the stoop below. Her face and hands were bleeding. As she pounded with her bare fists on the fragments of glass in the panes, she screamed in a high-pitched, unnatural voice: "He has come! At last he has come! I am glad, he is here!" People who happened to pass by at the moment rushed forward to catch her in the event she should jump or fall while others ran into the house after Mr. Dalmaden. But the girl did not fall. Her mother seized her from behind and held her till help arrived. A few moments later Dr. Mendoza arrived and the crowd of neighbors and curiosity-seekers dispersed.

The incident was the talk of the neighborhood that evening, and then for the first time I heard from my mother what the meaning was of the words of the demented woman. She had mistaken her father for her returning bridegroom. It was in expectation of his arrival that she had been sitting all those years patiently at the window. She had lost all notions of time, and now had also lost all sense of place and distance, for she would have stepped off the ledge without hesitation.

Had she once had a lover, then? And why had he abandoned her, a girl of such striking beauty and sweetness? Yes, there had been a man many years before to whom she had been betrothed, a stranger he was, a cantor from Amsterdam who had first come to Gorcum, by special arrangement, to participate in the services at the local synagogue on the high holy days. For a year or so he made regular visits to our town, lodging over the week ends first at Dr. Mendoza's and later at the Dalmadens. He was a thin young man with wavy black hair, always dressed in black and carrying a silver-topped cane. When he walked he nodded his head with every step, very dignified and important. On Saturday afternoons and on Sundays he was seen promenading arm in arm with Judith, in company with the whole Dalmaden family, Mr. and Mrs. Dalmaden in front, both attired in their best clothes, he in the old shining frock coat and top hat and she in her black-silk dress.

Judith was an exceedingly beautiful girl then, tall and slender, with coal-black eyes and eyelashes so long and thick they cast a shadow on her pale olive skin. The young lieutenants of the garrison all saluted her and rattled their sabers on the cobblestones to draw her attention as she passed by. And the cantor had given her a ring, too. That was known by the whole town. She still wore it. When she sat by the window in her solitary vigil she was always taking off that ring and putting it on again and polishing it and holding it up to the light to admire its big topaz. And then the cantor ceased his visits. Nobody knew exactly why, but it was said that he had quarreled with Mr. Dalmaden on the subject of the dowry or that he had expressed his disappointment over the small amount Judith was to bring

with her into marriage. At any rate he was never again seen
in Gorcum.

For a time thereafter Judith also disappeared from sight.
She was hiding her shame and sorrow. That lasted a few
weeks, until the rawness and the severity of the blow wore
off, and she was again seen walking out with her parents
and sisters, just as if nothing had happened. She seemed to
have forgotten her bridegroom. But that was an illusion.
As time passed she grew distant and aloof, walking swiftly
through the streets, looking to neither left nor right and
not returning anyone's greetings, as if she were perpetually
in a hurry and distracted and worried.

To her familiars and to the neighbors who stopped her
to say a kind word, she brought up the very subject they
were avoiding in order to spare her feelings. She spoke of
her bridegroom and of nothing else. She spoke of him as if
he had been a rich man, a wealthy merchant or a prince.
She seemed to forget that people knew very well who he
was, a simple cantor, a young man without standing or
fortune. She would tell people that he had left but for a
short time and would soon return for her. He was coming
in his own carriage from Amsterdam, to take her to her
new home, after a honeymoon in Paris and Berlin and other
great cities. He was preparing the house for her, buying
the costliest furniture, tapestries, and richly decorated sets
of dishes and rugs and crystal glasses and brass lamps. Oh,
he was a rich man, never fear, she would say with a smile
and a coquettish turn of her head. She was going to be
happy and an envied woman. Look at the gorgeous ring he
had given her to plight his troth. It was but a cheap little
bauble and the stone probably false, but Judith pretended
that it was one of the most expensive jewels in existence.

Gradually the home that the absent groom was preparing
grew into a palace in the girl's sick imagination. It was a
castle, an estate on the Amstel or in Wassenaar near The
Hague. She was always changing the location of that idyllic
place. She had been on a visit there, she said, and had never
seen—no, never known that there was such splendor in the
whole world. And soon, very soon, she would leave Gorcum

for good to install herself as mistress of the enchanted dwelling. And everybody to whom she talked was invited to visit her and stay as long as they liked, for there were no end of rooms and servants on the estate for the guests.

She spoke wistfully and earnestly that way, and people nodded their heads and smiled at her, and did not contradict her, realizing that her mind had succumbed under the blow of disappointed love. But the bridegroom never turned up. Tobias had searched for him and found him one day in Amsterdam. It was said he had given the man a thrashing, but that was not true. He had met the cantor in one of the streets of the capital, had seized hold of the lapels of his coat and lifted him up that way from the ground with one hand. But he had not harmed the man. He had put him down again with a curse.

When Doctor Mendoza came into the house that afternoon after Judith tried to jump from the window, she was sitting on the bed in her room busily sewing a gold-colored ribbon to the hem of an old dress. Before her on a chair stood a cloth-covered box filled with worthless, shiny trash: curtain rings, thimbles, umbrella knobs, broken spoons, children's trinkets, and such stuff. Repeatedly she plunged her hands into the box as if she were searching for something, and all the time she was singing in a loud voice like someone who walks alone in the fields. Her mother and sisters stood huddled together in a weeping group in the corner of the room. Only Judith was gay and cheerful as she had not been since the days of her youth. She kept jumping up from the chair and running over to the cupboard to bring out more clothes and rags and trinkets, stuffing and heaping them all into the box.

At last the great day had come, she was saying. She had seen her bridegroom. He was waiting for her downstairs. "I always told you he would come, and you would not believe me. Have you seen him, too, Doctor?" she asked the physician as he entered the room. "I have indeed, my dear," replied the Doctor gravely. "But I saw him only for an instant. He told me he was very busy and could stay only a minute. He did me the honor of asking me to bring you to Amsterdam as quickly as possible. Are you ready, Judith? Put all your things together, will you, while I go out to order the carriage. We leave in an hour."

And so they did. The Doctor's large coach was brought from the stable and Judith was installed in the rear by her father's side, holding in her lap the box of trinkets. Dr. Mendoza sat with David, who drove the horse.

At midnight they reached the small town of Vianen just across the Lek River, where they halted for a rest at a hostelry located near the ferry. The inn was owned by a Jewish woman of the Doctor's acquaintance. He went into the house, where some lights were still burning, and explained the nature of their sad journey. The hostess thereupon came outside and stepping up to the carriage, she said: "Please come in. I'm glad I was still up, although it's after midnight. But my niece is visiting me, you see, and so . . ."

"My good woman," Judith interrupted the hostess, "you should know how to keep your distance. Please remember that you are speaking to a princess."

"Oh, I really didn't know you were a princess," exclaimed the hostess, feigning surprise. "Please forgive me. But won't you step down from your coach now, Princess, and come inside to drink a cup of tea and warm your feet?"

Visibly elated over the woman's changed tone, Judith smiled her consent and, taking her father's arm, but still clutching the box of trinkets, she walked into the guest hall with great dignity. After they had been sitting for a time around the large table, drinking tea, Judith, overcome with fatigue and the warmth of the fireplace, grew drowsy. Her head nodded and the fluttering of the eyes showed that she was fighting back sleep with difficulty. Observing his patient's condition, Doctor Mendoza suggested that they let her sleep, and continue the journey after daylight.

As David was preparing to take his sister to a room upstairs, a young girl walked into the room who was to change completely the tragic significance of that night for David. She was tall, of pleasing appearance; gentle hazel eyes, a firm nose, and a mouth of deep coral-red that showed a row of gleaming white teeth. She looked a youthful copy of the hostess of the inn and was introduced as her niece.

When the girl had greeted the company, Judith, turning to the hostess, said: "A charming person you have there, my good woman!"

"Yes," agreed the hostess, "she is not bad-looking, is she? But she doesn't belong here. She's from Amsterdam."

"Has this girl an occupation?" asked Judith again.

"No," replied the hostess, "not yet. She has just finished school."

"In that case," said Judith, "I may take her in my service, for I am on my way to my estate, you see, and I need a lady in waiting." And with that she opened the box she carried and spread its pitiful contents on the table before her.

"You can all see my treasures here," she said. "The only thing I lack now is a diadem for my hair on my wedding day. But David has my orders to buy me one on our arrival in Amsterdam."

The niece looked at Judith in uncomprehending astonishment. David took her aside to explain his sister's condition and the object of their journey. Then the girl returned to Judith and said: "Princess, your diadem is here. I have it upstairs. I will bring it down in a moment." She left the room and brought back a strip of gold foil or tinsel in the shape of a crown—one of those ornaments worn by children at birthday parties, or by grownups at rural wedding feasts. Judith almost snatched the pressed-paper crown from the girl's hands and placed it on her own head. "Yes," she said, "this is the article I ordered at my jeweler's. I am glad it reached me before I see my bridegroom."

When Judith was safely in her room and the others had retired, David returned downstairs, intending to stretch out on a bench by the fire. But he did not sleep a wink that night. For downstairs he found the niece clearing off the table, and they sat talking till daylight. They had fallen in love at first sight. The girl's name was Jetta Bernard. She was the daughter of a well-to-do diamond merchant in Amsterdam. She married David in 1923, and in 1942 accompanied him when the Jews of Holland were driven to the slaughterhouses of Poland by the agents of international fascism.

It's hard to go back to the Latin grammar after two months of freedom and wandering up and down the countryside without any sort of dignity to support. It's still harder to think of a classroom from which for the first time in five years the red, clean-scrubbed Flemish face of Fons Boogaert will be missing. At home everybody goes around with a heavy heart because of the condition of our old dog Prince. His days are numbered. During the vacation he has gone totally blind. The sadness of early fall pervades the atmosphere. Summer is about to leave us. The parting is particularly painful this year. Some years, after a torrid season full of thunder and scorching heat, summer quits us suddenly toward the end of August or at the beginning of September in a wild burst of storms, of pelting downpour and raw mists, slamming the door with a bang, as it were, in making its exit. This year it seems unable to tear itself away. It's going out with dragging feet, reluctantly, sighing with regret. It lingers, sick with the love of life.

The clarity in the air is so amazing that you can distinguish the shape of men across the river. The blue of the water is more blue and the violet of the Forest of Altena in the distance is lighter than I've ever seen it at this time of the year. The trees are coloring slowly. The vines on the garden walls are turning from brown to purple. The cherry trees are scarlet, the mulberries golden yellow. In the bluish dark of the acacias their tiny oval leaves are fading like starry sparks. All you can do is wonder at the world's sad beauty while listening to the whispered lament of the dying summer.

But there's happiness, too, in those moments of home-coming, a feeling of belonging to one little corner of the earth, a feeling of friendship with familiar flowers and trees and wells and old houses, and of responsibility for something, for a patch of earth, for a tree, for a dog, for a brother. Perhaps it's well that the feeling does not last long enough to degenerate, as well it might, into nostalgic sentimentality.

But what can be done except wander about aimlessly today? Kees is working on the sketches he made during vacation. He's painting a garden today. Oh, not such as any gardener ever laid out. No, not a garden like that, but one that a Dante, or another Southerner, might dream of; a garden full of flames and fire with the sun vibrating in every leaf, in which a pair of lovers sit under pale-green palms on a pink bench and little girls with unbelievable citron-yellow hair play in the burning sand. I've never seen any garden like that, I told him this morning. Well, you see it now, he replied curtly. Are you by any chance, I asked him next, protesting against something or other again, is that it? My question made him smile, but he frowned the next instant.

He has no time to talk now. He scarcely takes time off to eat and drink and is up before dawn. He's painting like a madman. A tornado is in his heart and the sun is in his head. Every hour is precious. How much longer will the light stay with us? It may be a question of hours. Strange man, Kees; half vagabond, half man of the world; well-read, urbane, with a vast background of ideas, and yet inclined to reverie and sadness, and so restless of spirit that he wanders off, away from Gorcum, out of Holland, for months on end as if a magnet draws him and who has nevertheless been heard to say that love of one's native land is the most melancholy of all loves because it is sister to despair.

Those travels of his are not sight-seeing trips. Except as the symbol of some idea, the background of history, or the framework of human interest, scenery has little attraction for him. Whatever he paints has a connection with history, with legend, or with life. He would never paint in Switzerland, for instance. The Alps are just meaningless lumps, and Niagara a sight you can witness any day in miniature at the pump. On the other hand, there are spots in Paris, in Avignon, in Carpentras, from which he can scarcely tear himself away. A house, a garden, a street, is sacred to him because a Danton, a Vincent van Gogh, a Tolstoi, a Pascal, once moved in or near. In the dark, last night, he played Wagner's *"Liebestod"* on the organ.

Kees' ancestors, my mother's people, came from Italy. They were Waldensians. Persecuted for their faith in the Piedmont Valley, they found refuge in Holland. There's tragic and somber blood in their veins. They are dowered with divine discontent, with the pangs of hunger unassuaged. Besides they have the malady of the sun; a secret *Heimweh* for the light —dazzling warm, limitless light. I'll have to walk without him today. I'll have to learn to walk alone anyway.

Leather-aproned, clog-wearing draymen are rolling vats of beer from a brewery float into the cellar of the Black Knight. The Black Knight is a tavern of the popular variety, probably the largest in town, much frequented by the artillerymen whose barracks stand just around the corner. Its reputation is not of the best, chiefly, it seems, because women entertain there in the evening with song and dance. There's also a Barbary organ inside. The crash and thunder of it fill the square with a doomsday roar whenever the door opens at night to let customers in or out. Ary's been in there, but I've never screwed up the courage. Uncle Alexander, who's a syndic, complains that it's the brewery interests that protect this dive, as he calls it, by frustrating any attempt at reform.

Around midnight the military patrol goes in and clears the place of all but civilians. If you want to see a fight, then is the time. One soldier was killed right there on the stoop last winter, knifed to death in the proper Brabant fashion, his bowels ripped open from one hip to the other. I saw them cart the dead boy away on a wheelbarrow. That time Uncle Alexander blasted away at the Black Knight for weeks on end in his newspaper. All to no avail. At the hearing held in the Town Council the brewery interests won hands down. They had the laugh on him. We're yet to see who laughs last.

There's an acrid, sour smell coming up from the open cellar. An oil lamp suspended from the basement ceiling throws a pale reddish glow on the stone steps over which lies a pair of greased sliding poles. Baker Blom with the pasty face and the fish eyes, an unlit cigar dangling from the corner of his mouth, has interrupted his afternoon nap behind the counter and saunters out of his shop next door to watch the unloading of the beer. He has assumed the national attitude for the occasion: his hands are in the pockets of his shapeless cotton breeches. One of the draymen, one Dirk de Lange, a red-faced, bullnecked, barrel-bellied specimen with a rusty mustache, is engaged in conversation with a blonde barmaid who has come outside, apparently to check up on the delivery. She holds a sheet of yellow paper in her hands and unsteadily peers at the figures on it while talking to Dirk. Chewing tobacco rapidly, Dirk looks intently at the girl's white neck and as far down her bosom as her dress permits.

The only man actually working is a middle-aged individual with a dumpy sort of gait who slowly pushes a hogshead in the direction of the trapdoor. He's Johannes Jakobus Kant, whose sole claim to distinction is the fact, of which he seldom fails to remind me when we meet, that he was the first person in the community to be confirmed by my grandfather. Some forty-odd years ago that was. Johannes Jakobus, grandfather called on him from the pulpit, mak-

ing a play of words on the man's name, *kant* yourself
—that is, turn yourself resolutely—against the world.
He smiles at me with a wan, painful smile. He's
probably thinking of that high moment in church
long ago. His feet probably hurt, too, for he has
fallen arches and moves with difficulty.

From the open cellar door comes the sound of a
deep bass voice:

> Oh, he was the tallest
> the fairest,
> the most upstanding
> royal grenadier!

Dirk glances at the hole whence rises the chanty,
then sideways at the girl again, scratches his ribs
under his leathern apron, and winks at the passer-by.

—Hey, Willem, he calls into the cellar opening,
is there any more room down there?

A man's face appears above the sidewalk. Lively,
blue bead-eyes travel swiftly back and forth between
Dirk and the girl, taking in the situation.

—There's plenty of room for a quick rough-and-
tumble, if that's what you mean!

All burst into laughter. Evan Johannes Jakobus
forces his face into a wry smile. The barmaid pokes
Dirk in the spleen and walks back to the tavern entrance, her hips swaying and her slippers clattering up
the steps of the porch. Dirk makes a clicking sound
with his tongue after her. Baker Blom's flabby paunch
shakes with silent and malicious mirth as he follows
the girl indoors. The dull thud of the hogsheads rolling and bumping from the skid on the cobblestones
is the only sound to break the afternoon's stillness in
the deserted Town Hall Square. The carillon in Sint
Jan's tower starts playing and a man dressed in a
frock coat and silk hat and carrying a cane suddenly
emerges from a side street.

—Hey, down there, make room in the bed, Dirk
calls into the cellar as his own wooden shoes rattle

quickly down the stone steps. Here's Joris de Ridder coming down the pike!

Willem's head comes up from the trapdoor again and turns in all directions until the eyes come to rest on the approaching figure in black.

—Holy God, so it is! The jumping Jesus in person. The silver-penised monster in the flesh. Quick, get out of my way, boys. Let me down.

Willem vanishes into the earth, slowly followed by Johannes Jakobus. From below come muffled laughter and giggles. It sounds as if the barmaid has gone to join the men down there after all. I am left helplessly alone to face Mijnheer de Ridder, wealthy property-owner, member of the Council, regent of the orphan asylum, pillar of the church, one of the meanest landlords in the town, according to his own tenants.

He made his money operating peepshows and similar amusements for sailors on Rotterdam's notorious Schiedam Dike. Besides, he's said to be stricken with a disease the ravages of which necessitated the amputation of a part of his sexual organs last year and its replacement with an artificial tube. The famous Doctor Maas, specialist in men's diseases, performed the operation. Our whole town knows about Councillor de Ridder's little mishap and chortles over it. On announcements of public sales and auctions to which Councillor de Ridder's name is officially signed and which are posted all over town, persons unknown are in the habit of filling in the details of the man's history with pencil scrawls.

Mijnheer de Ridder is clean-shaven and stands more than six feet in his stockings. With his stovepipe hat on he looms as tall and thin as a pole. His face has a cadaverous color corroded to a yellow tint by envy and avarice. He draws up his nose and stretches his upper lip as if forever on the verge of sneezing. When he grins, as he does now, he shows a double row of blackened stumps of teeth. He's the most loquacious bore in the community, so that everybody tries to dodge him. But I am caught. There is no escape.

—It's a delight to see you, my boy, he begins his inanities, and then rants on, without interruption, without waiting for an answer to his own questions, until eventually he'll be out of breath, I hope.

—I dare say you're glad to be back, my boy, in Van Arkel's Ancient Fortress. When does school open exactly? To work, to work and to study, that's the only balm for the thirsty soul. I always say it's science alone that gives food to life and that causes man to strive for a higher goal. Without doubt you've visited some highly interesting and picturesque spots in our dearly loved fatherland during your vacation. I want to hear about it. Where did you go this year?

—I really can't understand people who go traveling abroad, can you? I mean when we have everything worth seeing and enjoying here at home in Holland. Beauty, that is, majesty of landscape, character, rugged coasts and smiling fields, good hotels, excellent transportation facilities, polite employees, security of life and limb. What more do you want? We simply don't realize how fortunate we are. I maintain there's no country like Holland, so glorious, so all-around great in historical achievement, in progress!

—How goodly are thy tents, O Jacob! Ha, ha! How goodly, indeed! It seems even God's word makes reference to us, don't you think? No wonder the poet sings of the sense of freedom and happiness that animates everyone who dwells on Holland's dear old soil. Do you know, I am a convinced believer and an emphatic proponent. . . .

But I'll never know what Councillor de Ridder proposes so emphatically. For on that assertive note, emitted with the swelling bosom of a public orator catching his first breath, the man suddenly breaks off.

He whirls around as if stung by a bee and peers down the cellar door.

> —Drip went the dripper
> please, Doctor Maas!
> Clip went the clipper
> close to his a . . . !

A singsong, whining male voice, as of someone holding his nose to disguise his identity, comes up from the depths of the basement. De Ridder's pig eyes narrow down to furious slits. He throws his head back in disdain, swings his stick, and walks off without another word.

—He's gone, boys, the old whoremaster! Willem's head is out of the trapdoor again.

—Jesus, what a bloody hypocrite! There's no country like Holland, eh? So great, so glorious! The bloodsucker! Ho, that was a good one though about the Bible! I never thought of it that way, that he's clipped as clean as any Jew man, I mean. According to the Scriptures, all right! Boy, oh boy! Johannes Jakobus, did you hear? Clip went the clipper! That got the old bullock's goat, what?

Curious how frequently that talk about Holland's greatness and blessedness and favored providential treatment crops up in conversations lately. People seem to have it on the tip of their tongues. My father read us from the newspapers only at noon today that some thirteen thousand miners were killed by an explosion in a pit near Carrières in France. And what was his verdict?—Blessed little Holland, he says with a sigh of relief as he refills his pipe. And he's not alone, by any means. News of the most diversified happenings evoke the same facile sort of commentary from our townsmen: Good old little Holland after all, isn't it?

It's easily said, costs nothing, saves thinking, and besides, I venture to say, judging by the note of unction that's usually injected, it suffuses the speaker's soul with a warm glow of patriotic satisfaction. They don't know what their own house looks like, for they've never been outside. But God's in His heaven and all's well—in Holland at least. That's all that matters. With some individuals that phrase has become a totally thoughtless interjection, a stopgap remark to pass the time of day, like saying that it looks like coming on rain, which is generally a pretty safe prognostication in this climate. . . .

There's Frans Hidding, the hunchback, with his nose glued to Noorden's shop window. As children we went to the School of the Bible together. He was a bright boy then, and didn't have that horribly crooked spine. One day he fell out of a tree in an orchard where he was stealing cherries. The farmer fired a shot of salt at him. That was the end of Frans' ambition to follow in his father's footsteps as a professional soldier. For three years he lay strapped on a plank. But even that didn't straighten his back.

His mother told my mother that since Frans is able to walk about again the Devil himself has moved into that boy, he's a raving maniac at times. Or rather he was. For he's quite tamed now. The Salvation Army has got hold of him. On Sundays he wears their uniform and plays a trumpet in their band. On weekdays he runs errands for Borstlap, the pharmacist.

That's what he's doing now, delivering pills and potions. Only the sick will have to wait, I fear, till Franskin has looked his fill at the nice things in Noorden's shop window. And from that window he'll move to the next, or better yet two doors farther down the street to The Sign of the Limping Magpie. They're Flemings, the people who run that place, another tavern, incidentally, or rather a *café chantant*, but with the emphasis on something much stronger than coffee.

I recall the time when a one-legged magpie in a cage hung next to the door on sunny days reviled passers-by with cries of "Crook!" and "Hypocrite!"

alternately. The magpie is dead now. But his ghost goes marching on. He has been stuffed and stands in a glass case in the window. Under one wing, on the side where the leg is missing, he is supported by a tiny wooden crutch. On his head is a miniature red kerchief of the kind the poorer women wear in the place of hats. Frans Hidding is inspecting the marvel now. For the ten-thousandth time, I expect.

What a lot of people on the street today! That's four or five I've met so far. And there's Dominie Blinkenberg. That makes six. Hats off to that Lutheran, I suppose. Not too far, not too much, now. He mustn't get the notion that I'm trying to curry favor. There, that was just right. He salutes like a soldier. Never takes his own hat off. Must be part of the Lutheran creed. Let's not expatiate on heresies, the day is too fine. Ah, that's better, here comes Beatrix Vossius! No question about it, she's one of the loveliest girls in existence. It isn't good manners to stop a lady on the street. Perhaps she'll let me accompany her part of her way. I like to hear her voice and watch her face and be near her. Maybe that's sinful. Turn, turn—O Lord, my eye from vanity. What the hell!

—No, Papa isn't back yet. He's coming in this evening. I'm running to the butcher's now, you see, to get his pork chops. You know that's Papa's favorite dish, sauerkraut and pork chops.

—Where is your Papa coming from, Beatrix?

—Oh, from Berlin.

—From Berlin? I thought he was there before?

—So he was, many times. But Papa doesn't go for sight-seeing there, you see. He's been sifting heaps of rubbish over there as usual.

—Still looking for Ovid's secret?

—That's his passion, you know that.

—You are my passion, Beatrix!

—No declarations, now. I'm going for pork chops.

—So you won't take a little walk today? Let's

make the round of the ramparts together, what do you say? Half an hour, if we walk fast. To the river then, through the park?

—What are you thinking of? Not today. Maybe tomorrow. Papa will be home in an hour or so!

I'd like to think of something else than her Papa although, I will admit, Vossius is a man of admirable character and very fine intellectual qualities. He's a master of erudition, in spite of his red beard and his elephantine size. He wobbles and staggers on his huge flat feet. His face is that of a hyena, said Ary once, and his soul that of a peanut. Maybe he has no soul, said Jetze, maybe his spiritual substance has been annihilated and he's just an empty shell, a body without a soul. How an enormity like that can be the father of so marvelous a creature as Beatrix is a mystery.

Still, Vossius is harmless. He's making a contribution to scientific progress, if you can call it that. He has only one aim in life, one hobby, one goal, one objective: to accumulate the necessary knowledge to write a life of Ovid.

That's why he is always sifting heaps of rubbish, as his daughter said. He has visited all the libraries in Europe. But he's stuck at present and has been stuck for the past five years. He can't discover why the Emperor Augustus banished Ovid. It's generally supposed that Ovid, walking around in the palace garden, saw something that had better been left unseen: his imperial patron with a young girl, or was it a boy? At any rate Augustus is thought to have told the Peeping Tom Ovid to take himself off to Sardinia. Vossius won't accept that explanation. He says it's unworthy of Caesar Augustus. He can't believe it and will never rest until he has found a better reason.

And so he digs and ferrets and ponders until he's as nearsighted as an owl in daylight. He goes through life blindfolded, as it were, has no eyes, ears, feeling, or taste for anything but Ovid and—pork chops.

He's like that specialist typified in O. W. Holmes' "Scarabee," the man who devotes a lifetime to acquiring knowledge of the minutest peculiarities of some obscure tribe of insects. Vossius' insect is called: What did Ovid see when Augustus wasn't looking?

We've another instructor at the Gymnasium who's looking for the weak adjective in old Saxon chronicles. Another scholar! But that about the pork chops and the sauerkraut is news! That's something I will dish up tomorrow, when school reopens. . . .

When it became known the other day that China is threatened with a fearful famine, press and pulpit in this town immediately put on a song and dance about blessed, happy, good, safe, God's own little Holland. It's growing as monotonous as the sound of the foghorns on the river. An earthquake on the island of St. Pierre! Blessed little Holland, of course! The war in Tripoli, a run on the banks in America, revolution in Portugal, the persecution of the followers of Baha'ullah in Persia, an outbreak of foot and mouth disease in Hungary, pogroms in Russia. Blessed little Holland! Miraculously preserved little Holland!

It almost goes like a litany. The poor sleep under the bridges in London—Blessed Holland. *Ora pro nobis!* An anarchist throws a bomb at the Spanish King—*ora pro nobis*. Blessed little Holland! The Burmese still practice human sacrifice. The Mafia makes the Sicilian countryside unsafe. The Serbs push their King and Queen out of the palace window. A nihilist shoots down Premier Stolypin in Kiev. Blessed, dear, good, safe, lovely, incomparable, unsurpassed little Holland! Always the same deadening refrain. It makes you think of that Pharisee who was overheard thanking God that he wasn't "as these others." You'd imagine that the rest of the world exists only to provide contrasts to show our advantages, so that we may pat ourselves on the back.

Of course, it's true enough that there are no earthquakes here, no famines, upheavals, wars, no volcanic eruptions. But what would an Italian say, for instance, if he were compelled to live here and were told that half our country lies well below sea level, that vast masses of water, millions of tons of it, hang virtually suspended above our heads? What would he do? He'd run back as fast as he could to the slopes of old Vesuvius and break into song at the familiar sight of the smoking lava. They say the sight of water frightens Italians out of their wits. They don't seem to like the touch of it much, either. How does the old saying go? Russians wash their bodies but not their clothes; Italians their clothes but not their bodies. We? Neither. We wash the façades of our houses.

There's a servant girl with a foot pump doing it now. Flaming red hair she has, of a kind that's known popularly as Spanish fly. She must hail from Brabant across the river. She's the type, luscious and lusty. Oho, if it's Mr. Marsman's house she's washing, she must be the girl who was caught *in flagrante delicto* with a hussar on the ramparts, last week, by one of those so-called midnight missionaries. It's her name that was read off in church last Sunday. Anna Maria something. She's to do penance, the dominie said, before she's readmitted into full communion. Much penance that child will do! Not with hair like that! Probably told her hussar she knows a safer place for next time. Now if she asked me, I could tell her of a spot where those snoopers of the midnight mission will never venture.

Foreign books and periodicals contribute not a little to that sickening self-glorification on our part. Every second visitor to Holland describes it as charming, picturesque, idyllic, quaint, historically interesting, peaceful; the people kind, industrious, frugal, clean, courageous, patient, intensely religious, polite, artistically inclined, hospitable, intelligent—and I don't know what else. Such compliments are eagerly translated and republished. Uncle Alexander, the editor of the *Gazette for Gorcum and the Five Seigneurial Counties*, always keeps a stock of that kind of article on hand. He has them on tap. He prints them on a day when news is scarce or when the rheumatism in his fingers keeps him from writing a piece himself. They appear under the standard heading: "As Others See Us."

What would he put in if he didn't have his clippings? Kees says that with his brother Alexander it's a case of *aut scissors*, *aut nullus*. As others see us! But he won't let us know how the Javanese or the Achinese or the Balinese or any of those peoples in Indonesia see us and our country! Devils from hell, they probably call us. Gin-soaked, sweat-smeared, red-faced, saber-rattling Dutch brutes. Oh, there's no doubt in the world that the Dutch are a good-humored and kindly people. But even so, things which would be unthinkable at home are not only thinkable but do-able and are actually done in Indonesia. In the parliamentary reports recently I read excerpts from a speech by a Roman Catholic member, a certain Mr. de Stuers, on the military expedition in the Achin uplands of Sumatra.

—How can the facts of what I rightfully qualify as a murder expedition pure and simple, said the man, be made to harmonize with the Christian banner which the Government waves so hysterically? When human beings, he went on, who valiantly defend their homes, their hearths, and their families are constantly spoken of in official communiqués as fanatics, I begin to grow puzzled about the meaning of our language. In school I was taught that such behavior was patriotism and showed an intense love of country. Are the glorious deeds of our ancestors also to be qualified as fanaticism? If the Government, he asked, pursues, as it says, a policy of pacification and civilization, a Christian policy, what then are these deeds of shame and horror in Indonesia?

Almost unbelievable that good, gentle, kindhearted

Dutchmen behave in such a manner that their deeds
can be described as acts of shame and horror! What
makes them change, anyway, when they get over
there? We are always led to believe that the English
are the most ruthless colonial administrators on
earth, who don't care a rap about the righteousness
of another people's cause when British interests are
involved. We are constantly, even now when those
events lie in the far-distant past, being reminded at
school and in church of the South African War and
of the wanton destruction by Britain of Boer independence for the sake of Witwatersrand's diamond
fields. But now the shoe is on the other foot. The
terrors of the South Africa "murder camps" for
women prisoners have been surpassed in Indonesia.
Now it's we ourselves who stand branded before the
whole world with Cain's awful mark.

—I have seen them, said that critic of our Government's colonial policy in full session of the Second
Chamber, I have seen the heaps of corpses of men,
women, and children lying in their burnt-out huts,
along the roads, in the cool forests, under the waving
palms, the work of Christian Dutch civilization, a
stinking, smoking human holocaust on the altar of
Mammon, a hecatomb of victims cursing the blue sky,
a sacrilege committed against nature and humanity.
And this, he wound up, is but one crime in a whole
long, sheer endless list of crimes committed by Holland against the divine name. . . .

That's Gerrit Huet coming out of Van Eck's bookshop over there. He's leaving this year for the university, going to study law. Gerrit was our comrade in
arms in the hectic days of the debating club and the
theatrical society when he nourished the idée fixe of
starting a newspaper, a real independent journal, of
national scope, of course. It was not to be tied up
with any of the existing political parties or schools
of thought, it was to be the unmistakable and fearless
spokesman of the common people.—If our rulers,

Gerrit used to argue, would consult their conscience
and listen to the people they wouldn't be so often in a
quandary. They'd discover what's fit to be done. For
the people are close to the heart of things.

—Oh, yes, yes, fine. No doubt about it, we'd say.
We're right with you. But where's the money to come
from? Have you thought of that, too? Publishing
costs something, you know? Oh, there was not going
to be any trouble about that. None at all. Gerrit had
it all figured out. All we'd need were five hundred
subscribers who'd pay two gulden each a month for
ten years. With the accumulated interest we'd dispose
of a quarter of a million. In ten years we boys of
seventeen would be twenty-seven. We'd be sitting on
top of the world and we'd found the true, independent journal. And how collect? Go from house to
house, of course. Ring bells. Challenge them. Beg,
persuade, cajole, force them, by God. Tell them Holland's got to be saved. We've not collected a cent,
but we've quarreled quite frequently as to what was
to be printed in the first issue.

A people with our record in the East cannot very
well sit in judgment on England. What puzzles me
greatly is the cause, the motive, the impulse which
turns us into barbarians away from home. Our ethical
standards seem to undergo a complete transformation the moment they are transferred from an essentially peaceful and relatively civilized atmosphere at
home to that of the colonies. Over there we become
arrogant, coarse, rude, intolerant, violent, and brutal.
Here at home the Government insists that every one
of its acts is predicated on the touchstone of God's
word. In Indonesia we disregard the most elementary
decencies of human life. We do not merely rattle the
sword and shake the mailed fist, as the German Emperor does, we of good, noble little Holland actually
wield the sword and bring down our fists. We hack
and slash and burn and maim and murder the most
inoffensive people on earth the moment they venture

to whisper a word of doubt about our claims of superior capacity to govern them.

Here at home we have societies for the prevention of cruelty to animals. In Indonesia we kill women and children, and it is we who do that, we, who claim to be followers of the gentle Jesus. And yet it's quite true also that at home our people, on the whole, abhor violence in any form. What makes us change, then, when we are abroad? The same thing probably that causes the English to resort to violence abroad: imperialism, the lust for domination, the craving for power, the thirst for profits: capitalism.

It's clearly the rankest nonsense to say that human nature does not change and cannot be made to change. We see it happening before our own eyes. The hunger for other people's property and wealth changes essentially kind and good-natured Dutchmen into swaggering, stony-hearted, merciless brutes over in the East.—It is not the consciousness of men that determines their existence, said Karl Marx, it is their social existence which determines their consciousness. All the talk of Holland's mission, the white man's burden, the need of acquainting the peoples of Indonesia with the Christian Gospel and elevating them to a higher ethical standard, cannot obscure the fact that we are out for loot and treasure and are as ready as any English imperialist to strike down anyone brave enough to interfere with or to protest against a policy of wholesale spoliation and enslavement of the native peoples.

Is it surprising that humble men and women have vaguely come to suspect that our "dominion over palm and pine" is not wholly the poetic idyl which the official apologists and the beneficiaries of our Government's colonial policy make it out to be, and grow ill at ease in their thinking about our role as a nation? Take Niek Goovaarts, the printer to the local synod, not a politician, a scholar, or a capitalist, or anything of that kind, but a poor man and an

ardent supporter of the Government of fundamentalists that sits in The Hague. One day last fall, while
I stood watching him in his shop as he ran off some
pamphlets on the foot press for the Java Mission
Board and the conversation shifted to the East
Indies, he suddenly asked me:—Tell me, Pieter, have
you ever thought of it how Holland can expect to
remain a free and independent nation when we trample underfoot the liberty of other peoples? There is
a God of justice, isn't there?

—Well, said I, not knowing really what to answer,
we only imitate the English. In colonial affairs . . .

—No, damn it all, Niek interrupted me angrily,
for he is a gruff man, I'm not asking you about the
English. I'm not concerned with what the English do.
England will have to save her own soul alive, in her
own way. I'm talking about Holland, about you and
me, about your father and your Uncle Kees and your
teachers, about Dries Dekker, the milkman, and
Paulus Kentie, the undertaker, about ourselves and
the likes of us who make up the Dutch nation. Are
we guilty of those crimes in India, yes or no? Don't
hedge now and try to worm out of it. Give me a
straightforward answer as befits a son of John Calvin.
What is it? How can we stand in God's house Sunday
after Sunday and have the blood of these innocents on
our hands?

—You see, Niek, the colonial question is linked up
with a great number of other questions. There are
some other matters to be considered first.

—Oh, you're one of those who believe in keeping
silent. You want the pigs to learn to die without squealing, is that it?

—No, but you see, Niek, the interests, the directors
and shareholders, of the large colonial trusts . . .
I began again.

—No, no, not the interests, don't hide behind the
interests. Where do *you* stand, by the living God?
Do you consider me and yourself guilty, yes or no?

I say that Holland can remain free only by practicing
a policy of strict morality in the foreign field. We are
not strong enough to ward off any foreign aggression. The Germans, the English, or the French could
take Holland in a week if they wanted to. Our strength
lies in our utter defenselessness. We have no other
protector but God! Then why make God's protection
impossible by doing what's evil? God cannot protect
murderers and robbers, can He? He can't go against
His own Law, can He? We all know in our innermost
conscience that the blood of the thousands of innocent
children slain in the Indies will some day be asked of
us, of you and me, because Holland, under the guise
of a tolerant, genial, and urbane little nation, in reality
does more than any other small people to raise the
whirlwind that's going to ravage the world. Let there
be repentance and contrition, I say, and let's turn up
a new road before it's too late!

—Would you set the colonies free, Niek? Would
you favor that?

—Yes, Holland must set the example. We are
God's people, God's elect, aren't we? Then we must
do what God commands: proclaim freedom for those
who sit in the prison house. Holland must tear this
evil of colonialism from her own breast, if it be at
the risk of death.

—The Japanese or the English would seize our
colonies immediately if we set them free.

—Maybe, but we as a people would be free of the
mortal sin of oppressing God's children in Java, our
brothers. Isn't that something?

—We will sink to the rank of Denmark as a nation.
We'll be poor as church mice.

—Are we so devilish rich, then, now? I can't see it!

—It all depends on your point of view, said Marius
de Vries, the grocer, who had come in and overheard
part of our conversation. If you agree that there is
such a thing as international morality, we are clearly
at fault. If there is no law of right and wrong in the

dealing of one people with another, we are as innocent as newborn babes. That was Marius de Vries talking, and he's an Elder.

I am entirely of the opinion of Niek Goovaarts, but only in secret, of course. I wouldn't dare say openly what I think of colonialism, except to Ary or Kees perhaps, for fear of being laughed at as a presumptuous, immature meddler who's not even dry behind the ears. I can hear the objections now that would arise should I open my mouth, and the ridicule: —What do I know about such complex economic problems as our relationships with Indonesia involve?— How dare a snotty schoolboy go counter to the general interest and defame the fatherland's chief honor and glory? The cheek, the impertinence of it! You would reduce Holland to the rank of Denmark, would you? You unpatriotic rascal, you red anarchist! That's what I'd get to hear. Still I can't help it: I think it would be a great gesture if Holland dared cut herself loose from that colonial empire that is second only to Britain's. That would be greatness indeed for the fatherland!

Cut the collective sin of colonialism out of our breasts, as Niek says, as France once tore the sin of anti-Semitism from her heart when the French people would not let a Jew suffer innocently on Devil's Island. France is greater for that single act, in my estimation, than for all the glorious campaigns of Napoleon and Louis XIV combined. It's good to have a clean heart, but to have clean hands as a nation is better still. May a man not wish his fatherland great in the things of the spirit? Does greatness consist only in being able to bully a weaker people and rob it of its lands and wealth by virtue of the un-Christian right of the strongest? Are the jungle's ways to be an example for Christians? I think the Danes have set a magnificent example to the rest of the world in abolishing their army. I wish we'd do the same in the colonial field. We say we are a Christian people. All right then, let's be Christians. If that is to be the case, the glorious task of our country should be expressed in terms of Christianity, in terms of the people's spirit, not in the spirit of a handful of capitalist bonzes and moguls of the East India Company who have been enriching themselves for generations from the enslavement of Javanese and other weak peoples.

The call of the highest aspirations of the human spirit—thought, science, art, religion and so-called civilization—is to serve the gradual embodiment of the Christian ideal in human society. The oppression and exploitation of others is incompatible with that process. As a nation, in our relationship with other nations we should begin to live a worthy existence. We'll have to, for if we persist in playing the role of a great colonial power, however surreptitiously we do it, however clandestinely, our sin will find us out: some day Holland will collect the wages of the sin of colonialism. Fool, fool, fool, impossible fool! Anarchist! Antipatriot! Yes, isn't Christianity foolish? An enterprise set up by God and founded in Jesus Christ to conquer evil by goodness? How high is that enterprise rated on the Stock Exchange in Amsterdam, in London, in New York? Is it worth quoting at all?

It all depends on your point of view, said Marius de Vries. Sure, everything depends on that. From the window of the dining-car of those new luxury express trains running between Cologne and the Hook of Holland, which do not even stop at Gorcum, our own town itself might well appear a well-ordered, ideal little community, so neatly walled in, so safe, so snug, so comfortable, so compact, so quaint, so picture-postcard colorful with Sint Jan's tower rising above the trees and the red roofs.

Still, I wonder what the inhabitants of the fish market around here would have to say about our little paradise if they dared talk? Their cottages stink and swarm with vermin. The water closet stands over an open drain in the kitchen and the whole family sleeps in one cupboard bed, a mere hole in the wall. Van den Oever, the policeman, told Uncle Kees that whenever he has business in one of these huts he's sure to find his uniform crawling with lice when he comes out. And then those four abandoned children in the alley across the way where my mother dropped in by chance that day. De Man their name was. Covered with sores were their bodies and their heads crawling with lice. Couldn't be combed or scrubbed clean, she said, no matter how she tried. And all these people sitting in their door fronts in the spring, emaciated, wasted, catching a little sunshine before dying of tuberculosis. But it's the English who are said to have all the slums. Blessed little Holland has nothing of the kind. Oh, no! We are so picturesque!

What we need here by way of picturesqueness is a roaring big fire or an earthquake, as they had in Lisbon. In the Fish Street quarter and in many another quarter. Or better yet, a revolution, a house-cleaning, literally and figuratively. Pestholes like these blocks of houses should not be destroyed by an accident, by lightning, flood, or earthquake. They should be destroyed deliberately. Man should have the honor and the courage to destroy them himself, intentionally, with benevolence aforethought. It would show that he had come of age, that he respects himself, that he has grown reasonable.

What was it Domela said in the parliament? The revolution will begin and will be completed in Holland the day the Christians start to put their Christianity into practice. That would include burning down a good part of our cities and that section of Drenthe Province where people actually live in dugouts, in holes in the earth. An immense, howling, crepitating fire, that's what would make Holland blessed. A big enough fire to be seen in Germany and in Belgium and maybe in England, where it would perhaps set a good example!

Couldn't we start the ball rolling, Ary and I and some others? Couldn't we break into one of the warehouses on the quay some dark night and get hold of a barrel or two of petroleum, sprinkle the stuff around this neighborhood and the rest? Hear the rats squeal and the legions of bedbugs and disease germs crackle in the flames and see all this pestiferous slum go up in smoke? Is that perhaps what Nero had in mind when he set Rome on fire: to destroy the fetid stews, the cesspools, and the cloacae of the Pistrinum quarter? If so, the man wasn't such a fool after all, but a benefactor of the human race. The subject needs further investigation.

The burning of Rome might make an excellent chapter for the book, or set of books rather, Ary and I plan to write some day. It's to be a universal history in the light of Marxism, every major event in human history explained from the point of view of the class struggle: the Trojan War, the journey of the Argonauts, the flight of Moses from Egypt, the adoption of a source god named Yahveh by the nomadic Israelites, the prophets, the Crucifixion, the Crusades, the Inquisition, the Commune of Paris, the promulgation of the doctrine of papal infallibility, the Russo-Japanese War, the invention of printing, gunpowder, and telegraphy—everything. It has never been done. Nor, says Kees, will it ever be done. But that remains to be seen. We already have seven boxes stuffed with reference notes and lists of books to be consulted.

What if a sudden high wind should spread the fire and burn down the whole town? God! If we are going to set the place on fire we'd first have to warn the inhabitants. We can't endanger their lives. But in that event we'd be found out. Our own warning would give us away. The people themselves would carry tales and be on the accusers' side. Let's see, now; we'd be charged with infraction, with destruction of property and endangering human life. Who would defend us in court?—May it please Your

Honor, we humbly submit that our intentions were both patriotic and religious. We wanted to do away with evil. Ours was an act of pure philanthropy. It's true perhaps that we endangered human life for a moment. But we did so only because human life has been permanently endangered here, generation after generation, since the thirteenth century at least. Those fishermen's cottages have been standing here six hundred years. The date is engraved in the façade: A.D. 1265. What does that A.D. mean: Anno Domini or Anno Diaboli?

—We wanted to end the danger once and for all by stamping it out. All those dwellings were foul and loathsome hearths of infection. They threatened the whole community, rich and poor, old and young. They were a menace to Your Honor's own children. Your Honor would not have let his dog live there. The people suffered in body and soul. We wanted to destroy the conditions that degraded them, destroy them at the root. We'd better not use the word "radically." That might set the judicial mind off on a tangent. The people who lived here had no opportunity to improve their minds by reading and study and the enjoyment of art. They hadn't decent enough clothes to present themselves in church. They were caught in the selfsame wheel that held their ancestors captive. Six hundred years of ignominy!

How would the Judge take that? He'd probably declare us crazy. Perhaps there would be a petition circulated amongst the townspeople to have us declared insane. That would be called the most charitable view that could be taken of the affair: misguided, irresponsible youths fallen under a bad influence. More likely he would call us housebreakers, incendiaries, murderers, anarchists, or Jesuits even, for invoking the theory of the end justifying the means, and send us to prison for ten, twenty years, maybe for life! Jan Verduin, the shoemaker, was in jail for five years. Jan killed his wife in an excess of drunken fury. He claims it was an accident. He merely wanted to give her the beating she deserved. He told me time passes so slowly for a man in solitary confinement that every hour seems a year and every year a century.

—The judges, he said, haven't a proper notion of time. In fact they do not know what time is at all. They cannot know, Time is an abstract conception to the man on the bench, the interval in which he does his day's work before he goes to see his mistress or sits down in the club for a rubber of whist before dinner. To the man in the cell, time is a torture, more fiendish and cruel than the slow fire on which they used to roast heretics and witches in the past. Time in jail is something that makes men scream and turns them into dithering idiots. . . .

It's starting to rain. Now, why didn't I take an umbrella as my mother suggested? Soldiers are forbidden to carry umbrellas. That's a military law. They must let themselves be soaked to the skin when on the march. They are supposed to be immune to colds, rheumatism, and pneumonia, I guess, or else they must enure themselves against these evils. It's not considered manly to carry an umbrella. Come to think of it, an army with umbrellas would indeed be an unheroic sight. And ridiculous to boot. Even so, ten thousand Freemasons carrying umbrellas stood in the pelting rain on the bulwarks of Montmartre during the siege of Paris and prevented Moltke from starting the bombardment of the city.

I wonder what entails greater suffering: solitary confinement as it is imposed in our jail or being shipped off to Siberia to live in some such House of the Dead as Dostoevski describes? In our local jail there are only women. All lifers. I never saw any of them, although I always glance up when passing by, always half-fearful, too, that I may really catch sight of a face peering through the bars of one of those small windows in the top story, the only part of the building that's visible above the high garden walls.

God! What would I do if a face really did appear there? Run? Wave a greeting? Shout something? What, for instance? A word of encouragement? That would be contrary to the law, which forbids communication with prisoners except through official channels. A prison window is not an official channel.

But then, we needn't worry, there won't be any face there. Those windows are too high from the floor in the cells for the inmates to reach—not even with their outstretched arms. Else they would be hoisting themselves up constantly by the bars to look out, see the street, see people moving about. That's precisely the essence of their punishment: they are cut off from the world. They are condemned never in all their lives to see anything except the walls of their cells and the gloomy gray corridors that lead to the dining-room and the chapel. That must be the heaviest burden of all: that constant awareness of being cut off from the world forever. Hell, I have been taught, is the consciousness of being cut off from God. But that can't be quite correct, that definition. The Psalmist says: Where shall I flee? To Sheol, the place of the departed spirits? Even there art Thou! God is in hell, too, then?

Those women in our jail wear hoods over their heads with holes for the eyes and mouth. Even at divine service they sit apart in individual wooden box-like cubicles that have a narrow slit for an opening in front so that they can watch only the pulpit and the minister in it. They are locked up in those boxes during the sermon. It's so horrible as to be unbelievable, says Uncle Christiaan; you can hear their breathing. Uncle Christiaan preaches once a month to the prisoners in his own town of Haarlem. You can't see their faces, but you can hear their breathing! When Uncle Christiaan comes home from a service in prison he locks himself up in his study. He can't speak for a whole day sometimes. He can't eat, can't drink, won't listen to music, he just sits there.

Our prisoners have a big celebration on the Queen's birthday. They are allowed to take off their masks at mealtime and they get a bottle of lemonade or orangeade each. One year it's lemonade, the next it's orangeade. The soldiers of the garrison that day receive a bottle of beer and two cigars after the morning parade. The officers wear their gala uniforms and a gorgeous bunch of feathers on their kepis. My brothers and I wear an orange bow in the lapel of our jackets on the Queen's birthday. Mother keeps those ribbons in a box with the sash of the same color Jozinus used to wear.

Jozinus is dead now. He's buried next to Grandfather. Only my mother knew what he was saying when he lay dying. Everything was paralyzed in his body except his eyes. They were big blue eyes and they moved quietly to and fro. In that way my mother knew what he meant to say. He asked her to play on the organ one day. It was on the first of May. While she played he closed his eyes and was gone.

Gone! Gone where? If death is the end, what is the meaning of life? That's the riddle of the universe. Will man ever fathom that mystery? Kees holds that the hope of immortality alone distinguishes man from the animals, that the certainty of survival is instinctive in man and therefore to be respected. Tagore, the poet, says that human instinct never deceives: the moment a child is born it turns instinctively toward its mother's breasts. He feels confident that when we die we will, in awakening to a new life, also turn toward and cling to something for support and succor in the realm of shades, that we will be intuitively aware of a higher protective presence awaiting us there.

But this is really putting the cart before the horse in that it presupposes an awakening in the first place and furthermore takes for granted the retention in death of a certain power of perception to detect and distinguish that mysterious power in the hereafter. To Tagore death is not an extinction of consciousness.

This is also the Christian view, or rather the Christian hypothesis: the divine hand and divine staff comforting and guiding us in the valley of the shadow of death. It's a beautiful and comforting thought. Yet when all is said and done it's mere speculation—a groping in the dark, wishful theological thinking and abstraction, mere edification stuff, as Ary calls it. It leaves you as skeptical as before.

Uncertainty remains to haunt us all our lives. The paradise Jesus promised to the thief on the cross and that nostalgic house of the many mansions in which He said He went to prepare a place for us are as ethereal and unsubstantial as the proverbial castles in the air. I read the *Life of Bossuet* by Massillon the other day. That man, that Hercules of Gallican sacerdotalism, surely knew all there is to be known of the hereafter, all the hopeful conjectures and comfort which theology has amassed on the subject and built up into an undeniably impressive system. Still Bossuet's deathbed appears to have been a cruel and long-drawn-out agony of uncertainty, an experience so horrible that the description of it by Massillon leaves the reader with a sense of anguish that grips him by the throat.

—Have you ever, I asked my grandfather one day, in all your long experience as a pastor, seen a really happy death, someone accepting death calmly, serenely, unafraid?—Only once, said he, and in that case the dying man, I'm sorry to say, was not a Christian. His answer threw me into consternation. Even Christians, then, people who profess belief in an almost material heaven with angels, golden streets, harps, and other paraphernalia with which the Oriental mind has furnished the celestial realm, fight to their last breath the summons to inherit all that glory prepared for them from before the foundation of the world. Bossuet screamed in horror. Calvin groaned with dread. Jesus himself sweated blood at the thought

of his impending passion. There's no edification in
the account of their last hours.

On the other hand, the ancients do not seem to
have been burdened with that awful sense of doom.
Death was a fact pure and simple to them, sublime in
its simplicity. They had no fear. With their last breath
they thanked Jupiter the Liberator. No whining, no
shedding of tears, no vain exaltation. Of one great
Roman it is said that nothing troubled his end, that
his parting was like the evening of a beautiful day.
Of another it is written that death was swallowed up
in the thought of the fatherland's perpetuity and in
the love of his family. Augustus had so easy an end
that he conversed till the last moment, and himself
announced, with a smile on his lips, that it was all
over. And Socrates? Is there anything more majestic
than the farewell to his friends? Cato the Elder fell
asleep without regrets or a sigh. Thoughts like these
run through the whole of classical literature, Greek,
Roman, and Hebrew alike.

When, then, at what point in history, did men
begin to be afraid of death? Tacitus is the first of the
Romans, as far as I know, who was beset with worries
and doubts on the subject of the final hour. Did he
perhaps know something about the Christian religion
and about the doctrine of the resurrection of the flesh?
It is the promulgation of that doctrine, not by Jesus,
but by His followers, as they waited in vain for His
promised return on the clouds, that plunged the
ancient world into doubt, skepticism, and demoraliza-
tion. It is since the advent of theological Christianity
that man's death has no longer been calm and happy.
A society that lived only in the hope of the Resurrection was dead, to all intents and purposes. Its cities,
palaces, and theaters became cemeteries, its temples
catacombs. Love was a crime, joy an abomination.
The Renaissance rescued Christendom from that
abysmal theological gloom. Calvin sought to bring it

back and, at least so far as Gorcum is concerned, he succeeded only too well. . . .

During that meal on the Queen's birthday the women in our jail are permitted to talk, the only time in the year they have that permission. Do they take advantage of the privilege? What do they say to each other? Do their tongues function after three hundred and sixty-four days of inactivity? Do they recognize each other?—Oh, is it you, Mrs. van der Zwaan? Well, I declare! I hardly recognized you. Your hair has grown so white, you know. Drink hearty, my dear! Isn't this lemonade good? The dear Queen! Long may she reign over us! And you, Mrs. Jansen, my goodness, haven't you lost some teeth? Another year gone, merciful Jesus! Surely, it's a hard job, repentance.

Repentance? I wouldn't call it that. What is done in those jails I'd call practicing a terrifying vivisection on the souls and bodies of human beings, a dissection so terrifying that the mere thought of it puts even those of a strong constitution in a cold sweat. No wonder Uncle Christiaan weeps. He has such a tender heart. What words of consolation can one speak in a prison like that?

—I sat in my cell five years long weaving mats, Jan Verduin told me. Toward the end it seemed to me that the door was standing open and that a small red light blinked at me at the end of a long tunnel. But the door wasn't open at all. I got up a thousand times from my stool to feel the lock with my hands. And there wasn't any tunnel or red lamp either. It was a hallucination. But it came back every day. Then I knew I was going crazy.

Siberia would be preferable, I think. Dostoevski's House of the Dead, with all its brutality, vice, filth, and stench! Dostoevski is the magnifying glass of the Russian soul. Who is our magnifying glass? Multatuli? Willem Kloos? That fop Louis Couperus? Stylists we have aplenty. It's their style that keeps

Dutch books from being translated into foreign languages. With translation the style is lost, and our writers have nothing but style. It kills them. It's not enough to write well. There must be an undercurrent of feeling, of sensitiveness. From the works of our most perfect stylists rises an atmosphere of unbearable ennui.

Perhaps they should be a little more negligent. Negligence is a great principle in art. Every sentence Anatole France writes is perfect, but there isn't one of those perfect phrases of his which carries as much feeling as a saying, apparently written without care or effort, by that tender and troubling Stendhal. France has erudition and intelligence. But intelligence alone is not creative. Aren't real great writers very often quite naïve and impractical persons, childlike in their simplicity, and guileless? Unless ye become like little children is more than a condition of entry into the Kingdom of Heaven. It is also that state of grace prerequisite to good writing. Dostoevski is simplicity and clarity personified. Through him it's possible to gain access to the whole manifold range of Russian life.

It's a strange thing, too, that mature and cultured people acquainted with Goethe and Molière and Hölderlin and Baudelaire are as easily captivated by Dostoevski as boys who read him for the first time. He writes from the fullness of his heart. His mind differs from that of our own littérateurs in its great measure of adaptability and background of ideas. He has walked with Christ. He knows a thousand small facts, each nothing in itself perhaps, but facts that, put together, make up the whole sense of life.

Napoleon said: Watch Russia, great things are gestating there. My father often says: One of you boys had better learn the Russian language, someday it will be useful to know what the Russians are saying and doing. Kees says the Russians are the most unpredictable people on earth. Why? They take the

Gospel seriously. Who was it that said that about the Russians being the only people who have preserved the true likeness of Christ in their bosom and whose destiny it is therefore, some day, when the peoples of the West have lost the road, to direct them into new paths of salvation? Who was it, again? Oh, yes, of course, I have it: one of those Dukhobors who stayed at Grandfather's house when he passed through Holland on his way to America. Piotr Veregin was his name. Grandfather received two letters from Tolstoi. Kees still keeps those letters. They're in the black cupboard in the bookroom upstairs. You'd think they're the original drafts of the Magna Carta and the Declaration of Human Rights, the way he preserves them in moth balls and tissue paper. Grandfather and Kees went to Rotterdam with D. A. Hilkof, Tolstoi's secretary that time, to straighten out certain difficulties with the steamboat companies about the transportation of the Dukhobors to Canada.

I wonder if it's true that the Tolstoi family originally came from the Netherlands? The name doesn't sound Dutch, surely. Perhaps it's a translation of the Dutch word meaning thick, firm. Ah, what does it matter! Tolstoi is ours as much as Russia's; he belongs to the whole human fatherland. Still, there does seem to be a certain similarity in character between the Russians and the Dutch. For one thing, our people have the same sound moral conviction of what's right and wrong. Both seem to be eternally worrying about God. Oh, how they worry about God! They long for God. Longing for God is religion.

One prominent German poet, I forget who, was so startled by the similarity in character between those two tormented God-seekers, Vincent van Gogh and Dostoevski, that before writing the life story of the painter he came to Holland and seriously examined the genealogy of the Van Gogh family for traces of Russian ancestry.—Vincent, he wrote, must have had Russian blood in his veins; in no other way can I

explain the appearance of a second Christian in our
time. Van Gogh and Dostoevski. True, both were
totally bereft of the aesthetic sense; both painted
saints with the features of human beings; both felt
the advent of a new ice period, a glacial petrifaction
in human relationships; both, in their humility, attributed the evil of our time to their own unprepossessing
and even repulsive features and character. But there
was no blood relationship between them, unless Dr.
Snetlage is right in holding that there's Slavic blood
in the Dutch people.

Slavs moved in here, he says, before the days of
Julius Caesar and again perhaps at the time of the
Great Peoples' Migration in the seventh century.
Quite possible! It's perfectly all right with me. Hun-
nish blood, Vandal blood, Celtic blood, Spanish blood,
Norman blood, Semitic blood, quite a hodgepodge!
Une salade, as the French would say, *une salade russe,*
well mixed! When you come to think of it Gorcum
could very well be a Russian town. We have everything here the Russian novelists tell us they have in
the average small Russian town, except the ikons.

But we do have the village idiot. As a matter of fact
on that point we surpass the Russians: we have no
less than half a dozen idiots and so-called innocents
walking about here. Only we don't look upon them as
saints or upon their gibberish as divinely inspired.
Perhaps we did formerly. It's an old, almost universal
tradition to look upon such people with a sort of
superstitious awe as illuminati, as strangely exalted
individuals who stand in some mysterious communication with the divine. In many places they are treated
with great kindness and indulgence. It has always
been so. King David let the spittle run into his beard
when he was captured by the Philistines in order that
he might be taken for a lunatic and as such be treated
with consideration. Clever trick that! As good as the
ruse de guerre of that missionary who removed his
wooden leg, his false teeth, and finally his wig and in

so doing scared away a crowd of seriously premeditating cannibals.

What became of the Dukhobors in America, anyway? What became of all those sectarians who migrated there from here and other parts of Europe: Mennonites, Gerardists, Quakers, Hernhutters, Peculiar People, Anabaptists, Labadists? Do they still exist? I wonder if they colored the brew a little in the melting-pot over there? That was the ruin of the Labadist community we went to see near Bolsward in Frisia with Kees. William Penn visited there one day and invited the brethren to America. He helped them build a communist colony in Pennsylvania and called it Bohemian Manor. Cromwell once dabbled with the idea of joining them. All that remained at Bolsward was a heap of stones and an inscription of a saying by De Labadie: He alone is superior to others who humbles himself and is the servant of all.

That's what the Pope of Rome calls himself, too, the servant of the servants of God, as he sits, not too humbly, in the splendor of his Vatican Palace. Servant of the servants of God and successor to Saint Peter. Saint Peter said to the blind man at the temple gate: Gold and silver have I not. But he opened the fellow's eyes. Miracles like that don't happen any more. They never happened, of course. Kissing the tomb of the Martyrs of Gorcum at Brielle is said to have cured a woman of water on the knee. Who was that woman? Where is she? Medical men smile when you ask them about such cures as are said to be performed at Lourdes, Kevelaer, and Fulda.

Plenty of people get cured in those places. But none stays cured. It's a momentary exaltation which gives them a feeling of relief and improvement. When the mass intoxication subsides they still have their tumors, dropsies, goiters, and palsied limbs. It's a highly significant fact that no cures are ever reported at Lourdes in wintertime. Little Bernadette seems a little sulky on cold days. She won't sing when there are no

admiring crowds about. Touching a box containing the
finger bones of Saint Boniface at Fulda is supposed to
cure diabetes. Will it? Not if you don't believe, the
monks told Uncle Christiaan, not if you doubt.

I saw myself a splinter of the True Cross in a golden
casket in the cathedral of Bois-le-Duc across the river.
There are other splinters elsewhere, in hundreds of
places. Glued together those splinters would make a
cross five times the height of Sint Jan's tower. What
haven't they got? The seamless robe of Christ over
which the soldiers cast lots on Calvary. There are
exactly forty of them in various Roman churches in
Europe. The Arabs at least keep only one of Mohammed's shirts. The blood of Saint Januarius that
liquefies once a year at Naples. The authentic hat,
the hat mind you, of the Virgin Mary can be seen at
Bagnara! Two bottles of her milk are kept in the
Convent of the Mater Domini near Naples. What
next! The last breath of Saint Peter in a jar, I suppose. Take a whiff, please! By God, it does smell of
garlic! . . .

Now look who's coming. Colonel van Maanen himself. He must have been inspecting the soldiers exer-
cising on the ramparts, else how would he be roaming
in this neighborhood? Should I take off my hat to him?
Yes, no. Yes, no. What shall it be? I am supposed to
show respect for the royal insignia on his uniform, for
his position, for . . . But he is boiling-mad at us.
He considers the gymnasiasts in general responsible
for his daughter's disgrace, the unreasonable man. If
anyone is responsible, it's Jetze. For it's Jetze who
wrote her a letter asking for a date, quite honorably.
As usual when he writes to girls, he ended the letter
on a note of high poetry. But the letter fell out of
the young lady's coat pocket and the directress of
the girls' school picked it up. She sent it to the girl's
mother. The mother gave it to the Colonel. The
Colonel sent it to our Rector. The Rector made copies
and sent them to Jetze's father and to the fathers of

Jetze's classmates. My father got a copy, too. The
Rector gave us a talking-to and a hundred lines from
Virgil to translate.

Jetze had no date, of course. But the girl started to
fool around with an orderly of her father's, a young
recruit who served at the Colonel's house as valet and
butler. And now the old man blames us. We turned his
daughter's thoughts in an evil direction, he says.
There, it's done! I tipped my hat to him. He just
glowered at me. That's what I get for my patriotism.
Ah, there's Ryer Dam coming down the street. Ryer
runs a bicycle shop, or rather rents out bicycles at
ten cents an hour. What's he doing up there by the
Dalem Gate? Probably trying to collect a debt?

—Did you see that, Ryer?

—What?

—Colonel van Maanen! There he goes. I saluted
him and he pulled a face at me.

—Serves you right. You disturbed his thoughts
about the country's defense. He was probably just
thinking of how to keep the Turks out.

—Busy these days, Ryer?

—My busiest day is Sunday.

—Sunday, Ryer? That's bad. That's the Sabbath.

—Look, Pieter, are you going to sing that song,
too? What in hell do I care about the Sabbath? Am
I to refuse business just to please the dominies?
When do people have time to take a ride out in the
country? On Sundays, isn't it? Old Dominie Strang
asked me the same question the other day. He says:
Don't you believe in God, Ryer? You know what I
told him? I says to him: Sure, I says, I believe in God,
but not in your God. My God is far over to the left,
I says, He likes freedom. My God likes riding a
bicycle on a Sunday and better yet, I says, a tandem
with a little lassie right up in front. That's what I told
him.

—Ho! You should have seen the face on him! He
swallowed as if he had tasted rat poison. God on a

bicycle, says he, a most bizarre idea! Make the most of it, Your Reverence, says I. You ain't going to have me burnt at the stake for it, are you? Not that, he says. Heavens, no, who spoke of that? I simply want you to mend your ways. So I came right back at him. I explained to him that young people prefer to go out on a Sunday and make love in the countryside, that they prefer that to sitting in church, see? But he says: Ah, but it rains so frequently on Sundays, Mr. Dam. They're apt to catch cold. They sit in the grass so often. So I says to him: *Eerwaarde*, Your Reverence, excuse my frankness, but a girl that's afraid to get her behind wet isn't worth the trouble. That's what I said. He walked off shaking his head. Why don't they leave people alone with their crazy ideas?

—What about the Sunday-closing laws, Ryer? Don't they apply to your business?

—Sure they do. That's the hell of it. People who want to go biking on Sunday must get their machines on Saturday night.

—Well?

—Well, what do you think they do? They ride out on Saturday night and do me out a lot of money. I can't charge them for the night, can I?

—Take the lanterns off, Ryer.

—Then they'll get fined by the police or they'll break their damned necks. What do you want me to do, kill my fellow Christians? Why don't you drop in at the shop? I got a new accordion, a pippin! A real Hohner! And, oh yes, Pieter there's a socialist meeting next Wednesday, I nearly forgot to tell you. Try to come out. A great speaker, Jan Regt. Regt'll tell them where to get off. I heard him before at the Field Day. Twenty-five cents admission. Tell your Uncle Kees, will you, and that friend of yours, Burgomaster Brandt's boy.

The last socialist meeting was held in the old warehouse back of Louis Swarthout's taproom. Duclou, the grocer, once used the place for the storage of vats of vinegar and mustard, but gave it up because of the rats. It poured rain that night, the roof leaked like a sieve and from the floor came an ice-cold draft. That was the night when Borstlap the pharmacist raised a rumpus by opening his umbrella in the midst of the proceedings. First he got a good laugh from the audience. But then the chairman denounced his gesture as an act of deliberate provocation. His protest that he merely wanted to keep off the rain was of no avail. Order! Order! Put that umbrella down, you bourgeois poison-mixer! Some of the young fellows who work out at the shipyard began to sing ominously: Oh, the people's wrath it's rising 'gainst the tyrants and their ilk! In the end Borstlap took the hint, put his umbrella down, and blew his nose. Just in time: one of the bouncers was coming down the aisle from the platform.

I could hardly see the speakers that evening, through the clouds of smoke from the cigars and pipes and those soot-belching oil lamps hanging from the ceiling. There was a strong smell of sweat and sour beer, of damp clothes and of wooden shoes stuffed with moist straw.—Place stinks like a sewer, said the principal of the denominational school as he entered the hall. But Kees came right back at him: Sir, do you think the catacombs smelled of violets? Tit for tat, that's old Kees' way.

When the windows were opened at last there was a new interruption. We could hear Swarthout's customer's come out into the alley alongside the taproom to relieve themselves. The whole assembly burst into laughter when a hoarse, croaking voice grunted outside: A piss without a fart is like a wedding without music. Comrades! Comrades! Don't let your attention be diverted by such vulgarities! Where is your proletarian dignity? Nardus de Smet, with the walrus mustache and the cork leg, who presided, banged the table and rang the bell. Still they laughed.

Then the house turned to unfinished business. It

appears that our Burgomaster, the cockeyed Baron Floris de Bruyn, won't let the civic hall be used for socialist meetings even for double or treble the usual rent.—Over my dead body, he told the committee. I'll see you in hell first. It is I, said he, squinting twice as hard as usual, it is I who am going to bar the road in this community to the forces of anarchism, atheism, and free love. So long as there sits a descendant of William the Silent on Holland's throne, there'll be no socialism in Gorcum. God, Holland, and Orange, he goes on telling the committee, is an unbreakable, eternal, threefold tie.—Three in one, eh, like Father, Son, and Holy Ghost? Nardus asked him.

Another of the committee members says to the Baron as he paced up and down raving at them and accidentally bumped his leg against a table: Man, why don't you look where you go, or else go where you look? That was a pretty mean crack. The Baron is very sensitive on the subject of his bad eyes. The report of the committee's interview with the Burgomaster took up nearly an hour.

I sat next to a man by the name of Klaas Bot who had brought his dog along. Bot runs a small shop near the Dalem Gate where he sells fishing tackle, charcoal, kindling wood, and hot water. I have also seen him in the costume of a mute with a cocked hat on and a long black cloak walking in front of funeral processions. The dog, a big shaggy mongrel, lay under the seat scratching and biting himself.

On the other side of Klaas Bot was Miss Helena de Wit. She's a feminist, a follower of Mrs. Pankhurst, and the first woman in Gorcum to wear bloomers when riding a bicycle. She has a rather inadequate bust, wears her hair bobbed—no hat, of course—a glittering pince-nez over small hard eyes, and no stockings. Annoyed over the dog's scratching she says to Bot:—It seems your dog has fleas.—Maybe, says Klaas. But you needn't worry: they don't go for humans.—Can't you put him out, she asks?—Can't

you get used to anything? comes back Klaas. With
that he winks at the dog, who looks up on hearing
his master's voice and wags his tail in perfect understanding. After that intermezzo Bot resumed chewing tobacco and spitting on the floor.

The more fiery and eloquent the speaker of the
evening, the more vigorously Klaas spat. Marx says.
Spit. Hegel says. Spit. Kautsky says. Spit. Bebel says.
Jaurès says. Troelstra says. Spit. Spit. Spit.—But
what in hell does the honored speaker say himself,
that the meat is better than the bones, like the rest
of us? That was Dorus Bommel interrupting. Order!
Order! Throw him out! Make that ass shut up!
Dorus, for God's sake, don't show your ignorance.

President Nardus promptly branded Dorus a hire-
ling of the *patronat* and of the Chamber of Commerce
and Local Initiative specially sent to the meeting to
cause a commotion. Wybe Hofstra dissented from
that opinion of the chair. Wybe said that in his opinion
Dorus was not an agent provocateur at all, but just
a damn fool who wanted to draw attention to himself.
—How are we to know, said Wybe, that there is such
an individual in the world as Dorus Bommel if he
doesn't reveal his existence now and then by making
a nuisance of himself? Great hilarity! Incident closed.
Another bang of the gavel. It's easy to see that
Nardus is a carpenter, the way he handles that hammer.

I saw Dr. Snetlage there. I don't think he saw me.
Better not. He stood in the rear. We all stood as
Nardus, in a voice of thunder, read the Communist
Manifesto: Proletarians of all countries, unite! You
have nothing to lose but your chains and a world to
gain! That's their creed. Their Apostles Creed, you
might say. If that is their Apostles Creed, what would
correspond to their Nicene Creed? Must be *Das
Kapital*, surplus value, dialectical materialism, *Vere-
lendungs Theorie* and that stuff. Ten times I have tried
to read that book. I still couldn't tell anybody what's

really in it. Creeds, whether Marxist or Christian, seem to be cosubstantially incomprehensible. Take that of Athanasius; it's labeled a creed for the removal of doubt. And then talks about somebody being begotten before the world of the substance of his mother. A helluva lot of doubt that removes! And whoever doesn't believe may he be anathema, cursed, ostracized, cut off, garrotted, drawn and quartered, buried alive, hanged, or roasted over a slow fire.

The Inquisition condemned every inhabitant of the Netherlands to death and murdered hundreds of thousands. I shouldn't say that. The Inquisition merely handed the poor heretic over to the secular authorities to be dealt with. There's a distinction! Our father John Calvin, too, shed innocent blood. But the modern Calvinists at least put up a monument on the spot where Servetus was burnt at the stake and wrote on it that their Father in God had made an unholy and terrible mistake. When will the Catholics put up a monument to the Huguenots or one tiny little commemorative plaque to the hundreds of thousands of Protestants slain by their Inquisition?

When? Never? They could not make such a gesture in a hundred years. That would come too close to making a confession of error. An authoritarian Church cannot show the least contrition without at the same time destroying or sapping its own basic claims to infallibility and to an exclusive possession of the truth. Rather than admit an error, it will try to cover up its confusion with more physical terror. Ah, you weep, Messire Galileo? You tremble at the sight of the thumbscrews and the rack, do you? And well you may. It's not by any means a pleasant sensation to feel your joints cracking. You weep? Do you recant your heresy, then, Messire, and do you admit that Mother Church is right when she teaches that the sun does move around the earth? Do I see you nod your venerable head? Ah, glory hallelujah, praise be to God! Another victory for the true faith!

To this day those people do not consider it immoral or uncivilized to persecute and punish a man for his opinions. Look at the exultation in their press over the execution of Francisco Ferrer, a schoolteacher who denied the magic properties of a consecrated wafer. Or that woman who was sent to prison in Burgos recently for having told her cronies around the pump that Jesus had brothers and sisters. To have let that remark pass might have given rise to doubt in certain minds of the validity of the doctrine of Mary-ever-Virgin. Now the doctrine is safe. It's true: the woman is in jail, isn't she? Isn't that proof that Mary remained a virgin in spite of at least five confinements? Believe or else . . . It's still the same story as in the Middle Ages.

Perhaps I had better not cross the bridge today. The first house on the other side of the canal is Pia van Houten's. Pia always raps on the window when I pass. She began it when my brothers and I went by on our way to and from the Froebel School, when we were knee-high to a grasshopper. She used to give us cookies then. We never thanked her; our mouths were too full. But today I really can't bear to listen again to the story of that litigation she carries on with the municipality about the ownership of the house she lives in. I've heard it a hundred times. I heard of the latest developments in the case only two days before I left on my vacation. It's been going on for eighteen years, that fight.

The municipality claims the house under a bequest by Pia's father. Pia argues that she is to have its use as long as she lives. Each anniversary of her father's death a bailiff and two assistants present themselves to claim possession. Pia pours the men a cup of coffee and sends them back to the Town Hall with a message to the Burgomaster to go to the devil. It's very humiliating for the Baron. If he should use force, he'd have the whole town against him. The people remember Pia's father, a rich man, owner of a dozen big

river boats, who left the bulk of his fortune to chari-
ties. So she sits by the window and knits and waits for
the next visit of the bailiff. Let's see, it's in September,
I think. They'll soon be due again.

She's a remarkable woman just the same, old Miss
Pia. She has her eyes on everything. Nothing escapes
her. The last time I sat down with her in her window
seat, the municipal architect happened to go by,
accompanied by three of his seven children. The
biggest, a girl, walked arm in arm with her father.
He held his other arm around the smallest one's neck.
—See that? Pia asked me. Touching, isn't it? Fine
picture of fatherly love, eh?—Yes, I said.—You make
a mistake, says she. He holds that big girl by the arm
so you won't see that her dress is torn at the elbow.
The little one he fondles that way so that people won't
notice that the three top buttons are missing from her
blouse. Pia has hawk eyes. Nothing escapes her.—It's
a pity, I said, speaking of the architect, that he has
to cover up his children's rags that way.—No pity at
all, says she. That's what comes of marrying a woman
eight years older than himself.—Is his wife that
much older?—Yes, says Miss Pia, his wife is a distant relative of his. She paid for his schooling. In
gratitude he married her. Now he's sorry; you can
tell that by the sour look on his face.

Pia van Houten herself was once engaged to be
married. Her fiancé was a young notary. She broke
off the engagement after twelve years on learning that
his grandmother had died in an insane asylum.—You
can't be too careful these days, said Miss Pia. On
Sundays when she goes to church she wears a long
black dress that hides the movement of her feet and
knees. You can't say that she walks; she glides. Her
head moves in so stately and steady a fashion that a
glass of water on top of her bonnet wouldn't spill a
drop. Some people refer to Miss Pia as Miss Kettle-
drums. That's because of her enormous bosom. When
she comes in Kees will say: There's the good ship

Pia sailing into harbor. You don't laugh, of course, for you're in church. Besides, the joke is too old. After she has taken her seat she looks around like a drill-master on parade to see whether everybody is in his place.

During the singing of the second psalm she passes her box of peppermints. It used to be a golden box, but now it's only an ordinary porcelain one. The golden one disappeared one Sunday while circulating in the pew right behind Miss Pia's seat. She says she's sure of the thief's identity. But she won't prosecute or lay a charge.—I'm letting the worm of remorse gnaw at the man's conscience, she says, until he's as miserable as Job on his dunghill.

If I go into her house, she'll probably tell me what sermons she heard in my absence. She remembers every word. In return she'll ask me what I have learned myself by way of edification in the towns I've visited. She doesn't want to miss a thing.

Jetze is capable of conversing with her for hours on end. He drank nine cups of tea in Pia's house one afternoon. Jetze is a great favorite of Pia's, because she knows his father. She agrees with Jetze's father on some subtle point of the doctrine of predestination.

It was Pia who discovered what went on in the garret of a house across the way from hers. Two girls had rented a room there. They kept their lamp burning long after midnight. Pia saw some soldiers dawdling about the bridge one evening and she put two and two together. And sure enough, it was true. Two hussies from Rotterdam, they were. They're gone now. The police forced them to leave. Everybody in town was sorry. It's uncanny the way that woman ferrets out people's secrets although she never leaves her house, except on Sundays when the bailiffs don't work.

Last October she said to me:—I wouldn't be in the least surprised to see Donker's bakery go up in flames some night. And two weeks after that, by the Lord

Harry, the house did burn. It was a noble spectacle,
incidentally, the way those sacks of flour shot straight
through the roof and exploded in mid-air. It was a
better show than the fireworks on the night of the
Queen's birthday. But how did Pia know it was going
to happen?—I live right across the way, she explained.
I knew that his business was going to pot. The hours
he spent loitering in the doorway, see, and the cautious, suspicious way he stepped into the street from
time to time to look at the building. I said to myself:
I wonder how much insurance he has on it. At night
he had a candle burning in the shop till about three
o'clock in the morning. Then he got up to put straw
and wood in the oven. I could see the glow from my
window upstairs. Then I thought of him looking at
the building as if he was calculating something and I
simply put two and two together again. Was I right?
But his father was an honest man, even if he died in
sin. May God have mercy on his poor soul!

—In sin, Miss Pia? How was that?—How's that,
you ask? Didn't your grandfather ever tell you, or
your Uncle Kees? It was a terrible scandal! It was
during Carnival week. There was a big affair one evening at the Flying Dutchman, you know, the tavern
on the Langedijk that's now called Café Merwestein
since the Jewish man took it over. Drinking, dancing,
and a costume ball. You can imagine what kind of
people went there. All those that live without God or
His commandments in this community were there.

And to that place went that foolish old man, Baker
Donker. He had no business there at all. I don't know
who put him up to it, unless it's that incendiary son
of his. All his life he had been an exemplary burgher
and a steady churchgoer. I believe he was even an
Elder in the chapel of the Dissenters for a time. I
don't know to this day what came over him. But they
dressed him up in a long robe, put a crown on his
head, placed a scepter in his hand, and made him king
of the ball. To make him look more royal they

painted his face with a gold wash. Then they hoisted him on the stage and there he sat on a big decorated armchair like a real king on his throne.

All that drunken crowd marched up to him to drop him a curtsy. Then the dancing started and he dozed off. He was in the habit of going to bed early, you see, being a baker. About midnight, when the revel was at its height, someone went up to him to offer him a glass of beer. They shook him, they called out his name; Donker didn't wake up. He had been dead for more than an hour. The excitement had been too much for him.

—Well, that wasn't so very scandalous, after all, Miss Pia.—Not scandalous? Wait till you hear the rest of it. They took the body home and called in the women to wash him and lay him out for burial. Those women tried to get the gold paint off his face. But they couldn't. They rubbed and scrubbed all night. There was no use. The paint had soaked in and dried in. It wouldn't come off. When they used turpentine the skin went pitch-black. And that's the way he went to meet his God, with a face as black as the night.— He must have caused quite a sensation in heaven, Miss Pia. A Dutch Negro! Ought to have been quite a novelty up there!—Oh, go away, you and your blasphemy!

One thing I've understood from Marx's books. It's something that haunts my imagination. I can't shake it off. Jan Regt, the speaker at the socialist meeting, touched upon it briefly that night. Marx talks about *die Zuspitzung der Lage*, the accentuation of the crisis in society, literally, the coming to a point of the historical process. In the era we have now entered, he says, there will be a series of nationalist wars in which the smaller states will gradually be eliminated in that they will virtually lose their independence by passing within the orbit or under the influence and protection of one or the other Great Powers. Then will follow a gigantic struggle between

the five or six major Powers, assisted by their satel-
lites, for the domination of the world and its markets.

However, this second contest of strength will not
be fought to a conclusive issue in one round of war
either. There will be a whole series of wars involving
well-nigh the entire human race. One world war will
scarcely be terminated before diplomatic maneuvering
begins for new alliances and new alignments looking
toward the next conflict. Powers allied in one campaign will be in opposing camps during the next round.
Ideologies will be created to change the noble ally
of one war into a subhuman monster who is to be
utterly destroyed in the next one.

These world wars will succeed each other with
ever-increasing rapidity. The brief intervals between
wars will be scarcely worth the name of peace, inasmuch as they will be utilized by the statesmen to
maneuver with feverish haste for new strategic positions and to prepare new political and military alignments for the next phase of the universal armed struggle. Each generation will in turn be called upon, as if
it were a law of nature or a divine command, to send
its children once, twice, or even three times to the
battlefields to be slaughtered in holocausts a thousand
times more inhuman than those sacrifices of the
Canaanites of antiquity who placed their newborn
infants in the white-hot metal arms of the Moloch
idol.

With the steady advance in the technique of transportation, and with science, industry, and capital
putting all their inventive genius, their energies and
resources, into the manufacture and perfection of
death-dealing and destructive instruments, that is,
ever more gruesome and devastating, war or the
preparation for war will in the end become man's sole
occupation and preoccupation. In our lifetime war will
in fact have become mankind's chief and exclusive
business.

The historical process is moving toward such a

cataclysm of horrors as even the towering imagination of a Dante could not conceive. And that's the period of history in which we are destined to live. Surely, not a very enticing prospect. No, it's a prospect to make one shudder. And it's not merely a bad dream —I wish it was, or a pessimistic presentiment induced by the sad sight of dropping leaves and lowering sky. It is an incontrovertible, verifiable fact.

Should it be considered fortunate or unfortunate that the great majority of men haven't the least suspicion of what's in store for them and for the world in the next fifty or a hundred years? And should they be told, or should they be left to nourish the illusion that war can be abolished by parliamentary decrees and peace conferences and goodwill meetings between statesmen? Or would it be more charitable to have their attention diverted from what is fundamentally wrong with modern society, as is being done now, by being fed spiritual food of the kind that Charles Kingsley, long before Marx, called "the opium of the people," that religion of resignation and human impotence which has already done so much to rob mankind of faith in itself and to break its will to reason and its courage to will and dare?

Strange things are happening in the national political field: water and fire are coming together: the Roman Catholic and the Calvinist parties have formed a coalition. The orthodox dominies are currently preaching from the text How good and lovely is it for brothers of the same house to dwell together in unity.

The justification for their cohabitation is the so-called antithesis invented by the Prime Minister Dr. Kuyper. The antithesis splits mankind in twain: believers and unbelievers; the sheep on one side, the goats on the other. Kees calls the coalition an anticipation on the Last Judgment. Fundamentally this move has nothing to do with theology, of course. Underneath all that subtle palaver we hear from the pulpits is a very real social-economic basis. What is happening is this: The reaction is closing ranks in the face of mounting social discontent. The growth of socialist thought and action puts the churches on their mettle.

It's a significant phenomenon, this coalition, in that it is a harbinger of things to come in other countries. It shows two things: first, that under their skin the official churches are sisters; secondly, that organized Christianity is willing to turn its back upon the poor, and consequently upon Jesus, the moment the established order of capitalism is threatened. Bon gré, mal gré, it reveals where its real interests lie and on which side it stands. It prefers a metaphysical, mythical, harmless Christ to a prophetic, social Jesus who talks of overcoming the world and of fighting it out to the bitter end. Christ is safe and sound; the churches prefer Him. Jesus is a disquieting Galilean carpenter's son who is moved with inner compassion for the masses.

The Catholic Church will reap the benefit of all this fatuous political maneuvering. Its position as the great, last bulwark of reaction in the world is strengthened immensely. The Protestant reaction joins hands with it. Not in Holland alone; the same is happening in Germany and in Hungary. Other countries will soon follow. Protestant countries chiefly. The Catholic Church flourishes only in Protestant countries. In so-called Catholic countries—France, Italy, Spain, Portugal—it's always in trouble, has to ally itself with the most brutal absolutism to keep on its feet.

How our Calvinists are going to collaborate with that old institution which they have so often identified as "the whore of Babylon" and "Antichrist" will be curious to watch. The Calvinists will have to become the protectors and apologizers of the Church of the Inquisition. Criticism of Roman Catholic politics will be squelched. Whoever ventures to point out that Rome has systematically fought every liberal constitution in Europe and the Americas, that it has anathematized every democratic institution from the public school to freedom of conscience, freedom of the press, and equal franchise, decrying them as "pestilential" and "evils that cannot be sufficiently execrated," that it has always placed itself squarely across the path of modern science and enlightenment, and that it declares legitimate the very servitude of which democracy vows to liberate mankind—anyone daring to remind his fellow citizens of the record of that Church will be told that he is disturbing unity, that he is attacking religion, that he is rocking the boat, that he is a red, radical, atheistic socialist.

There is indeed an antithesis in this world; but it does not run the way the Christian theologians say it does. It opposes the bourgeoisie, the ruling classes with their Christian Churches, to the *Habenichts*, the world's weary and heavy-laden who have Jesus on their side. The nearer the day comes when I must stand in the pulpit of my fathers, the more I am distressed. Sometimes I feel that I will get by, as so many do, without bothering about the economic and social question. Why make enemies? Why inject controversy and contradiction? And what difference will it make in the end if one insignificant person in a forlorn corner of Holland speaks out? Will that change anything in the situation?

But then there comes a fellow like Niek Goovaarts who shakes me all to pieces when he says:—No, by the living God! If you know, tell me straight! Don't dodge the issue! *Kleur bekennen*, acknowledge, show your color! Only what we experience personally, our right to free examination, our inner self-determination and autonomy, can make us free and independent and bring about our redemption.

The six-o'clock train is in. There's Mr. van Laan leaving the station, and there's old Vossius. I wonder if he has solved the riddle of Ovid this time. It doesn't look like it, his face is as thought-burdened and worried as ever. And there, heavens, is Joris de Ridder again! I must run; I couldn't stand a second encounter today.

Chapter V

NOBLE BY BIRTH

ZEGER van Rietvelt was the first boy to come to school wearing a bowler hat and spats and sporting a silver-knobbed walking-stick. In the case of any other student, such foppish apparel would almost certainly have met with frowns and headshaking on the part of the school authorities and most likely as well with an order from the Gymnasium's uncompromising censor to cease the practice forthwith. In Zeger's case it was different. The instructors treated that boy with a deference and an anxious partiality that sometimes bordered on the obsequious. He was above the law, so to speak; or if that expression be too strong, it can safely be said that in his case the rules and regulations governing the conduct of ordinary mortals were noticeably relaxed. The reason was simple: Zeger's father was a baronet, or, to give the Dutch equivalent of that title, a Jonkheer, and in addition one of the wealthiest landowners in the province, or for all I know in the Kingdom of the Netherlands. How much land the Rietvelts really owned I am not prepared to say, but from hearing Zeger's boasts on the subject one may easily have gained the impression that they did not lag very far behind the royal family itself.

His people claimed descent from the lordly house of Arkel, whose early Jans and Willems, if not the actual founders of Gorcum, were, on the indisputable authority of hoary documents, the seigneurs who had fortified our town in the twelfth and thirteenth centuries against the Counts of Holland. Besides building the walls and the fortifications of our city and its five turreted gates, the Lords of Arkel had distributed castles and strongholds all over the neighborhood to resist the encroachments of the slowly gathering might of a Central Power in the medieval Netherlands. Their five principal fortresses outside Gorcum stood in the near-by villages of Arkel, Rietvelt, Kedichem, Eeterwijk, and Leerdam. As may be seen, the first letters of the names of these localities form the word Arkel. Of this illustrious house our friend Zeger was an indirect offshoot.

But the Counts of Holland had long since exterminated the main branch of that turbulent race. The bones of the Arkels had turned to ashes, and the dust itself had vanished. The marble tombs of twenty-odd of these Lords, adorned with their peacefully reclining effigies, were ranged in a long row under the organ loft in the Great Church of our town, and a commemorative stone plaque in the façade of a military bakery marked the spot near which the last of the glorious name, Willem XXIII, died fighting against the pikemen of the hereditary enemy of his house, Jacqueline of Bavaria, Countess of Holland and Hainaut. Willem van Arkel, the inscription said, fought with surpassing bravery from nine in the morning till three in the afternoon against five thousand of Jacqueline's mercenaries who had entered the town by a ruse. Later in the day, he and a few knightly companions, having been separated from the main force of Gorcum's defenders, were pressed into a short narrow street by hundreds of the enemy, who entered the alley from both sides.

Willem and his friends, seeing their escape cut off, stood with their backs against the wall of that house which was a bakery in my youth and laid about so doughtily with their swords that before long a pile of dead and wounded lay about them. They were brought low in the end by some enemy soldiers who had entered the house from the rear and who poured boiling oil on them from the upstairs windows. That the particulars of that unequal battle, which took place on December 15 of the year 1417, have been so accurately preserved we owe to the fact that the Countess Jacqueline, who watched the affray from a point near by, demanded a report from all eyewitnesses of the death of the man whom she had intended to marry after having defeated him. Death saved the gallant Willem from a fate that was reserved for the Duke of Gloucester and two or three other princes whom Jacqueline married thereafter in rapid succession.

"Since the day of the last Willem's death," the inscription goes on to say, "the age-old cry 'Arkel, Arkel forever!' has not, alas, been heard in this land and will never be heard again." The castles of the Arkels, too, had been leveled with the ground. Of the one that once stood inside Gorcum proper, the so-called Blue Fortress, the mightiest of the lot, dominating the confluence of the Meuse and the Rhine, there remained but a pair of stunted towers, which were used in modern times as military arsenals. A deep moat, known as the Devil's Ditch, which was filled with a poisonous green ooze, marked the spot where the main structure once reared its impressive might. The Devil's Ditch now lay outside the town walls and was said to be haunted by a legion of screeching ghosts who on appropriate occasions, such as nights of storm or heavy frost when nobody was likely to be about to verify matters, filled the air with an eerie and doleful lament for the dead heroes of Arkel. Another castle, the manor house now occupied by Zeger's family in the village of Rietvelt, some ten miles from Gorcum, massive though it still was, constituted but a fragment of the huge castle with towers, drawbridges, dependencies, and moats which the old drawings in the museums showed to have stood there in the glorious past.

Zeger boarded at the Rector's house in Gorcum. For this reason the other boys weighed their words carefully when in his presence. Besides being an insufferable snob, the Jonkheer's son was a confirmed talebearer and informer. Extremely tall for his age, Zeger had blond hair almost the color of platinum and a boldly turned-up nose that gave him a decidedly supercilious mien. He had a habit of throwing his head back in a sudden jerky movement. Ostensibly to keep his lank hair from falling into his eyes, the gesture could also be taken as one of contempt for his fellow students and for the world in general. For a long time Zeger scarcely addressed his school companions by as much as a word. He came and went virtually ignoring their existence.

During the first two years he sat in the high, old-fashioned form to my left. His was the seat nearest the window. He would dangle his long legs on the outside of the form while keeping his eyes stedfastly averted from what went on in the classroom. None of the instructors ever reproved him by as much as a word or a look for this display of hauteur. He was an indifferent student, and in later years, when some measure of verbal communication had been established between him and the other boys, he remarked more than once that he was not attending the Gymnasium in order to prepare for a career or a profession, but merely to pass the time until he should be old enough to assist his father in the administration of the ancestral estates.

On Saturday, when school closed at noon, the young nobleman went home to the village that bore the family name. That homeward journey was his hour of triumph. He visibly enjoyed this compensation for the humiliation of having been forced to spend the week in the company of inferior creatures. A carriage bearing the old Arkel coat of arms, and drawn by two magnificent horses, stood waiting for him at the curb in front of the school. Zeger would emerge from the building walking with measured steps. Silver-handled cane under his arm, and slowly drawing on his kid gloves, he would throw his head back in a characteristic manner and arch his eyebrows to their ultimate height. He took as long as possible over the path from the door to the edge of the sidewalk, thus prolonging pleasure and triumph.

A footman, silk hat in hand, carried his satchel of books and then ran ahead to open the carriage door. This lackey wrapped a heavy woolen plaid around his young master's knees before closing the door, and then climbed to his own seat by the side of the liveried coachman on the driving box. The whip cracked, the horses' hoofs scraped on the cobblestones, and with a deafening rattle the landau flew through the streets. On the way toward the Arkel Gate, shopkeepers and others, recognizing the seigneurial equipage, uncovered their heads. To these salutations Zeger responded by tipping his own hat in a casual, nonchalant manner as if he were a feudal prince acknowledging the homage of lieges and chattel slaves. The whole performance was a little ceremony that many of his classmates never tired of watching and, it goes without saying, to Zeger's intense satisfaction, for the boy reveled in pomp and circumstance.

As time went by Zeger grew less overbearing in his attitude toward his schoolmates. Not only did he learn to speak civilly to them, but occasionally he joined in the discussions of the debating club which met on Wednesday afternoons. But he stedfastly refused to come to Uncle Kees' studio, where many of us forgathered after school hours on other days. Once, I remember, Ary Brandt's invitation brought on a heated altercation, perhaps the first of many that followed in the ensuing years.

"Come along," said Ary to Zeger on that occasion, "and smoke a pipe with us like an ordinary Christian! What are you afraid of? Nobody is going to tell the Rector, I'm sure!"

"No," Zeger drawled back, a little hesitant, groping for words, "it isn't the Rector at all, you see. I don't care for what the old man says. I was just wondering—eh, eh—whether a painter's studio is rather a—a—a—fit place for a Rietvelt."

"Well, of all the damned conceit!" shot back Ary, bristling with resentment. "Not a fit place? Then what on earth is a fit place for a Rietvelt? Is it perhaps over in Achin killing defenseless women and children, or what?"

With that remark the fat was in the fire and the quarrel flared up so vehemently that others had to separate the two boys to prevent them from coming to blows. For Achin, as Ary well knew, was a sore point with the members of the Rietvelt family. The truth was that Zeger's father, Arnout van Rietvelt, had served as a major in the colonial army and had taken part under Generals van Daalen and van Heutsz shortly after the turn of the century in the so-called pacification of Achin, a territory settled by Arabs and situated in the northwestern part of the Island of Sumatra.

In that campaign, it was said, Major van Rietvelt had distinguished himself by extraordinary bravery. A row of ribbons on the lapel of his coat attested to a grateful official recognition of services rendered to the fatherland. In itself this was nothing extraordinary; there were hundreds like him. It was not the man's heroism that Ary had in mind. His sarcastic references concerned the ugly rumors that circulated in Holland about the nature of those military expeditions in the northern parts of Sumatra. Returning soldiers had dropped more than hints that what in official language was described as a series of brilliant feats of arms had in reality been a display of ferocity uncommon even in a centuries-long history of ruthlessness and violence in the treatment of Indonesian natives. The tales soldiers brought home about the Achin episode in Dutch colonial administration were often too harrowing for words.

An outsider hearing Ary's reference to the killing of innocent natives might have passed it over as an irresponsible schoolboy's flippant remark about certain aspects of Holland's colonial policy. But not Zeger! Zeger knew perfectly well what Ary had in mind. He took Ary's words as a personal affront and an insult to his father. For the nobleman's son was well aware, as was everybody else in Gorcum, of the rumors current on the subject of Jonkheer van Rietvelt's personal share in the Achinese atrocities. He had commanded a company of Dutch troops in the late war in Sumatra and had come out of the East with the comically odious nickname of "The Cannibal."

For this, it must be said in all fairness, he was himself largely responsible. The man never missed an opportunity to boast about his own exploits, the dangers he had faced, the daring attacks he had led, and the cruelty he had not hesitated to employ against the women and children of "those fanatical Achinese." He never stopped talking about it. When he recounted some of the bloodcurdling details of the bayonet work of his soldiers or the employment of artillery against the straw huts of the natives, and when his listeners put their hands over their ears to shut out the sound of his voice, he would burst into fits of boisterous laughter and exclaim: "Yes, you people think that war is a big jollification. But I tell you it must be made as hard and ruthless as possible for the enemy. The more terrible you make it, the quicker he gives in. You can't expect to conquer an empire and keep it and hold those damned yellow monkeys in check by sitting at home in Gorcum and drinking hot chocolate on Sunday evening after church."

That was the way the Jonkheer talked; a resolute, fearless man, who was not intimidated by any sentimentalities about loving one's enemies when Holland was in danger. Not he! For that is the way he interpreted events in Indonesia. When some of the native tribes stirred in their huge prison which was their own country and rattled their chains, the Jonkheer at once began to raise a hue and cry about our fatherland being in danger. Men like him did not know that our fatherland was in danger all the time we went on oppressing others.

And then there was the Jonkheer's valet, old Piet Harte, the veteran with the cork leg, who followed his master like a shadow when he came to town. He was a well-known type in the community, and on the whole well liked. Yes, that man, more than the Jonkheer himself, was responsible for the savage nickname which the villagers of Rietvelt and others had fastened upon the lord of the manor.

Oh, he was a fine one, that Piet Harte, a drunkard and a brawler who did not care what he said or by whom he was heard. "I shed my blood for Queen and fatherland," he used to shout, "and I would like to see the man who will deny it!" Always challenging that way and ordering people out of his way or daring them to touch him. "This leg," he would shout, stamping down one of Gorcum's streets, staggering from one tavern to the other, "this leg is proof that I did my duty when the country was in danger! And what did you do?" With such questions he would rudely accost the first citizen who happened to come along. "You hid behind your wife's skirts, I bet!" He would unscrew his cork leg just below the knee and holding it by its rubber tip like a club with a heavy knob on the end, he would swing it menacingly above his head.

Not that anyone paid any attention to Piet Harte's drunken bravado or felt the faintest inclination to dispute his claim to glory. People moved out of his way when he came roaring down the streets, a fierce bully with a brutal, drink-sodden, purple-patched face and a bristling, turned-up yellow mustache, to whom fighting and brawling was a delight in spite of his crippled condition. I saw him one Sunday evening with one blow of his iron fists knock down a policeman who had gone to remove him from the Salvation Army's meetinghouse, where he was creating a disturbance. How many times Jonkheer van Rietvelt had pulled his flunky out of such scrapes, or bailed him out of jail, probably no one, least of all Piet himself, would have been able to recall.

Many times, too, I heard him tell—for he spoke to anybody who cared to listen—of the way he lost that leg of his in the jungles of Sumatra, where he had served the Jonkheer as private cook and valet. Strange to say, in so phenomenal a battler it was not in actual combat with the enemy that he had been wounded. He claimed that one day he walked into a trap of the kind natives set for tigers, a steel-pronged contrivance that upon snapping shut can inflict a mortal injury. In his case the teeth of the trap had been dipped in a particularly potent poison.

Maddened by pain and unable to free himself, Piet had started to crawl back to camp with the trap attached to his leg, but loss of blood so weakened him that he was forced to give up. Half-fainting, he resigned himself to the inevitable. It was at this point that Major van Rietvelt, attracted by his batman's earlier cries for help, appeared on the scene. The Jonkheer quickly unfastened the trap, but detecting the ominous marks on Piet's flesh where the venom was doing its deadly work, he did an extraordinary thing. Fearful that his servant and fellow soldier would be a lost man before they could reach a doctor, the Major then and there amputated Piet's leg.

"Yes sir, he chopped it right off with his saber," Harte used to say, "without hesitating a moment and without batting an eyelash. 'Piet, *jongen*,' the Major said to me, 'that leg has to come off. I'll fix you in a moment, Piet, don't worry! Just set your teeth for a moment!' Holy Christ in heaven, that man had nerve. Fortunately the bone was broken by the trap," Harte would say, "fortunately, else I don't see how he would have cut through. He just groaned and chopped. It didn't take long, and I didn't faint either." That is the kind of man Major van Rietvelt was, not squeamish or a milksop at all, a man of whom you might well believe that he had fully earned the award for "extreme coolness and resolute action under a most murderous enemy fire."

With what bold courage, too, he had fought at the crossing of the Singkel River, wading into the water up to his chin, straight into the fire of the entrenched Achinese riflemen, and then racing up the further bank firing his revolver and slashing with his saber right and left before coming to direct grips with the enemy! For a long time that was one of the most widely discussed episodes of the Sumatran campaign. One of the Achinese chieftains, a son or nephew of the pretender to the Sultanate, who was the real animater of the revolt against the Dutch usurpers, had faced the Major there in person and been killed by him in a terrible hand-to-hand combat.

It came about this way. When Major van Rietvelt, after losing more than half of his men in the crossing, reached the northern bank of the Singkel, he and the troops that remained were in danger of being cut to pieces. They were in an exposed position and the Achinese riflemen continued with deadly effectiveness to pour shot into the clusters of sorely bewildered Dutch soldiers. To have delayed for the purpose of regrouping upon reaching the farther shore would have been suicidal. On the other hand, to retreat meant annihilation in the water. Without a moment's hesitation, therefore, the Major gave the order to advance, although that course of action was fraught with no less hazard than to remain on the spot or to fall back.

The Achinese held their fire until they learned what their opponents' next move would be. Had they remained in their trenches, they could probably have stopped the oncoming

Dutchmen in their tracks and wiped them out to the last man. Instead they impetuously tumbled out of their defenses and came running downhill upon the badly outnumbered Dutch troops.

The last of Rietvelt's men had scarcely emerged from the water and were splashing up the riverbank when the Achinese rushed them. In an instant it became a case of each man for himself, and retreat was out of the question for either side. A bloody melee followed in which Dutch bayonets clashed with native daggers and krises. In the twinkling of an eye both sides lost all semblance of formation. The hillside was covered with stabbing, lunging, swearing, and pummeling white men and brown men who were presently rolling over the ground gouging each other's eyes and tearing at each other's throats. In this kind of close fighting the crooked krises of the Achinese, which resemble the saw bayonets the Germans used in World War I, were doing a deadly work. Disemboweled Dutch soldiers or men with their throats slit or otherwise horribly mutilated were lying about in all directions, writhing in agony or screaming in pain and terror.

Suddenly the young Achinese chieftain, recognizing Major van Rietvelt by the insignia on his uniform as the leader of the Dutch, raced forward with his kris poised to strike. The Major fired his revolver at the man, but missed. When a second pressure on the trigger produced no detonation, the Major threw away his pistol and drew his sword.

For a moment the two men fenced harmlessly, then the Achinese with a sudden swift gesture struck the Major a sharp blow on the wrist, causing him to drop his saber. The Dutch commander—I heard him tell the story himself— believed that he was lost at that moment. Blood was streaming from an ugly wound on his arm while the fierce foeman screamed exultingly and made ready for the kill. Without paying the slightest attention to his injury, the Major hurled himself at the Achinese prince and throwing his arms around him brought him to earth with a thud. In their fall the kris slipped from the young Sultan's hand, so that both men were now disarmed. They held each other in a viselike, deadly embrace face to face, muscle against muscle, bone against bone. Wrenching, heaving, and panting, they rolled toward the water's edge.

Right on the brink of the stream, the Achinese prince gained the upper hand. He was on top of Rietvelt, and disengaging one arm from the Dutch officer's desperate embrace, he pressed his thumb into the Major's left eye with all the force he could muster. Van Rietvelt yelled to his men to come to his aid. But the Dutch soldiers were too busy with their own attackers. Each man faced at least two of the enemy. They could not disengage themselves to come to the aid of their commander and probably did not even notice his plight or hear his cry for help in the tumult of the battle. At any rate, nobody came to the Major's rescue.

The Achinese chief now had the Dutch officer where he wanted him: in the water. The Major was still fighting and kicking and bumping his head into his opponent's stomach and chest, but he could not shake off the young man, who was slowly forcing Rietvelt's head under water. In a minute the struggle would have been over. The Major felt himself slipping. Yet, determined that if he was to perish, he would take his enemy with him into death, he summoned his strength for the last struggle. By that almost superhuman effort he managed to roll on top of the native prince.

In the same instant, the Major, seeing his enemy exposed and struggling to regain a hold, sank his teeth into the man's throat and bit through the larynx. Just then Piet Harte, who had disposed of several Achinese (the battle at the Singkel took place nearly a year before the accident with the steel trap), rushed up and stabbed the native prince through the eyes with his pocketknife.

That was the story of the Major's military fame, which I heard not only from Piet Harte, but from Zeger and from his father as well. It was on account of this exploit that the villagers of Rietvelt and many Gorcummers referred to the Jonkheer as "The Cannibal." But only behind his back, of course.

In spite of their frequent disagreements and their volu-
ble and sometimes quite acrimonious bouts of wrangling,
it must not be thought that there existed a deep and abiding
animosity between Zeger and Ary Brandt. To the contrary,
these two psychological opposites seemed ineluctably drawn
toward each other. They were friendly enemies, as the saying goes. At times, it is true, they could scarcely hide a feeling of mutual annoyance and irritation over the mere fact of
finding themselves in each other's company, and they bick-
ered and quarreled without end, yet they seemed to like it.
In the process of squabbling and jangling their spirits
warmed toward each other. The end of the fiercest argument left them in the best of humor. They never parted in
anger, and often walked off arm in arm. And they renewed
the pleasure of quarreling and disputing when the next
chance presented itself.

Fundamentally, I think, Zeger was a simplehearted, good-
natured fellow, but an enfant gâté who had never encountered anyone in life who dared to correct or contradict him.
Perhaps that is why he found it exciting when Ary charged
into him with blistering denunciations and refutations of his
pet ideas. Secretly he thought a great deal of Ary. I think
he would have liked nothing better than to make of him a
devoted friend. But his pride and cynicism prevented him
from speaking of things that he dismissed as sentimentalities. He never unburdened himself to set his soul free.

On Ary's side there was, unconsciously perhaps—or at
least unavowedly—an infinite compassion for the rich
Squire's son. He considered him the most underprivileged
boy in the world, in spite of all his wealth and social promi-
nence. Beneath Zeger's cold and supercilious behavior,
Ary's sensitive heart felt the hunger for friendship. Yet
Ary had strong feelings himself, and a good deal of pride
and not a little irony and he, too, often hid the generous
impulses of his nature under a blustering, challenging
behavior, so that the ice between the two really never quite
thawed.

With Dalmaden, the Jew, it was an entirely different
matter. In his presence Zeger grew strangely quiet. Not

that he had any reasoned antagonism toward the umbrella-peddler's son. There was, of course, an immense distance of caste and class between them, and this, one need hardly say, counted heavily in a country and a community where the people were divided in such airtight, separate compartments that the brethren of the same house of Holland were as strange to each other as if they were of a different race or hailed from different planets. Even so, David Dalmaden, it so happened, was indeed of a different race. He did not act differently, he did not speak differently, he did not even look differently, than an ordinary Dutch boy. He was different just the same. There was something in David's personality that seemed to jar on Zeger's nerves. Zeger seemed to feel the racial difference more keenly than anyone else in school. When David spoke, Zeger listened attentively with his mouth slightly agape, but his eyes turned questioningly from Ary to Jetze or to Fons Boogaert and myself, as if he wanted to say: What is this strange fellow trying to put over? Do you understand him? Do you trust him? What a queer mental twist he has! When I told him once that David's father was a scholar, Zeger replied: "A scholar who makes umbrellas—don't make me laugh!" "Don't forget that Spinoza ground lenses," I said, "and that he was not an inconsiderable thinker, or that Saint Paul was a tentmaker and Jesus a carpenter."

"That may be true," Zeger replied, "but they were Jews, all three of them, and first-class troublemakers, as far as I can make out. Jews are that by nature anyway, revolutionaries, troublemakers. They are always questioning and challenging and disputing. They never leave well enough alone. What makes them do that?"

"Their creed!" interjected Jetze. "It stands for justice!"

"No, their creed has nothing to do with it," came back Zeger, "or maybe you are right, maybe it has after all," he added, "if you mean that their creed is *floos, mazuma, geldmacherei*." He rubbed thumb and forefinger together as if he were counting money rapidly.

"If you think that is the Jewish creed," replied Ary, "I expect to see you succeed to the position of high priest or whatever it is that the Jews value most. For if there is a bigger *geldmacher* (money-maker) in these parts than your own dear papa, I have yet to hear of it."

"Leave my father out of it," said Zeger curtly.

"Very well, I will leave your father out. But then let me tell you, Zeger van Rietvelt," Ary continued, suddenly very seriously, "that you have not the least right to speak contemptuously that way about any people's creed. What of it if there are some good-for-nothing Jews in this world, some Jewish criminals and Jewish usurers? In the first place, you have never seen one of them around here in Gorcum, I'm sure, no more than I have. But even if there were, would you judge the Dutch people or their creed by the acts or behavior of some discreditable individuals, or the French people by the murderer of Ravachol?[1] You wouldn't, would you?

"You judge the French and the Russians and the Germans by their poets, by their philosophers, their thinkers and their intellectuals. You judge the Germans by their Hegels and Kants, by their Nietzsches and Schillers and Goethes and Luthers. You don't judge the Germans by the doings and thoughts of the dregs of humanity in Hamburg's Sankt Pauli quarter, or by the saber-rattlers of Potsdam, or by the asinine, pompous Junkers of Prussia, the land-owners. . . ."

"Leave my father out of it, I warn you again!" Zeger said curtly.

"I am leaving your father out of it," went on Ary, "I'm leaving him out definitely, I'm speaking of intellectuals and poets and artists. I'm saying that it's by their words and acts that you should judge a people, and that goes for the Jewish people as well. Writers, thinkers, poets are the men who express the innermost thoughts of a people, a people's soul, its hopes and aspirations. A poet shows you the soul of a people as in a mirror. Tolstoi, for instance, and Dostoevski show you the deep, innate religious character of the Russian.

[1] Ravachol was a bandit of whose depredations the newspapers were full at the time.

"Why are we taught Latin and Greek in this school? Because we want to learn what the Greeks and Romans thought and did. Do we have such a high regard for the Greeks and Romans of antiquity because of the grafters, the prostitutes, the assassins, the rakes, the homosexuals, and the monsters of depravity who swarmed in droves around the Parthenon and the Forum Romanum? Or is it because of old Homer and Virgil, Cicero and Demosthenes, the Stoics, Alcibiades, Euripides, Plotinus, Socrates, and all the others? You have a deep admiration for Hellas, don't you, and for ancient Rome? Well, do you think the Jewish psalmists and prophets are of any less significance than the Greek and Roman philosophers and poets and orators? Whose books have done more toward molding Western civilization, those of the Jews or those of the Romans, do you think? You have no right to speak at all, it seems to me, till you have done a little reading. You haven't read a single Jewish book, not even the Bible. . . ."

"I have read Karl Marx's *Capital*! That's a Jewish book!" interrupted Zeger triumphantly.

"Have you now? Have you really?" asked Ary in his most sarcastic vein. "One could never think so from hearing you babble. But what of it? What of Marx?"

"Doesn't Marx, the Jew, turn everything into a money question? Doesn't he reduce everything to sordid, materialistic considerations?" asked Zeger.

"He most certainly does," Ary agreed. "But you must consider that it's the question of bread and butter and clothing and shelter for the millions of starvelings in this world that Marx discusses. Marx discusses that question, and he says so plainly, because that question is uppermost in the minds of the vast majority of our fellow human beings. That question must be solved, he says, before the real history of the human race can begin. All that has preceded—life in the caves, the struggle against ferocious animals, against nature, against pestilence, against rival tribes for the possession of the world's goods—all that is merely preliminary, prehistoric, he calls it. Now must begin the struggle against poverty.

"Only after that is won can we turn our thoughts freely to higher things. Man must be liberated from material cares before he can profitably turn his thoughts to higher things. A man who's hungry has no interest in the paintings of Rembrandt or in the music of Beethoven. Nor does he feel like talking about the meaning of God, and other metaphysical subjects as to the why and whither of the human race, when his wife has contracted tuberculosis by being forced to live in a stinking slum, and when his children are cold in their rags and hollow-eyed and miserable from malnutrition. I firmly believe myself that the average man would prefer to think and talk of beautiful and noble things, but is kept from it by the reality that he sees around him and which he feels in his own body."

"Very well, very well," interrupted Zeger again. "But that is not what I was saying. I said Marx was a Jew. I meant that it was the Jew in him which brought up this disagreeable subject of poverty, that he is the man responsible for the idea of the class war, which is dividing the world into two classes. I mean that it was the Jew who put material considerations first."

"Marx wasn't writing of his own material circumstances," replied Ary. "Marx was personally tolerably well off. I dare say he could easily have gotten himself an appointment as a professor in economics or philosophy in any university, or he might have become a great and honored journalist if he had chosen that course. He had a good mind, you will admit that, and he had excellent manners. I've heard it said that he was even a bit of a snob, although I think he was entitled to some superbity. Intellectually the man stood shoulder-high above his contemporaries. He became the champion of the world's oppressed. That was not a popular thing to do. You can't expect to rise in the world, become a Cabinet minister or a university professor or a big landowner, if you honestly stand up for the rights of the poor. You are immediately called an enemy, and rightly so, for you are an enemy of the class that would perpetuate the division of society into rich and poor, exploiter and exploited.

"It was an immense love for man that motivated Marx. He had nothing to gain personally by going to the trouble of explaining the nature of capitalist society. It was directly at variance with his personal, material interests, and he ended up a poor man, a very poor man as a matter of fact. That is the greatest thing a man can do—feel compassion for his fellows. And if you still insist on calling that putting material considerations first, I can cite you one Jew—no, ten other Jews—who definitely and intentionally put spiritual considerations first: Isaiah, Amos, Da Costa, Spinoza, Jesus."

"Spinoza? Jesus?" exclaimed Zeger. "Didn't the Jewish people themselves drive out the one and kill the other because these men insisted on the pre-eminence of the spiritual? Doesn't that show the Jewish character, the Jewish people's character?"

"The synagogue excommunicated Spinoza for the same reason that Calvin excommunicated Servetus, or for the same reason that Gomarus here in Holland drove out Arminius, or for the reason that Pope Alexander VI had Savonarola burnt at the stake. They had their religious differences, and it was customary in the past to act barbarously when religious differences arose. And as to killing Jesus, I ask you: Did we, you and I, kill Jan de Witt or Boniface? Did Michael Faraday, Huxley, and Darwin kill Thomas à Becket, or did the Bohemians kill John Huss? Do we ever hold it against the Greeks that Socrates was executed in Athens, or do we blame the contemporary French nation for the massacres of Saint Bartholomew's Day and of the Albigenses? The Jews now living certainly have nothing to do with that judicial crime committed in Jerusalem by a Roman governor two thousand years ago. They have less to do with that episode than these men there whom you see laying down a row of new cobblestones in the street have to do with the killing of Indonesian natives by . . ."

"Are you bringing that up again?" asked Zeger angrily. "You always start with Jesus or Mohammed or Karl Marx and end up with my father!"

"Your father? God forbid! Nothing is farther from my mind," said Ary, bursting into laughter. "I have no personal grudges, Zeger, old boy!"

"Then what should I read, Ary?"

"Read? Why not start with the Bible?"

"I've read it, Ary, really I have!"

"You've read the whoring stories, you mean. You've never read Jeremiah on antimilitarism, I bet!"

"Oh, Ary, I can't read that stuff. It's too damned serious. Why didn't one of those Biblical writers dish up a story like those in the *Thousand and One Nights*?"

"I see your point, and I see at the same time that you've never looked inside the Bible," answered Ary. "Now it's to be one thing or the other with you, Zegerkin, my boy. Do you want to go on nourishing your damn-fool bourgeois notions about Jews, or do you want to make a serious inquiry into the Jewish creed, or rather into the psychology of the Jewish spirit? What is it to be? If you can make up your mind and you want to study a little Judaism, we can go to the sources. We have them right here in Gorcum. We could call on Doctor Mendoza some evening, that is, if the Rector will let you out after dark. The old Doctor has the books and he will gladly loan them to you, as he does to me. And we will all get a good glass of wine into the bargain."

"Fine," said Zeger, "I'm for it. I will come along. I like Dr. Mendoza immensely. He's a good Jew. But why did you say just now that you're sure I've never looked inside the Bible?"

"Because if you had you would know that the Bible has a dozen stories as good as any in the *Thousand and One Nights* and that, among other things, it contains the most erotic piece of Oriental literature in existence."

"What's that?"

"The Song of Songs!"

"Oh, but Ary, now you're going too far altogether. You shouldn't say that," broke in the violently blushing and agitated Alfons Boogaert, who had listened silently up to that point. "The Song of Songs is to be understood allegorically. It's a mystical dialogue between Christ and His holy bride the Church. Isn't that so, Pieter?" He turned to me for support.

"Yes," said I, somewhat sententiously, "that's also John Calvin's interpretation."

"That lets me out, gentlemen." Ary shook his head. "We've landed in the realm of theological speculation and miracles. There I draw the line. You two," he said, pointing to Boogaert and myself, "you can settle that question between yourselves. Only I beg of you not to come to blows!"

"Why should we come to blows?" asked Fons innocently. "We are in agreement, didn't you hear?"

"Are you?" queried Ary. "If you think you are, ask Pieter exactly which church is that holy bride with whom Christ is supposed to be conversing mystically in the Song of Songs. Is it Rome, Geneva, Moscow, or Oxford? Maybe you two will have to agree that the bridegroom is a bit of a polygamist—will you?"

"Don't talk so cynically, Ary!" Fons almost shouted. "You speak altogether too superciliously of holy things. I did not want to break in just a minute ago when you talked to Zeger, but you hurt me terribly."

"How so? I'm sure I didn't intend to offend you. Good heavens, what do you mean?"

"You compared the death of Our Lord with that of Socrates and Jan de Witt. Ary, there is simply no comparison possible in those cases. In Christ's death there was much more involved than a miscarriage of justice or a lynching bee. When Our Lord was crucified, that was God's Son, God Himself, dying for the sins of the world. There was the Resurrection, too. If Christ hadn't died and risen, where would we be? How poor and miserable would we be! No hope at all! Life would be hell."

"Theologically," replied Ary calmly, "there is indeed a great deal more involved, that's true, but not historically, not objectively." But Fons wasn't listening any more.

"If I did not have my Jesus," he said with a burning face and eyes aflame, "if I did not know that He lives, I would not want to go on living myself. I couldn't. I couldn't."

Zeger, who stood by, looked at Fons with wide-open eyes of astonishment. He took me aside and said: "Does he really mean that? Do those Roman Catholic people really believe such things?"

"Believe is a weak word," I said. "In the case of Boogaert it is more than belief, it's a factual experience. That's the central interest and fact of his life."

"I didn't think such people existed nowadays," said Zeger. "Do we have any of them in the Protestant Church?"

"There are quite a few yet," I said, "although their number is diminishing fast."

In the fifth year at school Ary, whose father was frequently away on official business—at least that was the name given to the affair that took the widowed rural Burgomaster on such unlikely occasions as week ends to Rotterdam and The Hague—became a fairly regular visitor at the Rietvelt mansion. He was then eighteen years old. For convenience he roomed with a private family in Gorcum, and seldom bothered to cross the river on Saturday afternoons, being almost certain to find his father absent. Instead he rode out with Zeger and returned on Monday morning in the famous equipage. This happened perhaps once or twice a month. More frequently, Ary remained in Gorcum for the week end, spending almost the entire time at my Uncle Kees' house and accompanying us on Sunday mornings on those long hikes, sometimes many miles distant, to some rural church to hear a sermon by a divine of whom Kees approved or whose doctrine he personally wanted to test and investigate. Shortly before the summer vacation preceding our last year of school, Zeger suddenly began to press us individually and collectively with invitations to spend a few weeks of the coming holidays at his home in Rietvelt. He held out prospects of horseback-riding, rabbit-hunting, boating and fishing expeditions on the River Linge near his paternal estates, and talked of other delights of that kind. But these attractions left us as unmoved as an invitation to spend our brief annual respite by a turn of enlistment in the Student Reserve of the army. He certainly received no encouragement from any of us beyond a few words of perfunctory acknowledgment, the more since we half-expected Uncle Kees to come forward with a proposal to accompany him on a month of wandering in the Flemish land, visiting the cities of Bruges, Antwerp, Ghent, and Ypres. On several occasions Kees had talked of making such a tour, and he had even hinted that we might extend the itinerary to include a brief sojourn in that queen of cities, Paris.

Now that a definite decision was to be made, Kees remained silent. He delayed and hemmed and hawed when the subject was brought up, until one day it was too late. Zeger had prevailed upon his mother to write to our parents and then there was no longer any escape. As a nod from a lord is said to be breakfast to a fool, so that letter from the gracious chatelaine of Rietvelt was as much as a command to our parents to send us there without delay. We were told that it was too great an honor to be disregarded, that it would be a most worth-while experience to be guests at an authentic castle and rub shoulders with authentic nobility; and finally that a refusal might be taken as an affront that would be fraught with disagreeable consequences in later life, when heaven knows to what important position Zeger might rise in national affairs and what influence he might exercise in our behalf if he remained our friend.

All our arguments to the contrary proved of no avail. We had to go. We were summoned to a command performance. Even Kees, upon whom we, and I especially, had pinned our last hope, failed us miserably. He said that his Flemish trip was set for another time and that we had better accept Zeger's invitation. The fact that David Dalmaden was not included in the invitation to Rietvelt, a circumstance we held to indicate the snobbish discrimination of the noble family, seemed not to make any difference with Kees. He refused to intervene, and in fact indicated that he thought a short stay at the mansion would do us a world of good.

So one afternoon, toward the end of August, Ary, Jetze,

and I stepped into one of the Rietvelt carriages and rode
out to the estate, depressed and rebellious in spirit and
determined to leave the place at the earliest possible
opportunity. We arrived at sundown and were welcomed
by the chatelaine, Zeger's mother, who, to our surprise,
left us alone again after a few moments of conversation.
Soon after, we ate together in a small dining-room, wondering all the time where Zeger could be. A servant girl
named Clara, a young woman with vivacious eyes who used
extraordinarily frank language, and who made a deep impression on Jetze, served the meal and then showed us to
our rooms. That girl had reddish-brown hair, a skin of
peachlike satin, and a mouth half-open, whether in sophistication or innocence I do not know. Before long she captivated our Jetze completely and on that score gave us no
end of trouble.

The quarters assigned to us consisted of a suite of vast,
walnut-paneled chambers located at the end of a long win-
dowless hallway in the east wing of the manor. They were
on the second floor and could be reached by an interior
stairway that was entered by a door, or rather a sliding
section in the wall of the main entrance hall. From that
door one went through a short dark passage or tunnel to
the foot of a flight of stone steps that ascended spirally
like those in a tower. Both the stairs and the long hallway
above were illuminated night and day by wicks floating in
linseed oil, in colored glass jars of the kind seen in church
sanctuaries or before ikons. These lamps were fitted into
iron brackets fastened to the wall.
Our rooms formed a self-contained, almost modern apartment with a sitting-room, a small library, bedrooms, dress-
ing-rooms, and a kitchen. The bathroom with its porcelain
tub and gaudy nickel-plated taps and fixtures was a distinct
revelation to us, as we had never seen one before. The only
bathroom in Gorcum was in the civic infirmary, an institution we knew only by its evil reputation as a place where
the sick who entered it generally lost their hope of recovery.
One peculiarity of the long hallway and our rooms was that

the heavy-beamed ceiling was so low that a man of average height standing on a chair could have touched it with his head. There were scarcely any ornaments in the rooms; a few faded family portraits were scattered here and there on the walls. In the small library there was a large oil painting of a young woman in a wedding gown. Except for the kitchen and the bathroom, the walls above the panels were uniformly done in dark-green brocade with gold-stitched flowers.

We elected to sleep in the main bedroom, where stood a chaise-longue and two enormous mahogany four-poster beds equipped with so-called heavens. From these canopies and along the massive sculptured pillars thick wine-colored curtains hung to the floor. Inside one of these high berths with the curtains drawn, one got the impression of being in a tent, but an utterly dark tent, of course. From the middle of the canopy, inside the bed, hung a thick knotted cord ending in a polished wooden handle in the shape of a closed horseshoe or stirrup. From that handle dangled a heavy silken tassel, reaching to within a foot of the pillows. The whole contrivance was a device to assist the occupant of the bed in hoisting himself or herself from a reclining to a sitting position. The tassel served to guide a hand groping in the darkness toward the handle.

At the head of the bed, but inside the square tent and just above the pillows, stretched a broad shelf on which stood a chamber pot. When I mention that the bathroom lacked a water closet, it will be clear why I called the apartment "almost modern." At the same time it explains the presence of the *vase de nuit*. Espying the polished horseshoe above his head, Jetze, imagining it to be a gymnastic appliance, at once tried it out. He managed to get his leg into the ring-like fixture, and was presently swinging to and fro, when the cord broke and he fell back into the pillows.

One climbed into the bed by means of a small, carpet-covered stepladder that stood at the side where the curtains parted. There was really such a mass of pillows, cushions, undersets, and props in those beds that it was obvious one was expected to conform to the old-fashioned Dutch custom

of sleeping in a sitting posture. And indeed, no sooner had
he sunk away in the immense feather tick which took the
place of a mattress than the ever-truthful Jetze began to
recite the well-known English bedtime prayer, but with a
variation befitting the occasion: "Now I sit me down to
sleep . . ." A moment later Ary's sepulchral voice was
heard in answer, from the abyss of eiderdown in the next
bed: "From the depths, O Lord . . . !"

These mock-pious exercises were interrupted by a knock
on the door and the appearance of a valet carrying an oil
lamp. Noticing that we were in bed, he inquired in a half-
amazed, half-injured tone whether we intended to go to
sleep without having eaten our porridge. We were out of
the feathers in a jump. Ary lighted some candles while the
valet spread a linen cover over the table and set fire to a
heap of dry twigs in the fireplace. The man then brought
in the tableware and a large tureen of groats cooked in
buttermilk, and we filled our plates. After putting a lump
of butter on the boiling-hot mush we poured some sweet
syrup of molasses over it. In my youth such meals were still
eaten in Holland before retiring, in the belief that it is
unwise to give the stomach a moment's rest. That belief
has cost many a good Dutchman his life.

While we were eating there was another knock at the
door. This time there entered an individual whose like for
ugliness I have never seen since. We stared at him open-
mouthed. He was gaunt and bony, more than six feet tall,
without a hair on either his head, his eyelids, or his brows.
He had the long scrawny neck of a vulture, wrinkled and
leathery, with a large Adam's apple bobbing up and down
like a dancing ball on a garden fountain. He was dressed
in a thick woolen chamber cloak, blue in color. His eyes
were unusually large and coal-black in a face the hue of
old parchment. The skin hung loosely from his lower jaws.

As he entered he mumbled something that none of us
could understand. Noticing our incomprehension, he suddenly removed from his mouth a double set of false teeth,
which he put in the pocket of his robe. Then, in a totally
different, high-pitched voice, he swore an obscene oath, and

giggled like a schoolgirl at our astonishment. Next he introduced himself as the Baron Otto van Rietvelt, our friend Zeger's grandfather. We promptly rose, and he was offered a chair while Ary asked if he would not do us the honor to eat with us. With another giggle and another oath, the Baron said he would be glad to join us, but he added: "I am like the midwife in this village, a certain Mrs. Welters, who says she cannot eat without drinking, nor drink without eating. That's a religion with me!" With that he pulled the bell cord to call the valet from the kitchen, and ordered four bottles of wine.

"I merely dropped in," said the Baron as he emptied the jug of syrup on his pap and swallowed a mouthful. "I really came to see if you were all comfortable. It's an old habit of mine. I can't sleep a wink, you understand, till I have assured myself that everyone is taken care of in my house. Just an old habit. I always did it when I was on maneuvers." He talked in short, clipped sentences and as he spoke tapped the table lightly with a blue-veined, deeply wrinkled hand.

"Every night I made the rounds of the farmhouses where my men were quartered to see how they were treated." He laughed again in his shrill, idiotic voice. "You should have seen how those boys installed themselves in the haylofts and all that, you understand, he, he! Not a whit abashed, by God! Not even when I entered. Real hussars! I served with the Hussars, you know," he added. "Twenty-one years . . . *Ritmeester*, captain of horse . . . I expect Zeger told you about that."

"With the Red Hussars, wasn't it, sir?" Ary asked politely.

The Baron almost choked on his porridge. "Red Hussars!" he fairly exploded. "Good God, sir, what do you take me for? Those fellows people call Red Hussars aren't hussars at all. Didn't you know? They are dragoons. A damned shabby lot. Anybody can get into that corps. I served with the Blue Hussars. Practically all the officers are noblemen. At least so it was in my day." The Baron emptied his glass in one swallow, refilled it, and drank that down, too, in one gulp. We took a little sip and found the wine disappointingly sour.

"I thought," I said, "that both regiments were of equal standing, that they both belonged to the Guard. Isn't there a regiment of Yellow Riders, too?"

The Baron's eyes blazed at me reproachfully and his toothless mouth dropped open with astonishment.

"The Yellows are field artillery," he stormed. "What in the name of God do they teach you boys in those damned schools nowadays? You don't know the army of your own country. Equal standing! Good God! Equal standing with Yellows and Reds! That's the damned limit!"

"Where were the maneuvers held, sir?" asked Ary, more than anything else to break the awkward silence that followed the Baron's outburst, for our friend was not the least interested in the subject, no more than Jetze or I.

"They were held, by God, where they were always held," said the Baron, "where they are still held, in Brabant, of course. Where else would you hold them?"

"Why always on the Belgian frontier?" asked Jetze. "Is that to scare our neighbors?"

"Exactly," came back the Baron, mellowing a little. "A damned treacherous lot, you know, the Belgians. We must always keep an eye on them! God knows what they're up to!"

"They are Netherlanders as we are," interjected Jetze. "The Flemings, in fact, are our blood brothers, the same people as we are, same language, same faces, same history almost. They just happened to become separated from us in the aftermath of the Napoleonic era. Somebody drew a line on a map in London or Paris, or was it Berlin? and said: On one side you people are henceforth called Belgians, and you on the other side, Netherlanders. And then these groups were told to hate each other after living together in peace for eighteen hundred years or more."

"Where, in the name of heaven, did you get all that nonsense?" the Baron shouted. "By God, I will have inquiries made by the Town Council," he went on as his Adam's apple jumped up and down like a wool-spinner's bobbin.

"If that is what they teach you about the Belgians in that school, I will have it stopped. The Belgians our brothers! Damned fine brotherly lot," he snorted in disgust. "And this in a Dutch school! Socialism, I call it, socialism and high treason. Believe me, I will see about it promptly." He filled his glass again, this time from the bottle standing in front of Jetze.

"You should by all means, sir," said Ary quietly, egging him on. "You are apt to discover a lot more. Do you know, for instance, what else they teach us at that school? They teach that our gracious King William lost the southern provinces, or what is called Belgium nowadays, because he treated the inhabitants as if they were a conquered colony, a lot of coolies."

"Good God!" shouted the Baron. "What infamy! Zeger never told me a word about that! Zeger shouldn't stay a day longer in that school! I will see his father at once." His eyes rolled indignantly from one to the other. "That school is no place for a Rietvelt. And that is what they dare say about a member of the royal family, about the great King William?" With that he drained Ary's bottle and started on mine.

"They say a good deal more," chimed in Jetze. "They say the King was a merchant at heart and that he lost out in the bargaining and then left us in the lurch to go to Berlin with a strange woman, yes, and became a Roman Catholic on top of all that to spite the whole Dutch nation."

The Baron's face looked as if he were about to have an apoplectic fit. The veins on his bony forehead swelled and throbbed and stood out like blue cords. His mouth was agape. He brought his fist down on the table with a crash. "The King a merchant!" he roared. "The King ran away! By God, that's lèse-majesté, nothing less, that's high treason unadulterated. What will we hear next? An Orange never runs away, sir!" he blazed up, sticking out his chest.

"No," said Jetze dryly, "that's true. But it rolls off sometimes when it's full of juice." The Baron was speechless. He sat staring at Jetze as if he had seen a ghost.

"Oh, maybe it isn't the Belgians at all we try to scare

with those maneuvers," I said, trying to change the subject
and unruffle our noble visitor's indignation. "The Great
Powers would never permit a war between Holland and
Belgium. England and the others are the guarantors of
Belgium's neutrality. And then I have never heard that the
Belgians are a warlike people."

"Don't bank on the English!" the Baron interrupted me
sharply. "Don't bank on them at all. They are a perfidious
and degenerate people. What didn't the Boers do to them,
for instance? A handful of Dutch farmers against Lords
Kitchener and Methuen and the cream of the British army,
Coldstream Guards, Black Watch, Seaforth Highlanders,
and all that! What did our Boers do to them? They made
hash of them! That's what they did! The English could
never have conquered the Boers if the German Emperor
had not sent a plan of strategy to London."

"More perfidy!" interjected Jetze. "Perfidy on the left
of us, perfidy on the right of us. Perfidy all over!"

"The English can't fight," said the Baron, shaking his
head impatiently with the interruption. "They have been
on the decline ever since they lost the only Dutch king they
ever had. That was their undoing."

"We are getting some novel views on history," said Ary,
chuckling. And addressing the Baron, he added: "It's a
pity, sir, the highly esteemed historian Yssel Ponthieu
could not hear you. Did you say William III was the greatest king the English had?"

"I said that," replied the Baron, "and I maintain it. I go
even further: I say he was the greatest prince we ever had."
He took a big swig of wine, but not from the glass. This
time he simply put the last bottle to his mouth.

"He did a lot of damage, too," objected Ary.

"What damage, in the name of heaven?" exclaimed the
Baron, aroused again.

"He is responsible for the assassination of one of the
greatest of Holland's citizens!"

"Whom do you mean?"

"I mean Jan de Witt," said Ary.

"De Witt was a traitor!" shouted the Baron.

"Whom, what, did he betray?" queried Ary quietly.

"He opposed the Prince," snapped the Baron.

"Is that treason?" said Ary. "No, mijnheer, there was nothing wrong with De Witt. The evil is in the history books. De Witt's epoch was fundamentally different from our own, but our history books pay no heed to the peculiarities and the mentality of another age. In De Witt's day Holland was a republic. Both De Witt and the Prince of Orange were servants of the Republic, the first as Grand Pensionary and the second as Commander of the Army. De Witt feared the influence of the Prince as a member of a family of hereditary military commanders. He saw that, inevitably, the Orange family would seek to gain sovereign power in the Netherlands. He tried to check the Prince's ambitions. The Prince in turn had De Witt put out of the way because the Grand Pensionary saw through the scheme."

"There is no proof! No proof at all!" said the Baron angrily.

"The surest proof is that the Orange family rules over Holland today, sir," replied Ary. "There is also proof that William III tipped De Witt's murderers and gave one of them, at least, a pension for life. It's the most outrageously scandalous episode in our history. That, and the execution of Jan van Oldenbarneveldt, another great patriot, by one of William's predecessors and fundamentally for the same reason."

The Baron looked about helplessly and nodded his head. "I see," he muttered, "I see: it's the schools and the books. You boys can't help it. It's the spirit of the age. We are growing thoroughly corrupt. It begins with throwing doubt on the most glorious achievements of our ruling house. Historical criticism, they call it, but in reality it's destruction of authority. Step by step we advance on the road to ruin until finally we'll have the great *Kladderadatsch* of the revolution and the canaille murdering and looting and raping without rein or check."

"We won't stand for it!" Jetze cried out fiercely with mock indignation.

"Stand for what?" asked the Baron.

"For the revolution!" Jetze replied.

"Right!" assented the Baron. "I'm glad to hear you say so. Do you intend to go into the army, sir?"

"No," said Jetze, "I am going to sea."

"I congratulate you." The Baron nodded approvingly at Jetze. "You have made a noble choice. I like sailors. And you, do you choose the navy?" He turned to Ary and me.

"No, sir," said Ary. "I'm going into the diplomatic service. I'm an anarchist. I can't stand the sound of sword-grinding and the creak of heavy boots. It rasps my nerves."

To our surprise the Baron burst into a fit of hilarious laughter. "Hoo, hoo, hoo!" he yelled, and he slapped his sides till the false teeth rattled in the pocket of his gown. He laughed so much that he fell into a spell of coughing and his face turned red and blue. But he still tittered and giggled in that sharp strident voice of his. We thought he had gone insane. All at once he stopped, wiped the tears of mirth from his eyes, and looked around with childlike innocence.

"Excuse me," he said, chuckling again. "I was thinking of something entirely different. That remark of yours made me think of my old comrade Count van der Poorten. Do you know Count Anatole van der Poorten?"

We said we had not the honor.

"Well, you see, Van der Poorten served with me in the Hussars. We came in together and we left together. . . . On the retired list, you understand. . . . Poorten is enormously rich. He owns no end of estates here in Holland and I don't know what big swindle in Indonesia his family carries on. They are as rich as Croesus, the whole clan of them. . . . We were always together. He is a good boy, but he likes the women. All sorts of women, you understand. Small, big, blondes, brunettes, fat and lean. He likes them all. I don't know how it is now, of course. He's getting on in years and the flame is burning a little low, I dare say. But in those days, in The Hague—I'm speaking of those days—many an adventure we had together in his town house in The Hague or in one of his country houses. He had the prettiest mistresses of any of us." The Baron made a clicking sound with his tongue as if tasting a delectable dish.

"Well, one day my friend Anatole goes and falls in love with a young lady, the daughter of a certain Mijnheer Langvoet. She was sixteen at the time, I think, sixteen or seventeen, I don't remember her exact age, but very young anyway, and beautiful as an angel. The rosy blonde type, you know, peaches and cream." He clicked his tongue again. "Anatole wanted to marry her, but the girl's father wouldn't hear of it. She was still going to school. Poorten insisted. He began to visit the old man and in that way learned that he was hard up, in debt over his head, on the point of bankruptcy. He offered to pay the old man's debts. . . . Paid them, too, by God, just like that, without any quid pro quo. . . . Went ahead and settled everything for the old boy without saying a word. That, of course, changed the situation entirely. Langvoet finally consented. But he says: 'Poorten, old man,' he says, 'I give you my daughter. I know you are a man of the world. I have been in the service myself, a Hussar. I know the life. Go easy with the girl. She's a child. She's innocent. She's a little angel. Respect her innocence for a few years, Poorten, promise me that!'

"Poorten promised the old man. And of course he was as good as his word, the word of a Hussar. He married the girl, moved into a new house, bought her jewels, horses, everything she wanted. Got himself some extra grooms. It was a show place.

"Still he did not abandon his old mistresses. That's understandable under the circumstances. His young wife served for ornamental purposes only, you might say. It gratified Anatole's aesthetic sense to have such a perfect beauty around and to show her off to his friends. In the meantime he visited his old girl friends regularly and, being a very methodical fellow, he marked the dates of those visits in a diary. He did that all his life—keeping a diary, I mean. He kept a diary even in the days when we were at

Breda[1] together. Of course, he could not very well write down anything about the precise nature of those visits to the demoiselles, because Adèle—that was his wife's name, Adèle—was in the habit of reading his entries when he was out and he knew it well. He wrote down those visits under expenses: 'Had my shoes shined today, twenty florins,' or 'My top boots shined again today, twenty-five florins'— entries like that.

"One day the young wife comes to him: 'Anatole,' she says, 'what are those expenses you note in your diary about having your shoes shined so often, and what a lot of money you pay for that. Heavens, I never knew shoeshining cost so much!'

"So Anatole sits down with her," the Baron went on, "and thinking that the time was come to explain to his bride the facts of life, he tries to tell her—oh, quite delicately, of course. He tells her he has certain old habits, acquired as a bachelor, and that he can't break off so easily. He explains the nature of his visits to the cocottes around town. She nodded and seemed to understand. But then, by God, she suddenly looks up at him in innocent amazement and calls out: 'And you must pay all that money for those dirty girls! My poor boy! My poor Anatole! And those damned cadets never pay me a cent!' Hooh, hooh, hooh," laughed the Baron.

Jetze blushed so much that he had to hide his face. But the Baron went on: "Wait, I know a better story yet. Shall I tell it to you?"

"No, thanks," said Ary politely. "My young friends here couldn't stand it. I'm something like their moral guardian, you see."

"Have it your own way," the Baron nodded. "It's a pity they can't take it. What I wanted to tell you is worth hearing. But if they can't take that, how about another bottle of wine?" And without waiting for an answer he clapped his hands. The valet appeared from the kitchen. He was a tall old man with white hair and a sad face who carried himself very erect, obviously an old soldier too.

[1] The Royal Military Academy is at Breda, Holland's West Point.

When the Baron asked him for more wine, he shook his head slowly but emphatically: "There is no more wine upstairs, sir," he said, "and I haven't the key to the cellar."

"It's a lie!" the Baron yelled back at him. "I know it's a lie. You have been instructed to tell a lie. I know you, Markus," and he wagged his finger at the valet. "I know you for the scoundrel you are. You're in the conspiracy against me. Well, it's up to you, I suppose. All right, you can tell them that you kept me from drinking. Go ahead and tell them! But tell them at the same time that you had to clean up the mess, too!" And with this he took one of the empty bottles by the neck and smashed the dishes on the table into smithereens. "There," he said, as he laughed his senile giggle again, "now go and tell on me, you damned traitor and *klikspaan* (tattletale)."

The valet looked at the destruction with perfect equanimity and said respectfully: "May I remind Mijnheer the Baron that it is after twelve, that mijnheer endangers his health by remaining up so late."

"My health is my own concern," retorted the Baron. "What is it to you, or to anyone else, what I do with my health? Get to hell out of here before I kick you out! Ah, if I had some of my own boys here, my own hussars, what a thrashing you would get, you Markus. They'd beat the life out of you, my man, at one word from me, just as we did to that fish-peddler in The Hague. What was his name again?"

"The man's name was Van Dusen, sir," said the valet humbly, and he added, opening the door: "I will wait for mijnheer in the kitchen."

"Wait or go! I don't care a damn! Do what you like, traitor!" the Baron shouted with mounting irritation. And suddenly in a much calmer tone of voice he said, addressing us: "This I must really tell you, gentlemen, about this confounded fish-peddler, I mean." He laughed and seemed to have forgotten his anger. The manservant walked out with a curious glance at his master, shrugging his shoulders.

The Baron sat down again and leaned over the table. "This fish-peddler, you see, had a daughter, Mina. She was a pretty girl and she worked as chambermaid in the house where I had my rooms. I took her out on a little excursion one day to Amsterdam and showed her our great capital, he, he! I took her on a boating trip too once, I think. Well, that's neither here nor there. I shouldn't speak about such things perhaps, he, he! But one day that girl's father comes to me and tells me that he expects me to marry his daughter, this Mina. He said she was enceinte and she named me as the culprit. I said I had not the least intention of marrying his daughter or even of having a liaison with her. I was through with her. She was not a minor. I had paid her her wages. She was responsible for her own actions—basta! The fool actually threatened me: he said he would inform His Excellency, the general commanding the garrison, and I told him, of course, that His Excellency was a man of honor and wouldn't even speak to the likes of him.

"Then I had him thrown down the stairs by my batman. That was this scoundrel Markus you just saw here. He was my batman for fifteen years. But this fish-peddler came back again and again. At last I lost my patience. I told him I would give him my decision about marrying the girl at the club and to meet me there one night after eleven. I had convoked all the junior Hussar officers and some Grenadiers, all friends of mine, to watch the fun. Well, he ran headlong into the trap. No sooner was he inside the club than we jumped on him, took his clothes off, and put him on the billiard table, face down. Then we beat him with the cues till he couldn't crawl and was begging for mercy. 'Mina, Mina, come and have a look,' we sang as we let him have it. Then we threw him into the street, naked as he was, and his pants after him. And then," the Baron doubled up with laughter, "would you believe it, the man was arrested for walking around undressed in the public street. I believe he got six months in the jug."

"Why didn't you behead him?" asked Jetze. "It seems to me that would have been more fun. Cut off his head and carry it around in procession through The Hague."

"That," the Baron looked at Jetze suspiciously, "that I don't think would have been allowed."

"But the other business, the beating, that was allowed?" I asked.

"Oh, we were allowed a great deal, anything in reason, of course." The Baron nodded. "The authorities in The Hague are very tolerant when it comes to the Hussars. They are the life of the town, and what a town!" he went on with an old man's loquaciousness. He sighed with the memory of it. "I could tell you a lot more," he mused, "but I can't talk without drinking and I refuse to drink water. Water is Holland's foe. I've no dealings with the enemy. Besides, water is for the fishes to swim in. It makes them dumb, he, he! Who wants to be dumb? Any of you gentlemen ever been to The Hague?"

We said we hadn't, but would like to.

"Ah, it's a jewel," said the Baron. "It's a delight! A dream city. Upon my soul, I always said that I liked The Hague better than Brussels or even Paris or Berlin. I visited abroad a good deal, I know what I'm talking about. I attended the maneuvers of both the French and the German armies as a guest of their General Staffs, and I had a good opportunity to taste of the life of these foreign cities. They don't begin to compare with The Hague. The Hague is so neat, so cosy and intimate. Beautiful shops, beautiful houses, plenty of entertainment. I don't think I dined at home a hundred times in the twenty-one years I served in the Hussars. Always on the go! Plenty of foreigners, too. Foreign ambassadors, artists, entertainers, women of all nationalities, he, he! Little brown Balinese girls included! Always on the go, indeed! Not a moment's rest . . ."

"For God and fatherland!" interrupted Jetze in a matter-of-fact tone.

"Indeed," assented the Baron, missing the sarcasm in our friend's remark. "Yes, the service is not exactly a bed of roses as some think."

"Mijnheer the Baron,"—Markus appeared at the door again—"I must insist that mijnheer come to bed now!"

"Get out!" roared Otto, "I am going to sleep here, in this room."

"No," said Markus firmly, "mijnheer comes with me."

And taking the Baron by the arm like a policeman, he led him out. Down the hall we could still hear him curse and giggle. "Traitor, ungrateful worm, conspirator, scoundrel. I know you, Markus! I know you!"

"It's the damned schools and the books, boys, by God!" Ary imitated the Baron's piping voice as he got into bed.

"Six months in the jug," murmured Jetze. "The bastards! Mina, Mina, come and have a look! The lecherous old goat!"

Zeger turned up in the morning just as we were being served breakfast in our lordly quarters by Clara of the coquettish eyes. The young Squire stayed a few minutes with us and then went back to bed pleading a splitting headache. This left us to our own devices, as we were on most of the following days. We spent our time roaming around the countryside, lay in the grass and tried to write poetry, and on two or three occasions went rowing. In the evenings we returned to the mansion, ate dinner in the family ciricle, and retired to our rooms to read or play checkers or dominoes. We did not ride horseback and we did not hunt after one disastrous experience when Jetze fired at a rabbit which, as it lay gasping in death agony, gave birth to a litter of little ones. Ary turned deadly pale at the sight, flung his shotgun down, and without a word went indoors. Jetze became physically ill, and we did not talk much that evening.

The only event of importance, at least the only occurrence at the Rietvelt mansion of which a vivid remembrance remains after all these years, was the dinner on Sunday evening when several of the notables of the neighborhood were the Squire's guests. There was talk of that dinner all week and the preparations for it on the preceding Saturday put everybody in a fever, so that even Clara was too busy to talk to Jetze, and we took ourselves off at an early hour in order not to obstruct the proceedings.

We came to know the Rietvelt property pretty thoroughly. It was more like a farm than one of those fabulous landed estates one reads about in novels, with tennis courts and golf links and parks and bridle paths. It was a place of work. From dawn to dark and even from dark to dawn there was a hovering unrest about the place, bustle and animation, coming and going without end. In the night when it was still, one heard the elementary gods stirring about, the wind rustling in the wheat fields, the sap rising in the trees, the whisper of the drying rye, the soft footsteps of the dripping dew, and a million bugs and flies buzzing and rushing about on their mysterious business. Once in a black rainstorm during our stay a calf was born, and the anguished mooing of its mother in travail awakened us. We heard a man shout hoarsely for rope and boiling water. Then again on another night it was a fox who got into one of the chicken coops, setting all the roosters and hens and chicks in creation crowing and clucking while the farm hands fired off rifles and shotguns as if the enemy were upon us.

Before the sun had quite flung off the shadows in the morning a thousand birds were singing and we could hear the clatter of pails from the direction of the dairy shed, and a moment later the metallic and muffled tramp of heavy boots and clogs of the men going out to the fields. Some mornings were foggy and rain-sodden, but most dawns during our brief stay came in sparklingly clear, even with a touch of autumnal crispness in the air, so that the horses' breaths looked like smoky trumpets. We had come in the midst of the busiest season. As the anniversary of the Battle of Waterloo lay behind, there were new potatoes on the table, but that did not mean that the potato crop was harvested. No less than twenty men and women were busy with that. Others in the meadows were bringing in the first hay.

There was, in fact, not enough help to go around. Even the kitchenmaids and the seamstresses had been called from their tasks in the manor and pressed into service. They walked behind the cutting machines spreading the hay out to dry. Everything was happening at once. The peas were bursting their pods. Long beans had to be cut up. Strange women were in the kitchen boiling preserves. There were battalions of young pigs in the sties, squealing and galloping to and fro. Nauseous messes were being cooked for them from kohlrabi. Women and children from adjoining villages were picking berries. Huddled on their knees in the long patches or standing in the shrubbery by the shore of the Linge River picking the red currants and black currants, these transient day workers were under the supervision of Piet Harte, the veteran, who sat by the water's edge in the shade of a pollard willow counting the baskets and, as the Dutch say, "doing himself good" from time to time from a large earthen crock of Schiedam gin.

Over in the beet fields other men were busy piling up the huge white bulbs in cone-shaped heaps along the road for the carts to pick up. The rain had washed the clay off the carrots and turnips so that they looked like small mounds of gleaming pink and yellow flesh, a picture to tempt any painter. And all over the place, which ran northward for several kilometers up to the horizon as far as the eye could reach, you could see Major van Rietvelt. Now he was here helping to repair a broken-down reaper, now there pitching sugar beets into a cart with a forked shovel, or running into the rye to investigate how far it had dried, always doing and doing, seeing more with that one eye of his than many a man with full sight, and pouring out orders, adjurations, objurgations, blame, and blasphemy and rushing about as if the buzzing in his blood was equal to the force in his frame. No, there was no idleness on that farm, no room for malingerers or lazybones. There was scarcely enough time to rest. The old injunction about making hay while the sun shines was there literally fulfilled. Work was like a tiger; it devoured people implacably.

We watched the men and women come in from the fields in the evening when the sun was gone and twilight had started. They dragged their feet and walked slowly. Even the sweat-streaming horses were tired and showed it by throwing their heads up and down wearily, rattling the burdening harness and shaking their manes. The Squire— he acknowledged it freely when he sat down to dinner— drove his people like a madman. The summer season is short in Holland, the climate is unpredictable, fall rains may come early and when they do they are ruinous. "It's only for a few weeks," he would say, leaning his elbows on the table and nearly dropping with fatigue himself. "Only a few weeks of hard work. They can sleep all winter if they like, but now it's wreck or ruin for all of us."

The farm workers might stand about for a while after supper smoking their pipes in front of the stables and cottages, or lie on the grass in the cool of the orchards, but at nine o'clock they went to bed and the lights went out all over the place. There was no time for banter or light-heartedness or amusements and no inclination for it either. The earth is a hard taskmaster. It bends the strongest toward itself before swallowing them up.

There were times when we felt ill at ease seeing everybody working his head off while we were forbidden to lend a hand anyhere. More than once we felt like going home, sneaking off to Gorcum, and probably would have had it not been for Jetze, who had fallen head over heels in love with Clara and would not hear of leaving under any pretext. Ary and I decided to wait till after the Sunday-evening dinner before returning to Gorcum.

Five large rooms in succession ran along the rear of the mansion. They were furnished in the old-fashioned Dutch style with heavy furniture, chairs, benches, gilt-framed mirrors, cupboards, enormous sideboards, and gleaming round tables, large and small. With the kitchens and the monumental stairway, these rooms, or halls as I should call them, took up the entire ground floor. Each room was separated by a set of folding doors. On the evening of the reception only the last of the folding doors, those giving access to the dining-room, were closed. Bouquets of flowers had been artfully arranged in every corner and on every table. In the music room, which was the first to be entered, huge potted palms stood along the walls. In front of the palms were rows of club seats of wicker. The rooms were illuminated by a thousand candles burning in the chandeliers suspended from the ceiling and in the massive silver candelabras on the mantelpieces.

The first arrival that Sunday evening was a lady to whom we were introduced by Zeger's mother. She was the Dowager Amelie Ten Eyck, a neighbor who seemed to be well on in years. She eyed us coldly through her lorgnette. Her face was beyond the help of rouge, withered and wrinkled like old wrapping paper, but her small dark eyes still sparkled. She inspected the rooms carefully, letting her glance travel over every object as she took small steps. The inspection was carried out with pursed lips. Shortly after her, the district school inspector arrived with his wife. He was a large, taciturn man, a well-known figure throughout the Land of Arkel. He wore a long black beard, which he constantly stroked. He bowed to the Dowager, nodded his head in the direction where Jetze and I were standing by the fireplace, and sank into a chair, pulling the tails of his dress coat forward and folding them on his knees. Picking up an illustrated periodical, he began to study it intently. His wife wandered into the next room.

The Dowager Ten Eyck, her hands folded in her lap, sat in a deep armchair in the middle of the last room, her face toward the open doors. Squire Arnout, our friend Zeger's father, a glass of brandy in his hand, strolled in leisurely, hesitated an instant at the sight of the old lady, then noticing that she had seen him, walked over quickly to her chair. As he bowed stiffly, she said to him: "I saw the Baroness Wenselaar drive by this morning."

Before replying, the Squire gulped down his brandy, then, glancing down cautiously at the Dowager from the corner of his eye, asked in a nonchalant tone of voice: "And how did she look?"

"She looked stunning," answered the Dowager. "She had on a new fur jacket."

The Squire laughed. "A fur jacket in summer, how odd! Still she always looks stunning, I must say, with or without a new fur jacket."

The Dowager turned up her eyes at him without moving her head and said: "Of course you would say that. All you men are in love with her."

"But isn't that going too far? A woman who is never

seen except when she drives by in her carriage?" Arnout returned. "Were you out that you saw her this morning?"

"No," said the Dowager, "I heard her carriage on the road and I trained my binoculars on her."

"Your binoculars?" asked the Squire, contracting his brows in surprise and shifting his empty glass from one hand to the other.

"Yes," said the Dowager, "I keep them in the window of my living-room. The house stands too far back from the road for me to distinguish people and things clearly with the naked eye. So I always have my binoculars at hand. Without them I would not know half of what goes on in our district."

A giant with a blond beard and childlike blue eyes entered the room. At the sound of his footsteps the Squire faced about and said, "Ah, there is our dominie! I have just learned that you preached an excellent sermon this morning, sir."

"Thank you," said the minister. "What are you drinking there, Squire?"

"Brandy," said the Squire. "Can I get you some?"

The Dowager asked the newcomer: "Dr. Satyn, do you ever visit the Wenselaars?"

The Squire watched the minister's face closely as the young man took a step nearer the Dowager's chair and bowed. "I was there only last week, madame," he said, "on the occasion of the Baron's sixty-fifth birthday."

"To be sure," the Dowager nodded her head slowly. "So it was, so it was. Good heavens, how time flies! Steeven is sixty-five."

"Was the Baroness wearing her new fur jacket?" interrupted the Squire, with a chuckle.

The Pastor looked at him uncomprehendingly. "A fur jacket? Upon my word, I didn't notice. Why?"

The Dowager stared coldly at the Squire and pursed her lips.

"How did you find them?" she asked the minister. "I mean where do they receive their visitors?"

The question seemed to startle the Pastor. His eyes flew

back and forth wonderingly from the Dowager to the Squire. "I was received in the small salon downstairs," he said.

"Always the same place," the Dowager nodded. "Of course, the Baron cannot be moved out of that room. How did he look?"

"The same as ever," answered the Pastor. "Possibly worse. His face is very pale and he sits by the chimney with heavy covers wrapped around his legs. He has a big fire going night and day."

At this moment Baron Otto strode into the room. He wore the uniform of a major in the Blue Hussars and all his decorations. His riding-boots, polished to a mirrorlike brightness, creaked. He seemed even taller than that first night he paid us a visit in our rooms. But now his vulture-like neck was hidden behind a high gilt collar. His features, too, now seemed of a finer grain, more sensitive. He came straight to the Dowager's chair and she gave him her hand. "Otto," she said, "are you well?"

"Of course," said the old Baron, "why shouldn't I be? If I felt any better there would be a scandal." He laughed at his own joke, but the Squire frowned.

"Who has his legs wrapped in covers?" asked Baron Otto abruptly. "Whom were you talking about when I came in?"

"About Steeven Wenselaar," explained the Dowager. "Dr. Satyn visited him last week."

"What were you doing there?" Otto turned to the Pastor. "Trying to convert that fool?"

"I went to congratulate the Baron on his birthday," said the Pastor.

"He's always having birthdays," chuckled Baron Otto. "That's all he ever has. Did you see his wife? A beauty, eh, what? I like her mouth, don't you? Red as a cherry. Fifty years younger than her husband, they say. Isn't it a pity? I said to my man Markus only the other day . . ."

The Squire deliberately interrupted his father. "Dr. Satyn was paying the Baron a visit. It was his birthday," he repeated.

"I know it was his birthday," said Otto, irritated. "You told me that before. What do I care about his damned birthdays?"

"He is in constant agony." The Pastor was bending slightly forward in speaking to the Dowager. "The slightest movement causes him excruciating pain. The Baroness is always by his side. She watches over him as over a child, she reads to him, serves him his meals, and massages his legs three or four times a day to ease the pain."

"He has his legs rubbed, eh?" asked Otto. "I thought so." He laughed his shrill piping giggle. "I thought so. That's just like him. But he won't leave her a cent for all her troubles, mark my word. A clear case of love's labor lost," he quoted in English. "I've known Steeven. I know that boy a long time, by God!"

Two men and a woman came into the room. One of the men was well known to us boys, a lieutenant of the Gorcum garrison, Jonkheer Hubert van Vredenburg, a pleasant-faced, broad-shouldered young man who was a member of the poetry society of which my father was the president. With him was Captain Folette, an officer with a huge paunch and dark eyes, who was totally bald. Both officers were in uniform. I had never seen the lady before.

Lieutenant van Vredenburg walked up to Baron Otto, clicked his heels, and bowed. The Dowager favored him with her most gracious smile as he bent over to kiss her hand. "You're the image of your dear mother," she said to him.

"We were just talking of Wenselaar's wife. Do you know her?" Baron Otto asked.

The Lieutenant blushed. "Slightly," he said. "I have met the Baroness but once."

"Where was that?" asked Otto.

Lieutenant van Vredenburg looked sidewise at the Baron and, increasing his air of caution, said slowly: "At the concert one night last winter in Gorcum."

"So she runs to concerts, that's interesting to know," said Otto. "Was she alone?" he asked.

The Lieutenant had no time to answer as the fat Captain

stepped up. Unable to bow because of his immense girth, he inclined his head deeply before the Baron.

"Folette," said Otto, "who was that woman you came in with?"

"She's German," replied the Captain, "Frau Stauffer, the wife of a new engineer at the iron factory. That's her husband over there talking with Dominie Satyn." The Captain nodded in the direction of a tall young man with a suntanned face who had his hair combed in a brush.

"Is he German, too?" asked the Dowager.

"Yes," said the Captain, "but he speaks Dutch."

"He must be a rarity," observed Baron Otto dryly, "I have never heard of a *Mof* yet who could speak Dutch."

"Otto," whispered the Dowager, "do speak a little softer. He might hear you."

"Can't I say what I like in my own house?" Otto returned. "What are all these Germans doing around here lately, anyway? What do they want?"

"They placed a big order for structural iron at the factory," said the fat Captain. "They are also buying up horses in the neighborhood."

"None came around here, so far as I know," said Otto. "Wish they would, by God!"

"Has Your Excellency some horses for sale?" asked Captain Folette.

"I should think we have," replied the Baron. "We have a dozen Brabant mares. I'll ask Arnout." He called to his son, "Arnout, are we selling those Brabanters?"

The Squire stepped nearer quickly and continued the conversation with Captain Folette.

Two maids, in black dresses with tiny white lace aprons, went around offering appetizers on large silver platters. Baron Otto put on his monocle and followed one of the girls out of the room just as Baroness Rietvelt came in accompanied by two young ladies and her son Zeger. Ary followed behind. The Baroness sat down by the Dowager's side. The two girls were Zeger's cousins, daughters of the Squire's sister. They were addressed as Freule Davina and Freule Hermina.

"I was glad to see you and your friends in church this morning," Dr. Satyn said to Ary. "You set a good example to the villagers here."

"Don't they come to church?" asked Ary.

"A mere handful, as you could see this morning." The Pastor smiled. "They really stay away from me, though, I am afraid," he added, "not from the church. I am not orthodox enough to suit them."

"How did they come to call you to this parish, then?" asked Jetze, who, being a pastor's son, was keenly interested in the subject.

"Oh, it's the Squire who settled that," replied the young minister. "They take the Squire's candidate. No one else stands a chance."

"But he does not go to church himself, does he?" asked Ary.

"Neither he nor his family." The Pastor shook his head. "If I could have that family, I'd fill my church."

There was a clatter of falling dishes and broken glass from one of the other rooms and the Dowager put her hands to her ears. Mrs. Rietvelt urged her husband to go out and see what had happened. A moment later the Squire returned holding his father loosely by the arm. The Squire's face was flushed with embarrassment and the Baron's wrinkles seemed to have grown deeper. It was clear that the two men had been quarreling. They were still talking in an angry undertone. Markus, the Baron's old batman, dressed up for the occasion in a dark-green livery with gilded buttons, followed immediately behind his old master. Dr. Satyn looked away quickly when they entered and began to talk animatedly to Lieutenant van Vredenburg. The fat Captain whispered something to the German engineer's wife which made that lady laugh so excitedly that she had to press her handkerchief to her mouth.

Otto fixed her with an astonished stare and, glancing around the room, saw that nearly all eyes were upon him. With an abrupt gesture he flung his son's hand from his own arm. "Leave me alone!" he said. "What of it if I spoke to that girl! Isn't this my own house, by God? The way you hold onto me, one would think I've been placed under arrest. I won't stand for it, by God! No, I won't sit down." His eyes fell upon Zeger's two cousins. "Next thing you know," he said, "they'll be sending me to Sunday school with you girls, or using me for some dirty dishwashing job. Fancy, somebody put a Bible in my room the other day, too. What in hell are we coming to?" The Freules blushed.

"Ottotje!" called out the Dowager, using the diminutive of his name, and wagging a finger at the old Baron. "Come here this very minute. I have something very, very interesting to tell you about your old friend General van der Veer." The Baron obeyed. He sat down meekly by her side on a taboret and began wiping his monocle with his handkerchief. The Dowager drew his head close to hers by pulling at one of the glittering crosses on his uniform.

Another landowner from the neighborhood, Jonkheer Tick, and his wife now made their entry. With them was Judge Bakhuis of the Cantonal Court in Gorcum and Dr. Potter, the local physician of Rietvelt, a gentle spirit, shy and learned and of delicate taste, who had published a book of verses under a pseudonym and who was known through the whole region for his interest in popular causes. He was no longer young. The white hair around his temples showed where the first frost of old age had nipped him. But the quiet blue eyes were tolerant and the firm mouth patient. The landowner walked with a stoop and smoked a cigar that dangled between his lips. He was a sallow-skinned, crumpled little man in the fifties with a graying walrus mustache and heavy purple pouches under his eyes. In striking contrast, his young wife flaunted her beauty. She was a head taller than her husband and moved with the stately dignity of a queen. She wore a low-cut blue-lace dress and her shoulders were bare. She had dark chestnut-colored hair that lay about her head in a fluffy aureole. One felt instinctively that all the secrets of night, of jeweled light, of whispering, laughing voices and rose-red carnations, were hers.

Lieutenant van Vredenburg settled his monocle in its socket with a little flourish and stared at her intently. So did the German engineer. Jetze sniffed at the perfume she brought in with her and said stupidly, "Roses of Picardy," and then laughed like a yokel. Judge Bakhuis, who was a Curator of the Gymnasium in Gorcum, looked over at Zeger, Ary, and myself standing by the window and nodded at us with a faint smile.

At the same moment the folding doors were swung open and the dining-room came into view.

"Is it true that there will be no maneuvers this year?" asked Jonkheer Tick of Captain Folette, who sat directly opposite him. The Captain put his wineglass down and said: "So I understand. There will be no general maneuvers. It appears that no funds were voted."

"No funds? Do you mean that the Second Chamber has not voted the necessary credits?" asked Squire Arnout.

"That's it." Captain Folette nodded. "They said they could not impose any more taxes this year."

"The Government did not ask for special credits," interjected Dr. Satyn. "A terrible lot of money had already been voted for the navy and for colonial defense."

The Squire looked quizzically at the Pastor for a moment, and started vigorously carving the meat on his plate.

"Oh, we are going to do our regular shooting for a couple of weeks in Zeist." The Captain addressed Squire Arnout. "I mean the artillery regiments are having their regular annual exercises."

"But no general maneuvers?" asked the Squire again.

"No, no general maneuvers," the Captain repeated.

"What do you think of that?" the Squire asked the German engineer. "No credits have been provided to give our army its proper training this year. I wonder what your Kaiser would do in that case? What would he do with a parliament that refused to co-operate in the national interest?"

"That is an eventuality which could not occur in Germany," said Herr Stauffer stiffly. "At least I cannot imagine such a challenge arising at all."

"The Kaiser would not tolerate such a parliament for a day," the engineer's wife spoke up. "And even if it happened, if credits were refused, I think every German soldier would march to maneuvers regardless."

"Bravo!" cried the Dowager. "That is the kind of language I like to hear. You Germans do have a feeling for your country. And your Kaiser is a marvelous man, *ein Prachtmensch*," she added in German. "He will not let himself be imposed upon by the politicians and the rabble. Here in Holland, it is a different story." She sighed deeply.

"That's not surprising," interjected Otto in a high voice, "when you know what contemptible, disgusting, stinking nonsense they teach here nowadays in the schools." He looked at his son, the Squire. "I meant to talk about that to you, Arnout . . ."

The Squire was talking to Frau Stauffer and did not pay any attention to his father. Ary threw me a swift smile. Dr. Satyn saw it and said, "You don't like the Kaiser?"

"I neither like him nor dislike him," said Ary. "I ignore him completely." Everybody burst into laughter. But the German engineer's face flamed red with anger.

"And the German Kaiser does not even know that you exist," he said sharply.

"I hope so," Ary smiled back.

Squire Arnout broke off his conversation with the engineer's wife and looked around the table. It was clear that he had not heard what had passed between Herr Stauffer and Ary Brandt. "I wonder," he said to the engineer, "whether you heard anything about the impression the Kaiser received on the occasion of his recent visit to this country. He was favorably impressed, I hope?"

"I am afraid," Herr Stauffer replied slowly, "that the impression was not of the best. His Majesty is said to have been very much annoyed by the affront to His Majesty in Amsterdam."

"In Amsterdam? An affront?" gasped Lieutenant van Vredenburg.

"Didn't you hear about it?" asked Judge Bakhuis.

"No, what happened?" inquired the Lieutenant.

"Why, the Socialists distributed tens of thousands of penny whistles," explained Jonkheer Tick, "and when the

Kaiser passed along the Damrak a hell of screeching and hooting broke loose."

"I'll be damned!" exclaimed Otto. "The canaille! Was the Queen with the Kaiser at the moment?"

"I don't know," replied Captain Folette. "If she was, the matter is even more serious."

"Yes," said Judge Bakhuis, "and the municipality of Amsterdam refused to repair the statue of the Maid on the Dam, although it was asked very urgently to do so by the Government."

"What's the matter with the statue?" the Squire inquired.

"One of its arms is missing, knocked off by lightning," remarked the Judge.

"Heavens above!" exclaimed the Dowager. "You mean to say the Kaiser looked upon a broken statue from the windows of the palace, the symbol of Dutch national unity with one arm missing?"

"Well, you have a Socialist majority in the Council of Amsterdam," said the Judge slowly. "What do you expect?"

"Socialists and traitors," replied Otto. "By God, I would know what to do with them!"

"I thought Wibaut was the only Socialist," said the Squire.

"Half the councilors are," the Judge remarked.

"It's a shame," said the Dowager. "But it has little to do with politics, I think. Our people are simply notorious for their bad manners, especially in Amsterdam. Don't you remember a few years ago at the Peace Conference in The Hague how the police had to be called in to protect the Chinese delegates? The street boys followed them around and pulled their pigtails."

"He, he, he!" laughed Baron Otto. "I remember. It was funny, I must admit!"

"Last summer," said Judge Bakhuis, "an Englishman who was making sketches in the fish market in Gorcum was driven off by the women. One woman threatened him with a knife. It was fortunate that he couldn't understand what they called him."

"Must have been choice language," the Squire remarked.

"It was even worse in Belgium," spoke up the German

engineer suddenly. "It appears His Majesty was terribly insulted by the King himself."

"By King Leopold?" asked two or three in unison.

"Yes," replied the German, "by King Leopold."

"What happened?" the Squire asked.

"It appears," went on the engineer, "that His Majesty spoke very frankly at the farewell dinner when almost the entire Belgian Cabinet was present. The Kaiser said it would not be long before he would make some important changes in the map of Europe. He said he intended to reduce France to its rightful proportions and that he intended to give French Flanders to King Leopold II."

"Well, what did Leopold say to that?" asked Lieutenant van Vredenburg.

"He did not say a word," came back the engineer. "Nobody else said a word. All those Belgians maintained an absolute silence. His Majesty the Emperor was deeply pained by that silence. But worst of all, in driving to the station right after dinner an incident occurred that will be long remembered, something we Germans cannot easily forgive."

"What was that?" asked the Squire as all eyes turned to Herr Stauffer.

"His Majesty was dressed in the uniform of a Belgian general, of course," went on Herr Stauffer, "while King Leopold wore the uniform of a German field marshal. As the Kaiser drove to the railway station in the evening, the streets were packed with people, but all their cheering was reserved for the second carriage, in which Leopold was seated. And why do you think they cheered?" asked the engineer, solemnly looking around the table. "They cheered, ladies and gentlemen, because King Leopold was wearing his helmet backside forward." The engineer looked with indignation from one face to the other. "Imagine, the great helmet of the Prussian Guard with the golden eagle! He had it on backward."

"Do you think it was deliberate?" asked Captain Folette in the silence that ensued.

"Yes," said the engineer, "I am afraid, Captain, it was a deliberate gesture, a deliberate affront."

Dr. Satyn tried to keep a straight face, but didn't succeed. Seeing Lieutenant van Vredenburg with his napkin stuffed in his mouth and tears of mirth rolling down his cheeks, the Pastor too burst into an uncontrollable fit of laughter. Otto slapped his thighs, screaming at the top of his voice, "Original idea! By God, what an idea!"

The engineer turned pale and seemed about to rise from his chair when the Squire called out, "I think it was a damned outrage, a true sample of Belgian vulgarity."

"Yes," assented Judge Bakhuis, "those Belgians have a damnably coarse sense of humor." Lieutenant van Vredenburg winked at Dr. Satyn and started to laugh again. "The Prussian eagle turned into a sparrow," he hiccuped. "Can you imagine Leopold with his long beard and his helmet on backward? God, that's rich!"

Jonkheer Tick saved the situation as another ripple of laughter started at the lower end of the table, by asking the Squire in a loud voice: "Have you heard that there is a move on foot to abolish the kermess (fair) in Gorcum? Who is behind that, do you think?"

"It's pretty clear who is behind that," answered the Squire, glancing at the German engineer, who sat staring stubbornly at his plate. "It's the orthodox dominies, of course. But they won't get very far. There are three market days in the week of kermess, two cattle markets and one horse market. The municipality of Gorcum cannot afford to give up that revenue. Nor the revenue from the amusements. Think of it, the owners of the carrousel alone pay a round thousand gulden for the concession. Figure what this means when you have so many amusements—a cakewalk, a circus, a cinematograph, and all the booths and tents. And then the people the kermess brings to the shops . . ."

"It's the taverns they aim at," explained Dr. Satyn. "All the taprooms, saloons, bars, and dance halls in Gorcum have permission to stay open all night during the week of kermess. It's a week of debauch and brawling. I forget how many were stabbed last year. The police were kept busy locking up people."

"Oh, it wasn't as bad as all that," and the Judge smiled, shaking his head. "The people have a right to amuse themselves. They must be allowed to let off steam once in a while."

"Why did you abolish the fair in Rietvelt here yourself some years ago, Squire, if I may ask?" inquired the Pastor.

"Well," replied the Squire, "it wasn't the fair itself I objected to so much. It was the aftermath."

"What do you mean, the aftermath?"

"I mean nine months after," said the Squire. "That fair of ours attracted the soldiers of the Gorcum garrison, you see, and we had an annual crop of illegitimate babies. Yes, and a lot of fighting and brawling, too. Make no mistake about it. Why, there were days, or rather nights I should say, when the jail was so crowded there was scarcely any breathing-space left. We had to shove the overflow into the basement of the municipal building . . ."

"That reminds me," interjected Jonkheer Tick, "when are that gravedigger and his pal going to be brought to trial?"

"This autumn, I think," replied the Squire. "There have been two postponements already. The business has become quite complicated."

"A clear case of necrophilia, don't you think?" asked Judge Bakhuis of the Pastor. "That sort of thing is very rare here in Holland and rare everywhere in rural communities. It's rather a disease of overcivilization and depravity. You can imagine its occurring in a city like Paris, or reading about it in ancient history. Here in Rietvelt it would seem impossible. Still, there it is, unquestionably a case of necrophilia. It's astounding. It frightens one sometimes to think what dark passions slumber in the souls of people. I always say we haven't yet begun to plumb the depths of the human mind."

"From what I have learned about the gravedigger's case," said the Pastor cautiously, "it does not appear to fall in the category—er—at all—er—of those strange aberrations to which you allude. It's much simpler than that. You would be surprised to learn what really happened." The Pastor looked in the direction of the Freules, who were listening attentively, and suddenly stopped talking.

"What is the gravedigger's crime anyway?" asked Zeger. "I've asked half a dozen people. Nobody wants to tell me."

"No one is going to tell you here, my dear," said Zeger's mother with finality. "That is not a subject we can discuss here at table." She smiled and continued: "I would much sooner listen to Mijnheer Brandt recite us something of the new poetry in the salon after dinner. I hear he is quite a champion of the moderns."

"Right!" exclaimed Lieutenant van Vredenburg. "Will you, Ary?" asked the Lieutenant with boyish enthusiasm.

"Yes, please, Mr. Brandt," Freule Davina pleaded. "We hear nothing but the old fogies at school."

Ary bowed gracefully in the direction of Mrs. Rietvelt and the young ladies.

"Will you recite us something from Willem Kloos?" asked Freule Hermina.

"Gladly," said Ary, "from Kloos or Verwey or Gorter or Roland Holst!"

"Those are some of the red brothers," said Captain Folette in an imposing, disapproving manner. "Anarchists!"

"They are great poets," said Ary. "I don't care if they are anarchists, bigamists, or teetotalers."

Lieutenant van Vredenburg thanked Ary with a grateful nod. Dr. Potter cast his eyes to heaven and smiled his faint, strange smile. The Pastor busied himself with cutting an apple and sprinkling it with salt.

"What is Your Reverence doing now?" asked the German engineer's wife.

"It brings out the taste better," the Pastor replied. "I learned it from a bishop in your own country. Please, try it!"

Frau Stauffer accepted a slice of apple and took a bite. "Indeed," she said, "it does taste better. Bishops certainly know their way in the world."

The servants now brought in the dessert, a huge fruit tart and Roman-ice punch. Jetze slyly reached under the tablecloth to open his belt a notch, keeping his eyes fixed on the crystal glasses of punch. He took a cigar, too, which Markus offered all the male guests. When Markus placed the tray before me I was on the point of declining, but Jetze began to signal desperately to me to take one. "For me," he whispered loudly. "For tonight before I go to sleep." Ary deliberately took a handful. He too had that passion for tobacco which some Dutch boys acquire at an early age, not clandestinely, let it be said, and from the indulgence in which not one of them has ever suffered a whit of harm at any time.

Above the babel of voices and the laughter I caught some tags and scraps of the conversation going on between the two squires. Jonkheer Tick, his face screwed into skeptical wrinkles, his elbows on the table and a fresh cigar dangling from his lips, was listening with an air of unconcealed impatience and disapproval to what his host was saying about fall plowing.

"I wouldn't think of it for a minute," he said, shaking his head vigorously.

"You can say what you like," came back the Squire, "I'm going to try it nevertheless. Think of the time you gain in the spring when everything needs to be done at once. I know it hasn't been done before in these parts. But on my last trip to Denmark and East Frisia I saw plenty of it. The Danish climate isn't much different from ours. If anything, it's colder. Why shouldn't I try it?"

"I should think they get much more snow up there," said Jonkheer Tick.

"More snow or less makes no difference," the Squire went on. "The Danes have taught us so many good lessons we ought to watch them carefully and take those lessons to heart."

"What have the Danes that we haven't got?" asked Squire Tick with a contemptuous shrug of the shoulders.

"For one thing they've ousted us completely from the English dairy market," replied his host. "And how did they do it? Is their cheese and butter any better than ours?"

"Of course not!" exclaimed the Jonkheer indignantly. "Whoever says that is an idiot!"

"Do you know how they got the better of us, Jan?" went on the Squire. "They introduced scientific methods of farming and marketing. We thought we could get along in the old way—every man for himself. We were so confident of the superiority and reputation of our products that we disdained all competitors, we underestimated them and ignored them. We didn't know what was going on. The Danes cooperated among themselves and crowded us out, and it will be a devil of a long time before we recapture that English market."

"It's socialism, if you ask me," said Squire Tick, pulling an ugly face. "They're rotten with it up there in Scandinavia."

Squire Rietvelt laughed. "Call it what you like, Jan," he said, "it does wonders. I wish you could see those farms in Holstein and Jutland. Perfect, I tell you."

"Well," said the other man, "things look wonderfully good with us, too, this year."

Now it was the time for the Squire to dissent. Things didn't look so promising at all, he thought. No, not for him at any rate. There had been a late spring and the last rains had beaten the first grass so heavily he had the machines mow it off. He was worried, too, about the rye. It was shooting up too fast. The potatoes were rotting in the ground. There had been altogether too much rain. And still he needed good prices for his crops in the coming fall, better prices than last year, because he was planning a lot of changes on the farm. For one thing the house and the barns needed painting. There hadn't been a lick of paint put on these past six years. On the east side of the house the sun was peeling off everything, giving it a dilapidated, neglected appearance. It was a disgrace, really. And he had to put down a new threshing floor, too, and on top of that he thought of installing a water system. Yes, a water system, nothing less. They had struck an artesian well in the middle of the apple orchard last summer and next winter, if there wasn't too heavy a frost, he was going to pipe that water into the house and the stables.

"That will cost you a pretty penny," said the other Squire, looking at his neighbor and smiling his cold smile. "Are you sure it isn't river water seeping in?"

No, Squire Rietvelt had had it analyzed. The only trouble was that old Van Daalen, the supervisor on the estate, was becoming an invalid, helpless with rheumatism most of the time. "The man is getting old," said the Squire. He was only good enough now to stand around, not much use otherwise. Still, in his younger days he was a phenomenal worker, a hustler, handy with everything. With a man like that, you never had any need of expert workers from town. Van Daalen would know how to lay down those pipes and install the pumps, and no trouble or worry about it. If only he were well. But he was ill and not likely to recover.

"Get rid of him," said Jonkheer Tick curtly, flicking the ashes off his cigar. "You'll be surprised when you start to figure it out how much profits a useless old fellow like that eats up. I never keep them for a day when they grow too old to work or when they start ailing. Work or get out, that's my motto."

"Well," Squire Rietvelt smiled back a little lamely, "that's something I simply couldn't do with old Van Daalen. He's been on the estate from childhood. In fact he was born on it. So was his wife, for that matter, and all his children. He started out as a plowboy for my grandfather sixty-five years ago. He has a share in the farm."

"Don't tell me now that you have started to parcel out the place among the noble peasants, like that man Tolstoi in Russia." said Jonkheer Tick, snickering. He rose from his chair as the hostess and the other ladies began to file out of the dining-hall.

"No," Squire Rietvelt laughed as he joined him, "I haven't got to that point yet, by Jove. I merely mean that Krelis van Daalen is almost like a fixture with us. He's part of the estate. It's hard to think of the farm without him."

"I run my farm to make money," said Jonkheer Tick. "I don't run it for the glory of God."

As the Squire walked out of the dining-room he joined the Pastor, who was speaking of his student days in Leyden to Ary and me. "Krelis van Daalen's wife is very ill," the Squire said to Dr. Satyn. "Perhaps you could look in for a moment one of these days. They live in the third cottage beyond the apple orchard." The Pastor nodded.

Coffee and liqueurs were being served in the next room, but most of the guests walked past the buffet into the room beyond and out through the folding doors into the garden.

The German engineer's wife, Baron Otto, Dr. Potter, and the fat Captain remained for coffee, sitting in a group around a small table. Seeing Dr. Satyn walk by, Baron Otto spoke to him as if it were the first time he had seen the Pastor that evening.

"Ah, Dominie," he exclaimed, "glad to see you! How is it going? Are you still fooling the farmers?"

"How so, Your Excellency?" asked the Pastor, more startled than amused. "What could I fool them with? They are far too clever for me!"

"*Nja*," said the Baron, "you know what I mean. Are you telling them all about heaven and the angels and the harps and the good times they're going to have up there?" He pointed upward and Captain Folette burst into uproarious laughter. "That was your worthy predecessor's strong point, you know, old Dr. Hooft," went on the Baron. "The fatherland of the pious, he called it. He, he, he!"

"I do believe in the immortality of the soul, Excellency," said the Pastor, "if that is what you mean."

"I thought so," said Otto with his irritating giggle. "But it's a weak point you mention there, my dear sir, a very weak point indeed. It's all good and well for you to talk about the immortality of the soul. It sounds pretty, I admit. It's poetry. How beautiful—life after death! Enthralling idea, really! But when you get as old as I am—I am past seventy, you know—it's an entirely different matter. Look, Dominie," he went on, taking hold of the Pastor's coat, "look, when you want to stay in the house, it's absolutely immaterial to you whether the Paris Express is on time or not, isn't it, or whether it will make the right connections?

If you happen to think of it, you say to yourself: The Paris Express, well, that's an excellent train, good cuisine, pleasant scenery and company, Paris is a noble city. But when your trunks are packed and you stand on the station platform, you begin to grow a little nervous. You look in the train directory. You look at the clock. Everything depends on accuracy. Do you see what I mean?

"Well, I am a man who has his trunks packed. I stand on the platform and I have looked in the directory, and I tell you frankly, Dominie, I don't believe there is any train, no train today, no train tomorrow, nor next year. There is no train ever. The outlook is hopeless. As the tree falls that's the way it's going to lie. We, too, we remain lying where they put us. If the soil is dry, he, he, he, you may have the good fortune that your skull goes on grinning for a couple of hundred years. But that's about all. There is no train, Dominie, no train, believe me, I know."

Baron Otto laughed again, but he suddenly stopped short and it seemed to me a flicker of fear showed in his dark eyes. "It's not a pleasant subject to think of when you lie awake at night and when you're past seventy," he said soberly.

"Oh, but I do think life has some deeper sense than that," spoke up the German lady. "I cannot believe that all this fuss, being born, being educated, worrying, laboring, and growing old, has no purpose. I cannot believe we are all running headlong into some blank wall, do you?" She turned to Captain Folette.

Mention of a blank wall apparently put Baron Otto in mind of something comical. He chuckled with suppressed delight, brought his head close to Dr. Potter's, and began to tell a story. "This is not for you, Dominie," he interrupted himself for a moment. "I wouldn't have it on my conscience for all the world to corrupt your innocent, youthful mind."

The Pastor, Ary, and I walked on. In the music room one of the Freules sat before the grand piano playing a Chopin nocturne while Zeger stood by to turn the pages. The girl played faultlessly, but without a trace of feeling.

We could look into the garden. The stars were out and the air was laden with the perfume of roses.

Zeger stepped through the glass folding doors to the stone terrace. With him was the elder of his two cousins, Freule Davina. She wore a simple dress of white crepe de chine cut in a style suggestive of J. L. David's painting of Madame Recamier. From a rather tight-fitting bodice and a high waistline the skirt fell down in large, ample folds to within a few inches of her ankles. She was really very short, but the mass of pale golden hair which lay in a pile on top of her head, and a pair of high-heeled shoes of dark-red leather, brought her face almost level with Zeger's shoulders. As she passed us, she was holding his arm and I could hear her talking to him in a low, pleasant voice. Out on the terrace, in the glow of light from the music room, I saw Zeger cut a red rose from the hedges that grew against the brick-pillared balustrade and pin it to Davina's dress. They stood facing each other, she laughing and standing on tiptoe looking alternately from his hands fastening the rose on her bosom to his face.

The Dowager, who had taken a seat by one of the unopened French windows, peered out at the couple. Dominie Satyn, Ary Brandt, and I stood behind her chair but a few feet away. She said to the Baron, who let himself down with a deep sigh into an armchair by her side, "They make a fine pair, don't they, Otto?"

"Who?" asked Otto, looking in the wrong direction.

"I mean Zeger and Davina," the Dowager said. "They're out there on the terrace."

"Possible!" replied the Baron. "I didn't notice them. How much has she got, anyway? Do you know? Does anybody know?"

"I am not talking of her dower. I think Davina is a beauty."

"Oh, sure," came back the Baron with a shrug of the shoulders. "Sure, why not? But so is Hermina a beauty. Eh, and that German woman over there talking with Folette, do you think she is to be despised? How old do you think she is? I don't think she is much over thirty."

"Beauty is a great good fortune," went on the Dowager, heedless of the Baron's remarks. "At our age, Ottotje, we need beauty around us, at least to look upon. We expect beauty from the young people. Maybe it's egotistical of me, but it gives me a deep sense of satisfaction to watch them." She peered again at Zeger and Davina, who stood talking earnestly on the terrace.

"What makes you think beauty is a great good fortune?" asked the Baron half-angrily. "I don't share your opinion at all. Beauty complicates things enormously for a woman. It puts additional responsibilities on her, it disturbs her dignity. Her face makes contact with anyone who looks at her. She can't help it. Her face urges itself on men. It speaks to them, even if her tongue is silent. It must be a damnable nuisance to have a beautiful face. It's a permanent indiscretion, by God! Do you call that good fortune?" The Baron laughed his childish giggle and with two fingers pulled up his Adam's apple from the depths of his stiff gilt collar.

"At least you were never troubled by the embarrassments of beauty," said the Dowager venomously. He looked at her sideways and laughed, and nodding in the direction of the young people on the terrace, he said, "I had better keep an eye open. Rietvelt blood, you know." He made as if he was about to rise.

The Dowager laid her hand on his arm. "Do sit still for a moment, Otto," she said. "You are as restless as a child with fever. Leave the young people alone. Don't forget we were young once ourselves."

"Young?" he queried. "Yes, that's true. But perhaps it would not be amiss to let the young ones benefit by the lessons of our youth. That girl Davina's eyes, for instance. Do you know, Amelie, they remind me very much of your own eyes when you were seventeen or eighteen. They have a peculiar glow in them, if I may say so: something irresistible. I watched her carefully at table. I don't think it's good for Zeger . . ."

The Dowager looked at him coldly. "I notice," she said, "that your memory is still good." The Baron rose.

"Please come with me," said the Pastor, "while I look in on Mrs. van Daalen, the wife of the supervisor. You don't know how I dread encounters of that sort." We went with him and in passing we saw the figure of our friend Jetze scurry into the darkness. The kitchen door was suddenly pulled shut from the inside, but slowly enough for us to catch a glimpse of Clara's eyes.

"What can you say in such cases?" the Dominie went on. "I mean when death is so near?"

"You can't very well say that there's no train," I suggested.

"Precisely!" came back the young minister. "Still, these people expect you to say something. They expect some magic, some formula, a word of consolation, something to hope for. Those are the very superstitions from which the people should be liberated. It's easy enough to talk against superstition from the pulpit. But what can one say to a person in the agony of death? I find it a most trying experience," he said as he wiped the perspiration off his brow.

At last we found the cottage, but we let the Pastor enter alone. An oil lamp shed its light through the open window. We sat on the grass smoking and listening to the sound of a piano coming from afar.

When the Pastor returned, he was more shaken than he had been before. "It's obvious," he said, "the end is very near. She could scarcely speak above a whisper. She was breathing with great difficulty and her words came by fits and starts. She told me it was very hard when you have worked all your life and brought up your children as best you can and you want a rest at last. She said she had been waiting, waiting for weeks for the Lord to take her home. She felt she was no earthly use to anyone now and in everybody's way. 'My man Krelis,' she said, 'has to pretend he's sick with the rheumatism so he can stay with me to the end. Dying, dying, dying, and still not dying. And the end won't come. The medicine cost an awful lot of money, too. But I am praying for the Lord to come and take me.' But I don't think she will have to wait much longer," said Dr. Satyn.

Ary and I listened in silence. Feeling no desire to return

to the party, we walked along the rear of the manor house. Passing the music room, we caught sight through the open windows of Lieutenant van Vredenburg standing near the piano, speaking and gesticulating slowly with his hands. No other sound but his voice was audible, although we could not distinguish the words. As we advanced we heard a burst of applause, and it became clear that the Lieutenant had been substituting for Ary in a recitation from the poets.

We went straight up to our rooms. The Pastor came up with us. He and Ary started a game of chess while I seated myself by the open window to smoke a pipe. The stars hung low, but there was no moon. Bats whirred by periodically, sweeping in under the eaves of the house. As my eyes grew accustomed to the dark, I could distinguish every object. Fifty yards away, on my right, there was a fountain and a small statue of Eros, to my left a small summerhouse. In the distance I could distinguish the pinpoint lights of workers' cottages. After a few minutes my attention was drawn by the sound of footsteps on the gravel path below the windows. I leaned out on my elbow, half-expecting to see Jetze and Clara. Instead I saw Captain Folette walk by with the German engineer's wife. They stopped and he pressed her against his round paunch, but she bent her head back and his girth prevented him from touching her face with his lips. The woman acted as if she wanted to turn back. The Captain held her firmly by the arm. Then they walked off rapidly and disappeared behind the summerhouse. I saw them no more.

"Did you get that, Pieter?" asked Ary, looking up from his chessboard. "Did you get that about that old man, Krelis van Daalen, having to pretend that he's sick with rheumatism in order to stay with his wife till the end? That's the most terrible pretense I've ever heard of. An eighty-year-old man has to simulate illness to remain near his dying wife."

Jetze came in. "Where did you go?" he demanded. "Everybody was asking for you."

We told him what had happened at the cottage and he fell silent. The Pastor left with a promise that he would look us up in Gorcum after the summer vacation.

"What's the mystery of the gravedigger's crime?" Jetze asked, getting into bed and lighting a cigar. "Everybody talks about it, but so furtively and incompletely, breaking off the conversation so suddenly and with such meaningful silences and knowing looks, that you get the impression it's something terribly scandalous. I asked Piet Harte and I asked Clara," he went on, throwing up his hands in a gesture of hopelessness.

"What did they say?" Ary wanted to know.

"When I asked Piet if there was a murder involved, he said, 'God, no! What those fellows did was worse than murder.' And when I said, 'What is worse than murder?' Piet told me, 'Go and ask them.' When I asked Clara she pulled a face and grew angry at me for even mentioning such matters."

"To whom did Harte refer when he said 'ask them'?" Ary queried.

"It seems there are two men involved, the gravedigger and someone else, the bell-ringer, I believe," replied Jetze.

"It must be some kind of sex crime," Ary thought. "If it wasn't, you'd surely have read it in the *Gazette for Gorcum and the Five Seigneurial Counties*," he said. "Your Uncle Alexander, the editor"—he turned to me—"does not consider such matters fit to print. You could tell by the indecent whispering and giggling going on that it's something shady, or they'd all be talking openly about it. Besides, didn't you hear Bakhuis say at dinner that it was a clear case of necrophilia?"

"What is necrophilia?" asked Jetze, jumping from the bed to relight his cigar.

"You should know, you've been learning Greek for five years. *Nekros*—dead, *philos*—friend, *philia*—friendship, a liking for," said Ary with the solemn intonation of a schoolmaster.

"You mean," asked Jetze, his mouth agape, "that these men are charged with . . . having performed the sexual act on a corpse?"

"I said nothing of the kind," Ary retorted. "I merely gave you the etymology of the word necrophilia. Besides, you needn't act so shocked. We know necrophilia was practiced in ancient times, and no doubt it is still practiced today here and there."

"Not in Loon," said Jetze indignantly, naming the village whence he hailed.

"No, not in Loon, nor in Rietvelt either," said Ary. "People don't have to. There are too many living Claras about. But in Egypt priests who were charged with the function of embalming are known to have practiced fornication on the bodies of virgins committed to their care. According to some authorities that's the origin of the disease called syphilis. Those priests would get a fine body in some back room of the temple at nights, where the embalming was done by lamplight, and then they'd get hold of the dead girl's hair."

"Enough!" called out Jetze. "God, you must have a perverted mind to think up such bestialities!"

"Beasts don't practice necrophilia," Ary returned. "That's one of civilized man's little refinements." But Jetze was pulling his shirt over his head and didn't hear.

From the local gendarme whom we encountered in the village the next day we heard disturbing confirmation of the strange affair.

"Those two are charged with opening graves," he said.

"To rob the bodies?" we asked.

"No, no," the bearded policeman said. "No, you can't say they were robbing the bodies. There was nothing to rob. They dug up two women. One of them was Dirk Mensert's, the lamplighter's, own wife, who had been buried only two days before."

"But they were the bodies of women they dug up?"

"What do you mean?"

"They didn't dig up the bodies of any men?"

"Men? No, not men. They dug up the bodies of two women."

"What did they do with them?"

"Ah," said the policeman, scratching his chin in a puzzled way, "that's not for me to talk about. The question is *sub*

judice. Only the court can speak of that or Dirk himself.
Why don't you ask him? There he goes!"

A shrunken little man, almost a dwarf, carrying a ladder
on his shoulder crossed the small square in front of the
municipal building that moment. He wore a cap, a leather
jacket, and greasy, baggy trousers. When he noticed us
looking in his direction, he averted his face and hurried
out of sight, not without a hasty, furtive glance before dis-
appearing.

"Who's that?" I asked the policeman.

"That's Dirk Mensert, the lamplighter. He's the man
whose wife they dug up. The other fellow is Bernt Sas, the
gravedigger. We have both their confessions."

"It can't be such a terrible crime," I said, "if the man
isn't even in custody."

"Well, it's bad enough," said the policeman pursing his
lips and nodding his head gravely. "Desecration of the dead
is a serious offense here in Rietvelt. Dirk will sure have
to sit for it a couple of years. We don't stand for that kind
of thing around here."

After that we dismissed it from our minds. What was
the use of asking questions; nobody seemed disposed to tell
us the truth. Besides, we had other matters to worry about.
Ary had more than once expressed his inclination to curtail
our sojourn at the Rietvelt manor and go home. Zeger
hadn't shown himself for several days. We were left entirely to our own devices, with everybody around us, man,
woman, and child, busy with farmwork. In the house we
felt too much like poor relatives who were privileged to
watch the habits and diversions of our betters. We read it
in the condescending attitude of the servants, who treated
us as if they did not consider that we really belonged. They
acted as if they were doing us immense favors when they
brought up our food and performed other small tasks for
us.

"We're wasting our vacation here," said Ary. "We
should go home and do something useful." But Jetze,
rooted by infatuation for the servant girl, would not hear
of returning. He would stay, he said, till they threw him

out, which was just what we feared. The affair with Clara was fast assuming serious proportions. There were bound to be questions asked. Jetze's father was not the kind of man to take such things lightly. He was a rigid disciplinarian and would certainly hold Ary and myself to account if anything went wrong between his only son and a chambermaid. This unpleasant situation disturbed our good humor.

We did return home before the term of our invitation expired, but not because Jetze was brought around to our view. Force majeure intervened. Jetze himself, in fact, suddenly and dramatically gave the signal to go. And if I tell of it here, it is not because of the importance of the incident, but because it happened on the evening of the day when we learned the secret of the lamplighter's crime, which in turn had an evil bearing on Zeger van Rietvelt's career, and may be said to have led to political repercussions many years later in the dark days of the Nazi tyranny in Holland.

That morning I broke the crystal of my watch and went to the village in search of a repair shop. It looked like another lost day. At dawn the rain of the night had turned into a steady downpour that threatened to continue steadily. Ary had borrowed some books from Dr. Potter and Jetze had driven into Gorcum on one of the covered market wagons to make some purchases. At the tavern where I made inquiries I was directed to a small cottage standing a few paces back from the road on the main dike street. When I entered, a bell, which was fastened to the door, set up a loud clangor. After a few moments I heard the shuffle of slippers in the rear, and presently who should enter the shop but the dwarfish lamplighter himself.

"Do you repair watches?" I asked him.

"If it's not too complicated, I can manage," he said.

"It's only the crystal that's broken," I said, holding out the timepiece.

"If that's all," replied the man, taking my watch in his hand, "I think I can accommodate you."

He sat down at a small table behind the counter, pulled open a drawer, and fumbled in it for his instruments.

"It's a bad day," he said, sighing heavily. "Altogether too much rain this year. The farmers are worried."

"It's the same every year, always too much rain," I replied, "and the farmers are always complaining. That's second nature with them."

He was picking the chips of glass from the dial of my watch with a pair of small pincers. He looked up at me as I leaned over the counter and said, "I hope you are enjoying your stay at the manor."

I said I was, immensely.

"I have been inside too," he volunteered. "Several times, in fact."

"Have you?"

"Yes, to wish the Jonkheer and Mevrouw a Happy New Year," he explained. "We all do that on New Year's Day. He is a generous man, Mijnheer van Rietvelt. He pours the Bols himself that day. The women drink persico. Lena had two glasses of it last time. Yes, we are fortunate to have such good patroons here in Rietvelt."

"No doubt," I said, "but who is Lena?"

"I thought you knew," he replied, looking up suspiciously.

"What makes you think I know who Lena is?" I asked.

"Didn't I see you myself talking to Izak, the policeman, the other day?"

"Yes, that's true, but he didn't mention anyone by that name."

He nodded and busied himself with the watch. He put the tip of his tongue out each time he tried to squeeze the new crystal in. I noticed that his hair was turning gray.

"Lena was my wife," he said after a pause. "She's gone. Died a year ago come next September."

"I'm sorry to hear that," I said.

"Yes, she's gone," he said with a deep sigh. "I'm not over it yet. We were sweethearts from the time we went to school together and right to the end. She said to me that last night, 'Don't wait long, Dirk. It will be so lonely without you.' That's what she said."

"God has her," I said perfunctorily.

"Thank you," nodded the man. "It's the only hope we

have. If we didn't have that hope, we poor people, what would we have?"

The watch was repaired. He rubbed the new crystal with a piece of chamois. As I paid him he asked, suddenly looking up, "Would you like to see her picture?"

"Very much," I answered.

"Come with me, please," he beckoned, shuffling ahead of me toward the rear of the shop. He led me into a room with a floor of large blue flagstones in which stood four or five crated boxes containing live rabbits. There was also a cookstove, a couple of cane-bottomed armchairs, and a large wooden bed. Near the window, with the light falling on it, hung a bird cage with a turtledove inside.

He pointed to an enlarged framed photograph in colors above the mantelpiece. The picture showed a young couple in wedding clothes. The woman held a large bouquet of flowers in her hand. She must have been almost a foot taller than her husband and her head was turned slightly sideways, as people do who squint.

"That's Lena," said the little man, indicating the photograph with a nod of his head. "That picture was taken twenty-two years ago on our wedding day." He stared at it himself for a few moments and muttered, "She's gone, poor girl, gone for good."

"We will all have to go some day," I said to fill the silence.

The rabbits were stirring uneasily in their cages. "I forgot to feed them this morning," said the man as he walked toward a corner of the room where lay a heap of freshly cut grass. Taking a handful, he pushed it through the wooden slats of the rabbit boxes.

"Yes, I know, we will all have to go some day," he said as he went to fetch more grass. "But I would willingly have cut off my right hand to keep Lena alive a little longer. Cutting off a hand can't hurt any more than what I feel here." He pointed to his heart. Then, looking up at the turtledove in its cage, "That creature up there feels as I do. It's pining away for Lena. It hasn't cooed once since she left. Before that it woke us every morning with its chortling and tortling with the first light of day."

"It's very sad," I commiserated, looking at the cage where the bird sat motionless on its perch, its swift-blinking, beady red eyes giving the only sign of life.

"Yes," he assented, "sad it is, and the worst of it all is that she is buried where she is buried."

"But where is your wife buried?" I asked, thinking that she had perhaps been a Roman Catholic and there was a question of unconsecrated ground involved in the affair of the opened graves of which the policeman had spoken.

"She's buried at the back of the cemetery, in the poor plot, near the ditch that runs along the back of the manor lands, where the dogs go at night and all the rats are. The place swarms with rats. They are all over. They even come over here. That's why I had to put the rabbits inside the house."

"That's horrible," I said.

"Yes," he answered, "you're right. It is horrible. That's no place for Lena, near that ditch. That's no place for her." Suddenly he added: "You heard about the trouble I'm in, I suppose?"

"Yes, I did hear that you are to appear before the court in the fall—is that what you mean?"

"Yes, I am to be judged, me and Bernt Sas. We committed a crime. Izak, the policeman, found out about it. Bernt was suspended as soon as they found out that something was wrong."

"Who is Bernt?" I asked.

"Bernt," he said, raising his eyes in surprise, "Bernt is the gravedigger. He's my friend. He lives in the fifth house down the road. He hasn't done a stroke of work since he was suspended. I too am living in daily dread that I'll be suspended in my official position. For if that happens we'll both starve to death."

"What is your official position, then?" I asked.

"I'm the lamplighter of Rietvelt," he replied with some dignity.

"Oh, yes, I knew you were," I said.

"It's a responsible position," he nodded, obviously pleased that I was aware of his social standing. "But nobody, let me tell you, has ever made the least complaint against me. You can see for yourself by stepping out on the road what kind of lighting service we have here in Rietvelt. Of course, you are used to gas lamps in Gorcum. But Gorcum is a big city. Here we have oil lamps. They burn well and the glass is spotless."

"I noticed that," I said.

"Did you really?' he smiled.

"Yes," I said, "one can't help noticing it after coming from Gorcum. The lamplighters in Gorcum do not seem to have their hearts in the business. Sometimes they leave the work to boys. What do young boys care whether the lamp glasses are clean?"

"Indeed, you can't expect that," he agreed, and then sighed again. "If I'm not sent to jail, I'll surely be suspended."

"What really happened?" I asked. "Maybe you are unnecessarily worried."

"No, really I have committed a serious offense. Everybody is agreed on that."

"What did you do, then?"

"Oh, it's a long story. But I will tell it to you. Aren't you one of the Van Paassen boys?"

When I said I was, he went on: "I thought so. Your mother was my teacher in Bible class. She used to come to Rietvelt every Sunday for years to teach us children. She was only a young girl herself then. Lena and I both went to her class."

"She will remember you when I tell her. She never forgets the names of any of the children she taught."

"I wish you'd tell her of the trouble I'm in," he said. "Maybe she could advise me. Maybe she could put in a good word with Judge Bakhuis at the trial. Do you think she would?"

"I'm sure she will," I said.

"Well, you see it's this way," he began. "There are twenty-seven street lamps in this village of Rietvelt. Three

of them are large ones. One of the big ones, you must have
noticed it, stands at the beginning of the lane of poplars
that leads up to the manor house. Another stands in front
of the municipal building, and the third is located near the
gate of the cemetery. The cemetery is just outside the village.
You passed it when you came here to Rietvelt. About the
time the sun sets I take my ladder and my oil can and I go
the rounds. I fill all those lamps, the big ones and the small
ones, and I put in enough oil to keep them burning till daylight. In the morning I make the rounds again to put out
the lights, trim the wicks, and polish the glass. That's been
my job here in the community since my father's death. I
took over from him.

"Now that night of her death I'm standing there on my
ladder near the cemetery gate looking over the stone wall
and thinking that it won't be long till Lena will be lying
there with all the others. As I stand there polishing the
glass all sorts of strange thoughts come into my head. I
thought of my father and mother and my sisters. Of course,
I knew they weren't there any more, because every seven
years Bernt digs up the graves of the poor and dumps
what's left of the bones and the coffins in a pit, to make
room for others. And so, as I stood there, I came to wonder
what neighbors Lena was going to have and in what corner
she was going to be put and how these neighbors were
going to behave toward her. For, heaven knows, I thought,
what goes on in a cemetery at nights with all those people
so crowded together.

"Maybe you think it strange I should have said these
things to myself? But that's the way it was, the thoughts
just kept coming into my head. Maybe, I thought, they do
meet and talk—the dead, I mean—maybe they just carry on
the way they carried on in their lifetime here in the village
of Rietvelt. Doesn't the Apostle say that their works shall
follow after them?" Dirk uncovered his head when he
quoted from Holy Writ, as was still the custom with old-
time Calvinists in those days.

"And so as I stand there on my ladder," he continued,
"and my eye suddenly falls on a dark patch of ground just

outside the wall, just beneath the spot where I was standing in the first row of graves. I peer into the darkness and I see that it is a freshly dug grave. Of course, I soon remembered that Mrs. Waters, the wife of one of our syndics, had died two days before Lena and that this must be the grave that Bernt had just dug for her. So I say to myself: If only that could be Lena's place, right in the first row, near the gate like that with all those rich folks around her, wouldn't that be fine? How happy she would be! She'd be lying right under the light of the big street lamp, too. She'd have a lamp of her own, you might say. And I'd come there every night as I always do and stand on my ladder and look over the wall and I'd say to her: Good night, Lena, rest well, do you hear! I've just lit the lamp for you!

"Of course, I knew it could never be, that Lena would never be buried there or anywhere near the gate. Everybody has his place in this world and Lena's place was not there with all those rich people. You can't expect that. Even in death, we poor people have to keep our distance. And so I climbed down and picked up my ladder and my oil can and I passed by Bernt's house to see if he was still up. I wanted to ask him in what place he was going to put Lena.

"Sure enough, the light was still burning at Bernt's and I went in. Bernt was sawing the planks for the coffin, but he stopped when he saw me and I asked him where he was going to bury her. He told me that he had no choice, that it all went by regulation and that it would be in the last row but one, where there was room for one more grave.

"'And who's to be her neighbor?' I asked him.

"'She'll be lying next to Peer Roeland,' says he.

"'The drunken sot who hanged himself last winter?'

"'Yes,' says Bernt, 'that's where it will have to be, Dirk, I'm afraid. You have no plot of your own and you have no money to buy one. So you'll have to abide by the rules.'

"Well," went on the lamplighter, 'that gave me such a scare: Lena next to that brute who ended in such a terrible way. I turned sick at heart at the thought of it. And then I told Bernt what I'd been thinking about standing on my ladder that night. But he said for me to go home and not to have such foolish thoughts. 'Never mind,' he says, 'where Lena is buried. Don't let that worry you. The dead don't know anything. They don't know what happens to them.'

"And so two days later she was buried, near the ditch, of course, and that would have been the end of it but for Bernt Sas himself. He comes to me the evening of the day after the funeral, just about the time I was going out to tend to my lamps, and he sets himself in that chair you're sitting in now and I give him a glass of Bols, thinking his rheumatism was bothering him perhaps, he looked so worried. But it wasn't the rheumatism. I could tell by the way he kept shifting from the chair to that box over there and then back again that there was something on his mind. At last when it was getting dark and I had to be on my way, he speaks up suddenly and he says: 'Dirk,' he says, 'I have something to tell you.'

" 'What is it, Bernt?' I ask, looking at him as he sat there with his face in his hands.

" 'Dirk,' he says, 'I've thought it all over. I've been thinking it over since the night she died, when you came to me.' With that he jumps up and takes me by the shoulders and says: 'It can be done, and it's going to be done. I've made up my mind about it. You and Lena have been good friends to me, the only friends I ever had. She looked after me when I lost my parents and when I was laid up three years ago she did everything to put me back on my feet. She was like a mother to me. It's got to be done, that's all!'

" 'What's got to be done?' I asked him.

" 'We're going to dig up Lena, and we're going to put her in Mrs. Waters' place near the gate,' he says.

"Well, you could have knocked me over with a feather when Bernt said that. I was dumfounded. I didn't know what to answer back. I started to shake from head to foot and got hot and cold just as if I had the fever.

"Finally I told Bernt that it wouldn't be right, that I had thought it over. Mijnheer Waters paid for his wife's plot after all, and what if he ever found out?"

"But Bernt said: 'He'll never find out. I am told he's had his eye on the Widow Bankerts for a long time. He'll want to forget about his first wife as soon as possible. He's a rich man, he's got other things to worry about than a corpse. He won't find out anything, because he doesn't want to find out anything in the first place. How is anybody ever going to find out? It will be a secret between you and me and we'll only have ourselves to blame if anything leaks out.'

"I could see," went on Dirk Mensert, "that his mind was made up. He wouldn't have Lena lying there next to that self-murderer. 'Come,' he says to me, 'take your ladder now and do your work. But don't light the lamp near the cemetery gate tonight. Leave it out or let it burn very low. We'll have to work in the dark. I'll meet you in an hour's time at the gate. You can go inside the graveyard; the door's open. If there's anybody around, keep out of sight. You can go and sit in the tool shed if you're there ahead of me.'

" 'No,' he said, when I protested that we wait till the next night and think it over in the meantime. 'No, we got to do it this very night. It's starting to rain. When that rain soaks in, the earth will be twice as heavy and we'll never be able to lift that coffin between the two of us.'

"*Heere God*," groaned the little man with the fearful memory of it, "God in Heaven, I hope I'll never have another night like that. I trembled the moment I left the house. When we began digging up those heavy clods of earth, Bernt told me to go easy, as I was making a noise fit to raise the dead. That remark set me shaking so much that the spade dropped out of my hands. I heard a fluttering and rustling above my head and my heart jumped into my mouth. I had to keep myself from crying out in fear. Bernt said that it was just the bats that house in the big family vaults, and that there were hundreds of them.

"It's all behind now, but the sweat starts pouring down my face when I lie thinking of it at night. After we had Mrs. Waters' coffin bare, we dug up Lena and we wheeled her coffin on a barrel to the front of the cemetery. Just as we had slipped a noose around the coffin and were letting her down beside Mrs. Waters, the terrible thing happened. We were letting the box down slowly when something happened that made my heart stand still: I heard footsteps. Bernt heard them, too. 'Down on your face,' he whispers to me. I plopped down and my hold on the rope slipped, the coffin tipped over and slid down into the grave with a noise that sounded like a clap of thunder in the night. 'Jesus, be merciful to us,' I said to myself, for I recognized the footsteps clearly enough. They were Izak's, the policeman's, making his regular rounds. We could hear him walk up to the wall and then his shoes scraping against it. A moment later his head appeared. He swung his lantern around a couple of times and dropped down again. We heard him try the gate next, but fortunately Bernt had locked it when he came in. At last we heard him walk off. Then Bernt said we'd have to work like lightning.

"So we got to work again. I slid down into the grave and found that Lena's coffin had burst open in falling down. Lena was under it. I told this to Bernt, but he said, 'Never mind that now, fill the hole,' and he starts shoveling in the lumps of earth. 'I'll rake it over in the morning,' he said. We filled the grave and then went to the rear of the cemetery, filled up Lena's empty place, and got out by climbing over the wall in the back near the ditch.

"While we were walking home and just as we passed the entrance of the poplar lane that runs up to the manor house, somebody steps from behind a tree and I see it's Izak. He stopped us right under the big lantern.

" 'Kind o' late,' he says.

" 'Yes, I couldn't sleep,' I told him, 'so I got up and went to Bernt and we went for a walk together.'

" 'Your clothes are all covered with mud,' Izak says.

" 'Yes, I stumbled, back at the ditch there.'

" 'Did Bernt stumble, too?' he asked.

" 'No, Bernt tried to pick me up and then he fell in himself.'

" 'Funny place to go for a walk,' says the policeman.

'Too bad you weren't in front of the cemetery.' As he said that he looked us squarely in the face.

" 'Why?' I asked.

" 'All hell was loose there a while back when I passed by.' He looked at our faces again in that searching way. But we didn't say a word.

"1 was afraid they would discover the crime right the next morning. But Bernt comes in late at night the day after and tells me that Izak didn't turn up at the cemetery till the afternoon and by that time all traces were wiped out. It was raining cats and dogs and Bernt had been early on the job.

"And so several months went by," the lamplighter went on. "We came together every night and we drank Geneva to quiet our nerves. We had such a guilty feeling that we hardly dared to walk in the streets. Bernt was getting more and more worried. 'That policeman smells a rat,' he kept on telling me. 'He visits the cemetery every day now, something he never did before.' It got on my nerves, too. Strange, though, I was brave only so long as Bernt was with me. So long as he was with me I could always talk him out of his gloominess. But no sooner had he gone than the fear mounted in my own heart. I couldn't sleep at night, no matter how I tried or how tired I was. When I dozed off for a while, I'd wake up in a cold sweat and shivering all over and looking around as if there was a ghost or something spooky in this room.

"Bernt couldn't sleep either. That's how we got into the habit of hitting the bottle every night. We never talked any more about what we had done in the graveyard, although it was never out of our minds for a minute. One morning, Bernt comes into my shop all smiling and cheerful and he tells me that Mijnheer Waters, our syndic, was to see him over at the cemetery that morning and ordered flowers to be planted on his wife's grave and also that a stonecutter in Gorcum would soon deliver a headstone.

"I had to laugh at that and Bernt, too. Our worries were over. At least, so we thought. But we were wrong. A month later Izak comes up to us one evening as we sit smoking a pipe on the doorstep and he says to me: 'Dirk,' he says, 'I want to ask you something about that night when I met you and Bernt walking in the rain near the manor house. Why didn't you light the lamp by the cemetery gate that night, Dirk?'

" 'It must have run out of oil,' I told him. But the policeman looked at me with a smirk on his face and he says: 'No, Dirk, boy, that isn't true. There was plenty of oil in that lamp. I watched you the next morning and you didn't pour any fresh oil in it. And still that lamp burned at night till way after dawn next morning when I watched you again and you opened the glass and blew out the flame.'

"And then Izak turns to Bernt and he says: 'You were awful busy, too, the next morning after I met you in the rain.'

" 'Yes,' replies Bernt, 'I had a lot of work to do.'

" 'Around Mrs. Waters' grave, eh, a grave that you had filled up two days before.'

"He didn't say another word and just left us sitting there. Bernt turns to me after the policeman left us and says to me: 'That *diender* knows everything. He watched me that morning. He suspected something when he met us there at the manor road and he verified his suspicions the next morning. We're lost, Dirk. We're going into the jug. You and I, three years, five years, I don't know how long. Lord Jesus in Heaven, what will become of us?'

"I made him sit down and take a drink and we started to talk about going out to the cemetery again and putting Lena back in her place. But Bernt said the summer nights were too short and there was a big stone on Mrs. Waters' grave. 'We'll have to wait till fall,' he said, 'when the nights are longer, then we'll do it.' And that idea, that we were going to make up for our fault, gave me back my peace of mind for a few days. But it didn't last long.

"One day around noon Bernt comes in and says: 'Dirk, it's all up with us. There were some officers of the parquet at the cemetery this morning. They opened Mrs. Waters' grave. I had to help. When they found Lena's body lying under the coffin, one of those officers went to fetch the

Mayor. The Mayor asked me for an explanation about the two bodies in the one grave and I couldn't find my tongue.'

"So there we were caught. I offered Bernt a drink and he takes the bottle out of my hand, puts it to his mouth and drinks it down in one gulp, nearly a quart of gin. Then we sat there without saying a word until there's a knock at the door and Izak comes in and says the Burgomaster wants to see us right away. Of course, we went up and I told the whole story, just as I told it to you now. Bernt was ordered to put Lena back in her own grave. A provincial police officer helped him, and after that Bernt was suspended. And now we are waiting for our trial."

The lamplighter started to cry softly. "Bernt says he will commit suicide if we're sent up," he added. "What can we do?"

"First of all, I'll tell my mother," I said, "and then my Uncle Kees, and they will see the Judge, I'm sure."

"He's a hard man, Judge Bakhuis," said Dirk.

"No, he isn't," I returned. "But he should know all the circumstances exactly before the trial. He should have time to think it over before he hears the official evidence in the courtroom. At present, I know he hasn't the faintest idea what really happened. Let's see what he says when he knows the truth. I'll come back some day next week, or at any rate before the vacation is over, and let you know what Judge Bakhuis thought of it."

With that we parted. I went back to the manor house and told Ary what I had learned about the crime. He thought the promise I made about informing the Judge gave us an excellent opportunity to leave Rietvelt that same day. Of course, we still had to persuade Jetze, who was absent with the marketers. He returned about dinnertime but we didn't tell him the lamplighter's story nor mention anything about our plans to return.

Dinner passed quietly. Zeger appeared with his two cousins, and the only guest who remained was the fat artillery Captain. The Squire told us stories of his experiences in the military campaign in Indonesia and retired early.

It had grown dark when we returned to our rooms. We lit the oil lamp and the candles on the mantelpiece and watched Jetze unpack a bottle of perfume. Ary told him what I had learned from Dirk Mensert, the lamplighter, and proposed that we go back to Gorcum to apprise Judge Bakhuis of the true circumstances of the case. Jetze fully agreed to the proposition, but wouldn't hear of departing the very next morning. Ary then began questioning him about the girl Clara and made allusions to the possibility of disagreeable consequences. But Jetze talked back angrily and the two were soon in a wrangle. I sat by the window smoking a pipe. A soft rain was falling. Suddenly my attention was sharpened by the sound of crunching gravel as on the night of the dinner. I looked out, and against the faint bluish background of the wall of the summerhouse, I could see the unwieldy figure of Captain Folette. I ducked back from the window and walked over to the mantelpiece to blow out the candles. I whispered to the others what I had seen. Ary at once blew out the oil lamp and the three of us cautiously approached the open window.

As our eyes became accustomed to the dark, we saw the Captain fumbling with the lock of the summerhouse, but he had difficulty opening the door, for presently we saw him put his shoulders to it and try to force it. We heard the creaking of the woodwork and a muffled curse. After two or three efforts the door gave away with a dull sound of rotten wood splintering to pieces and we saw the Captain step inside.

"What does he want there?" whispered Jetze.

"He's waiting for someone, obviously," I said.

We saw the man come out again, walk a few steps up the path, and return to the summerhouse. It was clear he expected somebody. But whom?

"The German woman has gone," said Ary. "I wonder who's his conquest tonight?"

As he spoke the Captain reappeared, walking on tiptoe, his hands in his pockets. He had come to a point directly under our window when we heard the sound of light running footsteps along the side of the house. The Captain advanced a few steps and we heard the whisper of voices.

Ary suddenly stepped back from the window. He had seen. I stepped back, too. There could be no doubt about it, the woman around whose waist the Captain threw his arms was Clara. Jetze stood alone for a moment watching them. We heard the door of the summerhouse close.

Our friend sat down on the chair by the window. Ary lit one candle. Jetze buried his face in his hands. Then suddenly he rose from his chair and walking to the table, picked up the bottle of perfume.

He took deliberate aim and flung it out into the darkness. The bottle struck the slate roof of the summerhouse with the crash of an explosive. Then he turned around and said, "Are you ready? I'm going home!"

We had our belongings in our bags in no time. We could hear windows and doors opening. People were running all over the garden. We heard someone speak about a strange sweet smell in the air. Ary took an envelope, put some money in it, and addressed it to Clara. Then he placed the envelope on the table, put a candlestick on top of it, and we walked out in silence.

It was ten miles to Gorcum. Before we had walked for half an hour the rain turned into a downpour. A carriage from the Rietvelt estate caught up with us near the village of Arkel, but we slipped off the dike road to let it go by. An hour later it passed us going in the opposite direction. At four in the morning we entered Gorcum's old Arkel Gate, and a few minutes later I dropped the knocker on the door of my Uncle Kees' house.

He came down and looked through the peephole.

"What's up?" he asked.

"Back from Rietvelt," I said.

"Come in," he said and opened the door. "I'm glad to see you all. But you are soaking wet," he remarked, looking at our clothes as we trooped in. "Did you walk?" I began to explain. "Let's have a fire before we talk," he interrupted. "What a wonderful night for a march! I'm sorry

I didn't know you were coming. I would have met you halfway."

By the side of the fireplace, with the logs crackling and roaring, dressed in woolen painter's smocks, we told Kees our adventure in Rietvelt from beginning to end while he cut slices of bread and cheese and filled the beakers with hot milk.

Chapter VI

MIJNHEER VAN ALPHEN'S DAUGHTER

THERE was only one girl in our class of seven. She was not a full-fledged student but an auditor. She did not follow all the prescribed courses of the curriculum and was exempt from competing in the annual examinations. Our girl's name was Adriana Maria van Alphen. To us boys she was just Yaan, since Yana, the diminutive of her name customarily given Dutch girls as a term of endearment, did not fit her personality at all. In the first place, she was somewhat older than the rest of us. She told us, more than once, that she was old enough to be our mother. This was a gross exaggeration, of course, and was only said in fun. I think she must have been nineteen when she joined the class; that is, when we were turning seventeen or eighteen.

But with that slight superiority in years she looked almost a mature woman. She was nearly as tall as Ary Brandt and powerfully built. Yaan had ash-blond hair, which she wore in thick braids around her head, and very dark eyes with a firm, rather large nose, and a sweetly, rather mockingly curved mouth. Her face was at once serious and gentle. She laughed easily, but tears also came quickly. She wept at concerts, for instance, for reasons we could not always fathom. Even at the sound of a hurdy-gurdy in the street playing snatches from Verdi's and Mascagni's operas, Yaan would often grow sad. But it must not be thought that she was the sickly-sentimental type. She was a most practical young person with a strong will and frank speech. She came to us from some finishing school for young ladies of the upper classes in the neighborhood of Cologne, and was a great help to us because of her fluent, idiomatic command of the modern languages, which gave us more trouble than Latin or Greek.

During her absence abroad she had traveled in England, Italy, and France. She had been as far East as Athens, an achievement for which everybody envied her. But what she told of the capital of modern Hellas did not always correspond with the exalted notions we entertained on the subject of the great center of classical art and learning. When I come to think of it, all of Yaan's stories about foreign lands left us with a vague feeling of disappointment or regret.

Everyone knew that she had discontinued her studies in the Rhineland quite abruptly, but for what reasons we could at first only guess. There were different explanations about her sudden return from abroad. Yaan herself said that a scandal at the young ladies' academy in Kreuzdorf had caused her father to fetch her back in a great hurry.

"What was the scandal, Yaan? Did it have anything to do with you?" we asked.

"No," she said laughingly, "not with me directly, although my reputation was slightly damaged, of course, by the mere fact that I was at the same school."

"Then it was something bad, just the same," we insisted.

"Bad? No," she replied, pursing her lips and shrugging her shoulders. "It was something that happens often enough. One of the young ladies discovered that she was pregnant, from causes unknown, of course. It was quite a sensation, and somewhat of a mystery, too. For a time we girls actually wondered," said Yaan with a mischievous look in the direction of Fons Boogaert, "whether there was going to be another miraculous birth, like the one in Bethlehem, you know. But no such luck! No little German Messiah was born. Just another future hotelkeeper. Everything turned out very prosaically. The piano teacher at the college, Mr. Do-re-mi we called him, turned out to be the unknown cause. He confessed and was dismissed, but he

221

honorably married the girl because she had a large dowry.
They're opening a *pension de famille* in Düsseldorf. Nevertheless, the school was almost ruined, as quite a few of the
girls were called home."

Now that may well have been one reason why Yaan's
father brought her back to Gorcum, but it was not the whole
story. The real cause was that Yaan herself had been unhappy in Germany and took advantage of the scandal to
return on her own account, on a day when she was least
expected. We knew the whole truth before long, for Yaan
could not keep a secret. Her heart belonged to a young
man in Gorcum, a young man of very humble origin who
was in her father's employ.

"I did nothing but weep all the time I was in Germany,"
she told us. "I wept in Kreuzdorf and I wept in London.
I wept everywhere they took me. When I came home I ran
up to my father and I said to him that if he left me abroad
another year, it would grow all dark in me forever," she
said, pointing to her heart.

But how had she become acquainted with this young man
in the first place? One could scarcely imagine two persons
more dissimilar in tastes and interests and farther apart
socially than Adriana van Alphen and this Hein Dermout,
she the only child of a prominent merchant with a mint of
money, who had servants at her beck and call and who had
been privately educated before she went to Germany, and
he, that boy Hein, a clog-wearing starveling brought up in
a squalid quarter of the town.

How did these two manage to achieve the well-nigh impossible: break down the rigid, ironclad system of social
reserve that divided the population of our town into
mutually estranged social clans? How was it done? Yaan
and Hein did indeed cross that boundary line. But at what
cost in pain and humiliation I would not be prepared to
figure out.

The way Yaan first met Hein Dermout was simple
enough. There was no strain or forcing of the social
amenities involved in that meeting. It was accident, nothing
more. It happened on the evening of the Queen's birthday,

when the municipality celebrated with a display of fire-works. The show was given on board an old disused ferry steamer. This boat was towed into the middle of the river for the occasion and there anchored. The citizens of Gor-cum and of the communities on the opposite side of the Merwede watched the pyrotechnics from the shores. Since the Free Blowers under the baton of the renowned Bee-thoven Bis were playing patriotic airs by the light of torches, Adriana and some girl friends had taken their position that evening on one of the high ramparts, within hearing of the band. It was the last day in August, and although a chilly breeze blew over the water, the girls had taken off their coats and spread them on the grass, wet with the evening dew.

Adriana was dressed in a flimsy gown of white lace and, like all the other girls in town that day, wore a sash of orange silk around her waist in honor of Her Majesty's anniversary. Suddenly the hissing and spluttering sparks of a huge roman candle, instead of shooting skyward, dropped in the midst of the crowd assembled on the rampart. Adriana was touched and her dress caught fire and a cry of horror went up from the bystanders. In panic the spec-tators scattered in all directions. Adriana scrambled to her feet and ran screaming down the pathway, her skirt aflame. The crowd gave her a wide berth. But one boy, who could not be immediately identified that evening, with commend-able presence of mind pulled off his overcoat, ran after the girl, and wrapped the garment around her. He then, most unceremoniously, flung her to the ground and rolled the frightened girl in the wet grass. In a moment the flames were extinguished. Adriana escaped with such minor burns that not a scar remained in later years.

A week later Hein Dermout was invited to call at the big patrician house on High Street, where Mijnheer van Alphen himself came out to meet him in the hall and led him into the salon and made him sit down and drink a glass of wine. After the boy had told his story and refused a generous reward, he was taken upstairs to see Adriana, who was still in bed, although rapidly recovering from her injuries. She took the opportunity to thank him for his courageous act, shook hands with him, and said that it was really the first time she had seen her rescuer's face. That night of the fireworks she had indeed felt how strong he was when he had thrown her to the ground, but had not seen his features. She was glad her life had been saved by such a good-looking young man.

Now what was a boy like Hein to answer to that? He just stood there by her bedside smiling shyly and hardly able to find words; a big strapping lad dressed in rough, ill-fitting clothes, twirling his cap in his hands and nervously fingering his light blond hair, which he had plastered down for the occasion with a liberal dose of water.

And that might have been the end of their acquaintance had not Mijnheer van Alphen, in talking with Hein of his family and their circumstances, discovered that the boy had left school and was now loitering around town without an occupation or much hope of finding employment. The result was that a month later Hein Dermout entered Mijnheer van Alphen's leather factory as an apprentice.

Adriana was then sixteen or seventeen, and receiving instruction from private tutors at home. When she was fully recovered she made a habit of calling for her father at his office near the leather factory and taking him home for dinner in the evening. Father and daughter could be seen walking home arm in arm, respectfully saluted by the citizens and stopping here and there to chat with acquaintances. It was soon noticed that Adriana arrived at the office a little earlier each day and that she sometimes spent whole afternoons at the factory, and what's more, that she spent most of her time in the room where Hein Dermout was working.

She spoke to him, too. There was nothing wrong in that, of course. It was natural that she should be kind to the young man who had rendered such heroic service. But she should not make it a habit, her father told her. She could come to the office as often as she liked. She was always a most welcome visitor. But she should stay out of the evil-smelling tannery. That was not a place for a young lady.

Mijnheer van Alphen was not long in suspecting the real source of Adriana's sudden enthusiastic interest in the technical details of turning raw cowhide into finished shoe leather. With a shock he realized that his generosity had led him to commit an error, an error fraught perhaps with disastrous consequences to the future welfare of his only child. Not that he breathed a word to anyone of his growing disquietude, least of all to Adriana herself. It was not in the man's nature to make a fuss or to betray an inward nervousness. Even so, alarmed he was, and determined to put an end to the foolish mooncalf play between his daughter and the lowly employee, and prevent it from maturing into an irrevocable love. He knew he had to act with dispatch and with resolution, for he understood the signs and knew the Dutch breed, outwardly often so unemotional and phlegmatic, but inwardly nurturing an unquenchable fire.

For a time Mijnheer van Alphen behaved, to all appearances at least, as if there were nothing between the two young people requiring his special attention. Although he could not help observing that the particular department where Hein Dermout worked drew his daughter as irresistibly as a magnet attracts steel, and that she kept on visiting the place at the most unlikely hours of the morning and afternoon, he went his way seemingly unconcerned and unruffled. He had his plans, nevertheless. But Dirk van Alphen was too cautious a man to show his hand by making a scene, to force the issue by dismissing Hein from his service or by challenging his daughter outright. That was not the way he went about his affairs.

He was never brusque or intemperate, nor did he like to pose ultimatums. In building up his business into one of the most flourishing in our province, he had learned to bide his time, to measure a favorable opportunity, and he knew by long experience how to gain his objective by quiet insistence, by bringing indirect pressure to bear at the right moment, never ponderously and bearishly but shrewdly and with deliberate calculation. By such means he had become rich and powerful, and by such means he would snatch

Adriana from the clutches of the man whom he had come to look on as a scheming adventurer.

He was aware that it would probably be fatal to his plans to cross Adriana's ambitions openly. She did not easily yield once her mind was made up. In fact, her father could well foresee that she would prove doubly stubborn the moment she realized that obstacles had been deliberately placed in her path. Mijnheer van Alphen need only consult his own conscience and probe his own character to measure his daughter's reaction. She was a chip of the old block.

When an invitation came to spend some months with relatives in England, Adriana had no suspicions that her father had engineered the scheme. Nor did it dawn upon her until too late that the pleasant trip from England to Germany was planned to be her last fling at freedom and that her entrance at a boarding school for a four-year course was designed to make her forget the face and the voice and gestures of her Hein. When she made that discovery, it was all over with her peace of mind. After two years she rebelled and came rushing home.

She frankly told her father why she had returned. He remonstrated with her gently, pointing out the social and intellectual barriers which precluded a continued friendship with the young worker, and warned her that she would become the laughingstock of her friends. But no more was said. It did not come to a rift between father and daughter. To the contrary, dutifully accepting his suggestion, she took some courses at the Gymnasium and continued her musical training under private instructors.

We, her schoolmates, were not in the least aware of the tension existing in Yaan's life, nor could we imagine the drama that was about to be enacted under our very eyes. Nobody but a few employees at the Van Alphen factory remembered anything about her precocious friendship with the young worker. If they did recall it, they were not talking about it, except perhaps in the intimacy of the neighborhood taverns in the evening. They took good care that their gossip did not come to the ears of their patroon. Moreover, it was two years or more since Adriana had paid her last visit to the plant. Who remembered what an irresponsible child of sixteen had said or done so long ago? Few outside of her immediate circle of friends and acquaintances recognized that child in the fully grown young lady, dressed in the height of fashion, who had come to stay at the big residence on High Street.

By that time, moreover, the object of Adriana's infatuation had disappeared from Gorcum. Hein Dermout was away doing his military service with the Blue Hussars in The Hague. Wasn't it possible that the poor boy would not return to Gorcum at all, considering the meager prospects of advance our town offered him? Mijnheer van Alphen was not disturbed at all. This Hein Dermout now lived in a cosmopolitan city. He was seeing life. He had decent pay. Wasn't it likely—no, inevitable that he would meet other girls, girls of his own kind, in the dance halls and cafés of the "Paris of the North"? An amorous adventure or two such as come so easily to soldiers and especially to cavalrymen, and Adriana was bound to be forgotten.

If after serving his time as a conscript he should continue in the service voluntarily, he would have a chance of rapid promotion to *wachtmeester* or adjutant possibly, with an assured pension and probably a cushy government job at the end of his term. Wasn't that something to be taken into consideration? Wouldn't that be preferable to coming back to the poisonous fumes of the tannery and his mother's slum cottage, or to loiter about the streets? Mijnheer van Alphen counted on Hein's common sense. The boy was not a fool. He knew which side his bread was buttered on. He should also know that he could not buck so powerful a man as the leather manufacturer if, perchance, his mooncalf passion had not been knocked out of his head. What was there to worry about?

That was the situation when Adriana joined our class. Hein Dermout was away. And while it was undoubtedly the memory of him and the desire to be near him again which had brought her back to Gorcum, she seemed to have fallen in completely with her father's views of the absent hussar. Anyone who remembered anything at all about her girlish

amorous escapade—if a walk or two on Sunday afternoons
in the local lovers' lane behind the ramparts and a few
hastily whispered words can be called that—must have
gained the impression that Adriana was resolved to forget
the past and was eager for everyone else to do the same. She
now seldom mentioned the boy's name even to Ary and me,
who were her early confidants in the affair that once troubled
her heart.

At school Yaan was cheerful and comradely with everybody. She took part in all our simple diversions, accompanying us to the riverside after school hours to see our friends
off on the steamer ferry, or attending the unconventional
sessions at the Sistine Chapel. Sometimes we took her along
for a walk or on Sundays on a long hike to attend service in
some distant village. One day she even rode out with us on a
bicycle all the way to the village of De Groot in Brabant
Province to be a witness of our setting foot on Belgian
territory.

When our debating and theatrical clubs went into the
discard, into the ash can of history, as Ary said grandilo-
quently, Adriana did more than her share to banish the
monotony of the long winter evenings. With her father's
encouragement, who, since his wife's death, lived in a mournful social isolation, she threw open the big family house
on High Street. One saw there young officers, fresh from
the military academy, very conscious of their uniforms and
their sabers, who twirled their first mustaches; apprentices
with noble names who served in local banking institutions;
young commissaries from the excise and revenue offices;
the local literati—Daan van der Zee, Top Naeff, Guido van
Gogh, the historian of Gorcum and a nephew of Vincent, my
Uncle Kees occasionally, and other painters, Corneille Henri
Ney in his gorgeous waistcoat, and of course a good assortment of gymnasiasts of all classes.

There were dinners and musical evenings, chess tournaments, card parties, and even dances, for the Van Alphens
were modernists who laughed at the narrow-minded Calvinist restrictions. As Adriana's classmates, Zeger, Jetze,
Alfons, Ary, David, and I had a standing invitation to drop

in whenever we felt like it. Only we could not take advantage
of her hospitality as often as we liked. We did not have the
leisure enjoyed by a girl who, as an auditor, did not have to
trouble her head about report cards or examinations.

Something must be said about the Van Alphen house,
because it was there that I received the first intimation of
the drama in which Adriana's life was subsequently
involved. It was an old-fashioned, patrician mansion, four
stories high and built in the style of the Dutch Renaissance,
Holland's Golden Age. To this day one may see hundreds,
if not thousands, of examples of that famous architectural
style in Amsterdam and Antwerp, the great trade centers of
the Low Countries. Of course, in so inconsiderable a town
as Gorcum there existed perhaps but three or four speci-
mens.

Six blue granite steps led from the street to the main
entrance. A heavy, carved oaken door, with a brass knocker
in the shape of a ring held in a lion's mouth, opened on an
extremely long hallway, paved with alternate slabs of blue
and white marble. On either side of the hallway was a row
of mahogany doors with white porcelain handles. Except for
an enormous crystal chandelier, refitted for gas, a brass combination hat and umbrella stand, and a red Persian runner
down the middle of the floor, there were no ornaments in the
hall. The spaces between the doors were white, as was the
ceiling.

The first door on the left opened into the drawing-room,
known as the "salon." This was a high-ceilinged chamber
with two tall, small-paned windows that afforded a view
of the principal street of Gorcum. On the benches on the
window sills stood some potted palms, and bluish metal
screens prevented passers-by from looking in. Outside the
windows, fastened to the lintels by extensible and reversible
brackets, were so-called "spies," or mirrors in metal frames.
Those spies gave the occupants of the window benches an
opportunity to look up and down the street without being
observed themselves. Curtains of green brocade draped the
windows, shutting out the light of day to such an extent that
even on the sunniest day the room seemed wrapped in twi-

light. On the walls hung Gobelins and portraits of elderly ladies and gentlemen and above the green-marble chimney shelf over a fine French water clock, a life-sized likeness of the founder of the Van Alphen fortune. He was a ruddy-faced, bespectacled, shrewdly smiling merchant in his middle age, dressed in the costume of a hundred years before. On the side of the room, facing the windows, were a set of huge folding doors, painted in light green with a thin stripe of gold to mark off the panels. When opened, as on those festive evenings when there was a large company, they revealed another room equally large, in which stood rows of high-backed upholstered chairs with red and green parrots embroidered on the back and the seat, and a gigantic buffet. In the center stood a round table. Its surface shone like a polished mirror. But then every object in that house—the floors, the doors, the banisters, the big dark sculptured cupboards in nearly every room—gleamed and sparkled as if a fresh coat of varnish were applied every morning. The flawless glass of the windows was as clear as crystal and without a speck of dust.

All this was the work of an ancient personage whom everybody addressed as Aunt Annabet and of whom it was said in town that she was so scrupulously clean that she would probably suffer an apoplectic fit should anyone ever discover so much as a particle of dirt even in so remote a place as the garret or the cellar. Aunt Annabet (the name is a contraction of Anna-Elizabeth) had been the Van Alphen family's housekeeper as long as anyone could remember. She had already been in the service of the mother of the present head of the family and that lady, Adriana's grandmother, had passed on to her reward some thirty years before. Aunt Annabet was thus as much of an heirloom as the cupboards and the paintings and the table silver. I do not know the precise relationship of Aunt Annabet to the Van Alphens. She was probably a distant poor relative. My mother, for some mysterious reason, referred to her habitually as "that unfortunate Annabet of the Van Alphens." Now when people spoke that way about a female person, I mean when they used the word "unfortunate" without any apparent reason, one could almost be sure there was some scandal involved, a sordid or disastrous love affair, an illegitimate baby somewhere in the background, abandonment by husband or fiancé, or something of that sort—some social irregularity that it was not polite to rake up, even though it was not necessarily to the discredit of the person concerned. The word "unfortunate" had a special meaning.

I must say that in Aunt Annabet's case it was rather difficult to imagine how there could have been anything out of the ordinary, either good or bad. She had always, as long as anyone could recall, been what she was: a shriveled little old woman who wore a ruffled cap and who shuffled around the big house from morning till night, scolding and nagging the servants in a shrill, high-pitched voice, up at dawn before anyone else and to bed only when everyone had retired. She had lashless eyes of a flat gray color over which seemed to lie a shell of mother-of-pearl; fish eyes they were called in Gorcum. But those eyes of Aunt Annabet had a sharp look. Nothing escaped her.

When I first came to the Van Alphen house, she used to sit on the window bench in the deserted salon in the afternoons, her colorless hands with their lusterless fingernails and leathery skin folded over a big, clean, carefully spread handkerchief and the Bible or some other edifying book lying open in her lap. For Aunt Annabet did not share the Van Alphen family's religious, or rather irreligious, views. She was a Calvinist. In nearly every sentence she uttered there figured some text from the Bible. When she opened the door for me the first time and I gave my name, she looked me in the face and said: "Young man, I knew your grandfather very well, but you don't resemble him very much. Still, 'Blessed are the dead which die in the Lord, for their works shall follow after them.'" On another occasion when I passed through the hallway with some of Adriana's French novels under my arm, she suddenly stepped out of one of the rooms and, seeing the books, which she recognized for what they were by their yellow covers, she pressed her lips disapprovingly over her toothless sunken mouth and said as she unfastened the latch on the door, "The wise shall inherit glory, Pieter van Paassen, but a fool carries away shame." To show her that I knew my Book as well as she, I said to her, "Judge not after the sight of eyes, Aunt Annabet." She glanced up sharply and nodded her wizened old head.

After that she treated me, if not exactly affably, with the considerate regard due to a lodge brother in good standing. She went so far as to throw me a glance of recognition in passing our family pew in church on Sunday mornings. Occasionally, too, during the endless sermons her silver monogrammed box of peppermints was allowed to circulate among the worshipers as far as my seat. In short, I was not entirely without hope that I had met whatever secret test Aunt Annabet applied to distinguish the goats from the sheep.

It must have been about this time, a year or so after her return, that I heard Adriana express the opinion that Aunt Annabet's mind was perhaps not as keen as it used to be. She told Ary and me as an indication of the old housekeeper's mental decline that whereas her recollection of persons and events in the distant past remained extraordinarily vivid, the present seemed to be slowly fading in a gray veil of forgetfulness. She could not remember things that had occurred yesterday or the day before, but spoke of persons long since dead as if she had just been chatting with them and of events almost forgotten by everybody else with a precision that would imply recent occurrence. Everyday household details, such as making up the menu for dinner with the cook, deciding on the food to be ordered at the butcher's and grocer's, or simply giving the gardener his instructions, gave more and more trouble to the old lady. A worried, strained look of bewilderment appeared on her face when she had to make up her mind, or answer a direct question.

Adriana mentioned, too, that unlike other years, Aunt Annabet seemed to look forward with apprehension to her birthday, an event which in the past had always been the occasion for a little celebration with a specially elaborate meal and presents and visitors, a day she enjoyed more

than anything else in the whole year. Now what could be the
explanation of that? Ary suggested that it was the gradual
disappearance of her old acquaintances and friends that
had plunged the old woman into these spells of gloom. Why,
asked Adriana, should old people be sad when other people
die? Adriana thought that the prospect of her birthday
troubled the old lady because it would require her to fix her
thoughts on the present, and concentrate for hours on what
went on about her in the house and what was being said to
her. It was too difficult for her to keep her thoughts together
that long.

The hours she spent alone in the empty drawing-room in
the afternoon dozing over her Bible or psalter grew longer
and longer. She did not seem to notice when the light of
day had sunk so low that her pretense of reading was mani-
festly untrue. And there had been two or three occasions
lately, Adriana said, when Aunt Annabet had overslept.
That caused a sensation, because it seemed as unbelievable
as the news that the Merwede had suddenly started flowing
back to its sources.

But Adriana was entirely mistaken in her suppositions.
The old lady's powers of perception had not weakened in
the least. She still had sharper eyes than many a person half
or even a quarter her age. Those fits of abstraction, her
sitting alone in the salon for hours sunk in reverie, her
preoccupied, pained looks and her disconsolate sighs, all
that had but one source—Adriana herself. Aunt Annabet
was worried about the girl she had brought up from earliest
childhood and whom she cherished as her own. Fact of the
matter was that Aunt Annabet suspected the truth about
Adriana and Hein Dermout long before anyone else.

It was on the Eve of Saint Nicholas, the night of the fifth
of December, that Ary Brandt and I got our first intimation
of the sad days that were in store for our friend. That night
a snowstorm raged, so that the usual joyful entry into our
town of the masquerade bishop on his white horse could
not take place. The biting frost that came with the snow
forced the host of children who customarily welcomed Saint
Nicholas and his black, gift-bearing servant to remain

indoors. But that did not prevent many celebrations from taking place in private homes. At the Van Alphen residence, for instance, the shutters were not closed—the only night in the year when that happened—so that the light from all the rooms, upstairs and downstairs, streamed in a ruddy glare into the wind- and snow-swept High Street. Everybody seemed to be going there that evening. Ary and I were stamping the snow off our shoes on the high stoop when a carriage halted and a whole swarm of young people alighted and stormed the entrance. Down the street other guests, arms laden with packages, were barging and floundering through the snow, calling to us to hold the door open for them.

The folding doors of the salon had been thrown open for the occasion. The double room looked like a hall, and the whole space was filled with a laughing, chatting, and carefree crowd of young and old people. We found Jetze sitting by the side of the buffet doing away with a plate of almond-filled pastry, called *boterletter*, quite unconcerned by the noise and bustle around him. Known to Aunt Annabet as a good orthodox parson's son, he was being served by that estimable lady herself, who placed cookies and coffee on a small table within his reach. Dr. Ney, his hands behind his back, stood by marveling at our friend's appetite. In the middle of the room by the table stood Adriana, looking mature and majestic in a long evening gown of dark-green velvet. She was busily unwrapping the parcels the servants were bringing in. Mijnheer van Alphen, his face as ruddy as a freshly washed boy's, was speaking in the ear of Dr. Mendoza, who puffed away thoughtfully at his cigar. With difficulty we made our way through the crowd to these gentlemen to wish them good evening. There were people sitting in the window seats and on the benches, but most of the guests milled about in the salon, out in the hall, and in the other rooms. There was a rush for the door whenever the metallic boom of the knocker on the front door was heard announcing new arrivals or a new delivery of packages.

In the music room Lieutenant van Vredenburg played traditional Saint Nicholas songs on the piano. Ten or twelve young boys and girls stood about him boisterously singing and shouting with glee. In a corner Zeger van Rietvelt was giving an exhibition of balancing one of the officers' drawn sabers on the palm of his hand without letting the point penetrate the skin. Jetze came in still chewing and went Zeger one better by balancing the sword on his chin. In Mijnheer van Alphen's study, we found a cousin of Adriana's who was studying medicine in Leyden and who was visiting Gorcum for the Christmas holidays. He was talking of the merits of homeopathy to our Burgomaster Baron de Bruyn and his wife. The serving here was done by two maids, directed by Aunt Annabet. They brought us hot chocolate and marzipan and fudge, traditional Saint Nicholas delicacies.

As soon as we had done our duty to the refreshments, we prepared to move on to the next place, for Kees too was giving a party, in the Sistine Chapel. We slipped quietly past the hilarious crowd in the hall and past the open door of the salon and were picking up our coats from the piles of garments on the chairs in the anteroom when Adriana spotted us.

"You are not going so soon?" she asked, with a gesture of disappointment.

We thanked her and told her we were expected at Kees' studio.

"But you can't go yet," she insisted. "I must show you the most precious gift I received today, and it's only to you two that I can show it."

"Oh, bring it to school tomorrow," said Ary. "It won't spoil, will it?"

"The evening will be spoiled for me if I don't show you," said Adriana.

"All right then, where is it?" asked Ary.

"Upstairs in my room," she said.

We followed her upstairs into her study. Then while we looked on she opened the big cupboard and from under a pile of papers drew out a parcel and unwrapped it. She held out a photograph at arm's length and cocked her head.

"Know who that is?" she asked.

"Yes," I said, "that's Hein Dermout."

She kissed the photograph of the young man in hussar's uniform. "What do *you* say?" She turned to Ary, pressing the photograph to her breast.

"He looks fine," replied Ary. "I've never seen him in real life, you know."

"He'll be here at Christmas, three weeks from now," said Adriana. "He's leaving the service; his time is up. And then we're going to be married."

"Married?" we asked almost in unison.

"Yes, married! We'll be married early in the New Year."

She laughed nervously and looked from the one to the other with a mute appeal in her eyes, again pressing the photograph to her bosom. Her breath came in gasps.

"Yaan," I asked bluntly, "is everything in order? Does your father consent?"

She bit her lips and her mouth quivered. "Father will never give his consent!" she said, bursting into tears. "Oh, Ary, Pieter, what am I to do?"

We were dumfounded by the announcement of a wedding followed immediately by Adriana's display of fear, and above all by the unmistakable note of anguish in her voice. "What am I to do?" It was a cry of despair.

I did not know what to answer her. I felt very sad myself. What could two inexperienced boys do whose knowledge of the world, not to speak of the eternally baffling complexities of the feminine heart, rested upon the scanty information derived from reading a few novels? What could they advise this heartbroken girl? Could I put my arms around her shoulders and tell her not to worry? Could we reassure her by saying that we would intercede with her father? But we knew in advance that such a promise would be meaningless. Mijnheer van Alphen would almost certainly indignantly reject any intervention in his private family affairs. One look at his stern face, at those straight thin lips, his inexorable eyes, and the heavy jaw, and you knew what a rebuff you would receive. He would most probably send us about our business, or even boot us out of his sight, quite unceremoniously and without any further talk. In what way would Adriana benefit from such an attempt at conciliation on our part? Wouldn't it rather aggravate her case by exasperating her father the more?

We were silent a moment as Adriana sobbed, leaning her head on Ary's shoulder. Then she dabbed at her eyes with her handkerchief and ran into an adjoining bedroom to wash off the trace of tears. But when she rejoined us she burst into weeping again.

"Promise me," she said as we started down the stairs arm in arm, "promise me you will always remain my friends. Promise me," she said again almost fiercely, as she gripped my arm so violently that it startled me.

"Yaan, for heaven's sake, be calm," pleaded Ary as we halted for a moment on the landing where we could see the milling crowd of revelers in the hallway. "What are you so excited about? Of course we'll always be your friends. You need never doubt that for a minute. Perhaps your father may not prove half as intractable as you think."

"You do not know Father," she said quietly, giving our arms a tug and starting to walk down again. "Once he has made up his mind, there's no budging him. Nothing in the world will make him go back on his word. And he hates Hein. He hates him. Oh!" Her mouth started to quiver and the tears began to well up again.

"Let's talk it over tomorrow," said Ary. "Come to the Sistine Chapel after classes. There we can talk in peace. Let's go over the whole thing. Maybe we can find a way. Maybe we can think of someone who could speak to your father. Perhaps you'll change your mind."

"Change my mind?" Adriana exclaimed under her breath, almost rudely pushing Ary away. "I will never change my mind. I cannot. You don't know me. You're not my friend."

"Yaan," said Ary gently, "I didn't mean it that way. I didn't mean that you would change your mind about Hein Dermout. I meant that perhaps you would postpone your wedding, think it over for awhile. What's the hurry? Hein won't run away."

"I have thought till I can think no more," she replied. And then she laughed as heartily as if there wasn't a cloud in her sky and in a moment she was swallowed up in the gay crowd in the salon.

Again we looked for our coats. This time Aunt Annabel came into the room.

"Why did Adriana take you upstairs?" asked the old woman, peering sharply at me. She was panting with excitement. "Why?"

"She wanted to show us a present she had received," I said.

"A photograph?"

"A photograph, yes."

"Of Hein Dermout?"

"Of Hein Dermout, yes."

"Oh, poor girl, poor girl!" wailed Aunt Annabet softly.

Adriana did not come to Uncle Kees' studio the next afternoon, nor ever afterward. Something occurred in the classroom the day after the Saint Nicholas party that made further discussion of her case quite superfluous. As far as we, her schoolfellows, were concerned, her problem moved out of our reach. In the morning when she came to school she was calm and bright and her usual cheerful self. She laughed and bantered with Zeger van Rietvelt, who occupied the form next to hers, as if she had not a care in the world. All trace of the night's agitation had vanished. Jetze and I walked out with her in the noon-hour recess as far as the Van Alphen residence and then continued homeward for lunch.

When I saw Ary again, shortly before two o'clock, I remarked to him that Yaan seemed to have recovered her composure completely, that she had made no reference to Jetze and me to the happenings of the night before, and I expressed the hope that everything would come out right. But Ary said: "If she were only less headstrong, or only half as stubborn as her father, if she would listen to reason and allow more time for reflection, instead of rushing pell-mell into marriage with that Dermout fellow, she might be saved. It might perhaps be possible to bring her around to other views. But then," he added, "we know her well enough to realize that that's asking too much. She's as obstinate as a mule, and I expect it to be a battle of wills to the bitter end between that girl and her father." A few hours later we knew that the battle was on and would be bitter indeed.

When the instructor of Greek, Dr. Vossius of the pointed red beard, entered the classroom to conduct the lesson of the second part of the afternoon, Adriana, who did not take that course, was packing her books preparatory to leaving. As she gathered the things on her desk, a pencil or a pen slipped out of her hand to the floor, and she stooped to pick it up. But in stooping over she did not act quite normally; that is, she did not bend over from the hips, but leaned over sideways, in the instinctive, self-protecting gesture of the expectant mother. Dr. Vossius, who stood by his table waiting for her to leave the room before starting the lesson, noticed the girl's awkward movement and stared fixedly at her for a moment. She too, as if aware that she had allowed herself to be caught off guard and wondering whether anyone had seen, looked up sharply. Meeting the Doctor's startled look and noticing his discomfiture, she turned as pale as a sheet and hurried out of the room.

"It was Vossius' look of surprise that drew my attention to the way Yaan picked up that pen," said Ary after school had been dismissed and we were walking to Kees' house. "I wonder how long the secret can be kept."

"Not an hour," said Kees, to whom we told the incident. "Vossius will already have told the Rector. The Rector will be watching her every movement from tomorrow on. She will betray herself again and a letter from the Curators will go off to Mijnheer van Alphen. And then the trouble will start."

And so it was. After the Christmas vacation Adriana did not return to the Gymnasium. For a time we saw no more of her. But we did see Hein Dermout, who was back in Gorcum. He hung around town, tramping the streets, vainly looking for work. Nobody wanted to have anything to do with the man who had brought dishonor to the name of one of our most prominent merchants. As far as Hein was concerned he might just as well have thrown himself into the river or moved to another town. In Gorcum he was

bound to find all doors closed in his face. Not that people
disliked or condemned him; as a matter of fact there were
quite a few who had a soft spot in their hearts for the
strapping, ruddy-faced young man, who had served his military term so well that he had reached the highest rank
possible to him before leaving The Hague. People were
simply afraid of offending Dirk van Alphen. They did not
dare to risk his ill will. The leather manufacturer was all-
powerful in the community. He could make men and break
them. But he could not break his own daughter.

Where was Adriana? It was as if the earth had suddenly
swallowed her up. Nobody had seen trace or sign of her
for weeks on end. Had she left town, or was she perhaps
seriously ill? No, it couldn't be that, for in the event of
illness in one of the big homes on High Street, the Burgomaster would certainly not have allowed heavy, rumbling
drays and trucks to pass by. That section of the street would
be barred to heavy traffic, or at least the cobblestones would
be covered with bundles of straw to deaden the noise. Nor
had anyone seen a doctor call at the Van Alphen residence.
Then what was up with the girl?

As inevitably happens in a small town where the range of
people's interests is extremely limited, tongues began to
wag as they had never wagged before. For everyone was
now aware of Adriana's condition and more than curious
to see what would be the outcome of her love affair with the
poor Widow Dermout's son. The most uninquisitive persons,
people who never seemed to take an interest in anything in
the world before, would stop you on the street and inquire
if there was perchance some news about the Van Alphen
young lady. When informed that there was none, they would
walk off shaking their heads significantly or making clicking sounds with their tongues. Was her father keeping her
prisoner to prevent her from going to Hein and running off
with him to be married? Who could tell? Had father and
daughter had it out and had she perhaps surrendered by
giving up Hein and by accepting some arrangement for the
baby to be born abroad and then placed for adoption, so

that the whole incident with Hein might be forgotten in time? Perhaps she had left town already.

There were all sorts of conjectures and opinions. But how could anyone really know what went on in the Van Alphen household when Aunt Annabet herself had not been seen in church for a month of Sundays and when the Venetian blinds on the windows of the distinguished house on High Street remained as mournfully shut as if there had been a death in the family? Even the servants were kept indoors, it was said. That they had been warned not to talk was certain. The gardener, for instance, who lived on his own, and who was shrewdly tapped for a little news, had proved as churlish and irascible as an angry bear, snarling back that he knew nothing and to leave him alone for the love of heaven. The man obviously had his instructions to keep silent. And if those instructions came from Mijnheer van Alphen, it was worth the man's bread and butter to obey. The leather manufacturer would not stand for any nonsense.

From Van Alphen's behavior in public surely nothing definite or enlightening could be deduced. You could not tell whether he was worried or angry, or whether in fact he knew anything at all. He went his way to and from the factory as usual, at his regular hours, and seemed not in the least nervous or distracted. Straight as a candle, his head thrown back almost defiantly and his umbrella crooked over his arm, he walked through the streets greeting acquaintances to left and right with his customary heartiness as if nothing in the world troubled him.

And then there was Hein Dermout. What had he to say for himself? With the shedding of the gorgeous blue uniform and the enormous bearskin busby of the Queen's bodyguard, the glamour had worn off a little. Not that he looked seedy or that he neglected his appearance. For a young man from that quarter of the town, with its brothels and taprooms and sordid eyesore of a hotel for transient beggars, Hein Dermout was a model of neatness. Even when he worked at the tannery in the old days, he was in the habit of shaving and putting on collar and tie in the evening before going out, while so many workers of his age simply kept their working clothes on and sat in those miserable half-lit taverns. Rather than lessening his self-respect, the two years spent in military service had accentuated his habits of neatness and punctiliousness. Still, the sudden change from the ornate uniform to civil clothes had a sobering and chastening effect. He was deprived of something—the official halo and the authoritative, impersonal, somewhat superior attitude which people unconsciously associate with the uniform. In his blue-serge suit and workman's cap he looked shorter, less important, and so humble, so pitifully unfitted to engage in battle with the most prominent and richest man in town!

But was he really fighting? Was he as determined as our Adriana was? Could anyone know? Could one speak to him as a friend of Adriana's and ask him how things stood with the girl and himself? Perhaps he would resent it as interference in a matter that concerned himself alone. Uncle Kees didn't think so. "Is it likely that a man in his circumstances, with the whole world against him, will resent a friendly word? Why, that fellow is starved for a kind look or a heartening word," said Kees. Ary remembered that Hein Dermout had in the past attended a few of our public debates, and was nearly always in the audience when out-of-town speakers visited us. That would be a subject to open a conversation with. He would speak to Hein.

It was not long before Ary had not only established contact with Hein Dermout, but had also managed, it soon appeared, to win the young worker's confidence. Before a month was over the two were fast friends. How did he do it? Such undertakings presented no difficulty to our Ary. Everything he undertook was done naturally and spontaneously. In the first place, he was kindness personified, in spite of a somewhat stern exterior. His approach to people, regardless of their station in life, was simple, without a trace of affectation or condescension. With Ary human bonds were stronger than class or blood. He had spoken to Hein Dermout as brother to brother. He had accosted him in the street, walked along with him to his mother's cottage, and there drunk a cup of coffee with him while talking about life in The Hague, about the beauties of that city and the environs, about the theaters and cafés and popular lecture halls and, inevitably, about the spread of "good doctrine" among the people, by which, of course, was meant the spread of socialist principles.

Hein told of visiting the parliament and of listening to speeches by the leaders of different political parties. He described their appearance and mannerism and their turns of speech. The two young men laughed over the pompous etiquette of our Second Chamber and the *Wichtigtuerei* of some of the ministers of the Government, the attitudes they struck and the affectation of their speech, the big foreign words they used, and the involved sentences with their paucity of ideas. Hein talked about the service, what life was like in the barracks, the extraordinary care lavished on the horses, which took far more time than the rest of the training, and how the chief topics of conversation among the hussars were drink and women.

He also told Ary of an incident that occurred once when he mounted guard outside the royal palace on the Noord-einde. On that occasion, it seems, the glass doors were unexpectedly swung open to let the Queen pass, and he, Hein, was thrown into such confusion and nervousness by Her Majesty's sudden appearance that in presenting arms he had fumbled his grip on his carbine and the weapon had clattered to the pavement. The Queen did not even look in his direction, but on her return, half an hour later, she had smiled graciously and even nodded her head approvingly at the manner in which he did the honors then.

Ary and Hein hit it off capitally together. And Hein's mother, too, was found to be a sensible woman—yes, a brave woman, Ary thought, for not having allowed her poverty and the sordid environment in which she lived to crush her spirit or embitter her temper. He was frankly happy about the meeting. For during that winter Ary remained in town in the evening, going home only on Satur-days, thus avoiding daily trips to and from the village of Altena over snow- and storm-swept roads and across the ice-filled river. He occupied a room in the house of the instructor of English, a grizzled but passionate fellow revolutionary who had married late in life and supported a family of six on his small salary. In that family circle Hein Dermout was almost a nightly caller.

Of course, they also spoke about Adriana and of the grave difficulties standing in the way to her marriage with Hein. There was no hedging on that subject, no false prudery. Hein looked upon his situation realistically and yet with the romantic dreams of a lover. I heard reports of these conversations at school, or in my uncle's studio where we went after classes, for Kees was also deeply interested.

"It all seems incredible to me," Hein told Ary. "It's so unbelievable that I grow dizzy thinking about it and I don't know any more whether it's reality or just a dream. Here is Adriana, the loveliest girl in town, the daughter of a rich manufacturer, an aristocrat, a man of power and influence, and here am I living in the Melkpad quarter, a man without a job, without education or manners. The contrast is too great. And yet we love each other to distraction. Sometimes I let my sentiments, my love for Adriana, carry me away and I see the future as a happy fairy tale. I forget the hurdles and the barriers for a moment and allow love to color everything. But it doesn't last very long. In the midst of my dreams my despair comes back and almost chokes me. The disillusionment is worse than a blow in the face. I realize all at once that I have nothing to offer her, nothing but trouble, humiliation, and maybe stark poverty. What can a girl like herself, used to luxury and servants and travel abroad, see in me? Why doesn't she just tell me to be gone? How can I take her with me into a life that holds out no promise at all? I really love her too much for that. I could not even ask her or make the attempt to live together. Every time I argue with myself and when theoretically I overcome the difficulties standing in our way, the reality rushes back into my consciousness and plunges me in darkness. I really don't know what to do any more.

"I'm like a man paralyzed, for on the other hand Adriana insists that we are never going to part. She knows my circumstances, of course. She knows every detail of my life.

I've told her everything again and again and she has visited my mother in our cottage. She has seen with her own eyes how we live. And she knows I haven't the smallest prospect here in Gorcum, or anywhere else in Holland, perhaps. When she visited me in The Hague last autumn, I told her I wanted to emigrate after my release from the army, that I wanted to go to America or to South Africa, to the gold fields to make a quick fortune, and then return to marry her, or let her come out there after I had established myself. But of that she wouldn't hear at all.

"She wouldn't even hear of waiting. She kept on saying, 'This is our country, here we belong and here we'll stay. It must be possible to find work and happiness in our own land.' And she also said: 'We're going to marry right away, now that we are young and can still love each other. I'm not going to wait.' That's what she says. So what am I to do?" continued Hein. "We must be married soon, you know. I simply can't run away now and sneak off to a foreign land and leave her in the lurch. The shame would kill my old mother. And then, this is the way Adriana wanted it, I mean the baby that is coming. After she became pregnant, she wrote me, 'Now I'm the one to decide, for now I have the instrument to force my father to let me marry you and at the same time I know that you, Hein, will never leave me.' There you are, that's Adriana."

"So there's no chance, then," asked Ary cautiously, "that there's any truth in the rumors that Adriana has left town already and is going to have her baby at some private clinic abroad? There are all kinds of strange rumors going around. People seem to think that in prominent families, in cases of this sort the babies often disappear. They are never seen or heard of any more. You remember the case of Flavia Sanders, the daughter of that rich family of grain merchants. Nobody ever saw her child after she went away to Paris."

"Oh, no!" Hein shook his head. "Nothing like that is going to happen. Adriana is still right here in Gorcum. She would reject with indignation the very idea of having an abortion. I don't think anyone has even mentioned it to her.

She's determined to have her baby. Why, she calls the baby her most powerful trump card, her biggest bargaining power. It's the baby, she thinks, that will pull us through."

It was in the Sistine Chapel, where Hein had dropped in one afternoon, as he did pretty regularly now, that he made these remarks.

"But how do you know all this?" Kees suddenly asked him. "How do you really know that Adriana is still here? No living soul has seen her for weeks. How do you know her father hasn't spirited her away, not to Paris necessarily, but to The Hague or to Rotterdam, for instance? There are such clinics in this country, too, you know."

"I am in regular communication with her," replied Hein. "I hear from Adriana every day."

"How can you? The Van Alphen house is hermetically closed. Nobody goes in or out."

"Just the same I get letters," said Hein. "I get one letter every night and Adriana gets one from me in the same hour."

"But there's no mail delivery at night," said Kees, shaking his head. "A special-delivery letter would surely fall into Dirk van Alphen's own hands."

"Oh, we don't trust the mails," Hein answered quickly. "We correspond by carrier."

"By carrier? Who can that person be that dares to brave Dirk van Alphen in his own house?" asked Kees, apparently still unconvinced.

"Aunt Annabet!" said Hein simply.

"Aunt Annabet?" we called out in unison. "Aunt Annabet! Well, of all people! Is she your *postillon d'amour?*" Ary roared with laughter and ran around the room slapping his sides. When he recovered from his outburst, he said, "Yes, yes," imitating Aunt Annabet's strident, high-pitched voice, "Yes, yes, the Lord works in a mysterious way his wonders to perform."

"He sure does," piped back Kees, also mimicking. "Indeedy, indeedy, we are laborers together with the Lord."

Not long after that it happened: Adriana and Hein were married. The news spread through town like wildfire.

We learned of it at school one day shortly before the afternoon classes reassembled. Although it created an uncommon stir in the community, the event had come off simply enough. That day Adriana awaited her father's return from the factory to announce that she was getting married. Mijnheer van Alphen was struck speechless, but pretended to be unaffected and calmly ate his lunch. It is not unlikely that he believed or hoped that Adriana would falter at the last minute, that she would not dare go through with the ceremony, but would throw herself on his mercy and accept his terms. Mijnheer van Alphen had more than once gained the upper hand in a business deal by waiting to the last moment before asserting his will and bringing his full power to bear. But if he expected a last-minute surrender on the part of his daughter, he miscalculated badly. At one o'clock Adriana walked into the dining-room and asked him whether he would not accompany her to the Town Hall. He turned pale, but did not answer her and even ignored her outstretched hand when she bade him good-by. He followed her to the front door, however, and held it open for her.

It was there, on the high stoop, within sight and hearing of several passers-by, that an angry scene occurred. Dirk van Alphen asked his daughter for the last time to reconsider. When she shook her head, his pent-up anger finally broke loose. He warned her that as long as she had anything to do with Hein Dermout she would not be permitted to cross his threshold again. When she walked off sadly, he lost control of himself altogether. He shouted a curse after her and slammed the door shut. That was the end.

Adriana was still crying when she arrived at the Town Hall, where the Burgomaster performed the ceremony in the presence of two of Hein's military friends, who were dressed in their hussar uniforms and who had come in on the morning train from The Hague to stand as witnesses. At two o'clock Dirk van Alphen knew, and half the town knew, that with all his influence and power he had not been able to prevent his daughter from marrying the man she loved.

Hein had rented a three-room cottage in the vicinity of

the Dalem Gate and there his mother, who was to take charge of the new household, awaited the couple upon their return from the Town Hall. In the afternoon a wagonload of Adriana's trunks and personal belongings arrived with a message from her father that he had these things removed because he did not wish to be reminded of a daughter who was to him dead and forgotten. Jetze and Ary took up a collection at school for a set of chairs with red plush seats and a set of dinner dishes, and in the evening Uncle Kees, who had sent over a big stove and a dozen sacks of anthracite, accompanied us when we went to extend our felicitations to our friends. We found Adriana unpacking her trunks and putting up her books and smiling through her tears. Then the stove was installed, and wine and cakes served, and Kees produced his flute. The two soldiers who had acted as witnesses came in and some other folk from the neighborhood and we serenaded the newlyweds with all the old songs appropriate to the occasion.

At nine o'clock Aunt Annabet arrived lugging an enormous hamper. She had brought with her a young pastor from one of the villages near Gorcum, a good orthodox young man of her acquaintance, and insisted that he bless the marriage, for said she, quoting Scripture as usual: "If the Lord does not build the house, in vain do the laborers labor thereon." So we witnessed the new ceremony and watched the pastor afterward drink a good deal more than the Scriptures prescribed for the stomach's sake.

But how was Hein Dermout to make a living? Surely, the three of them, husband, wife, and mother, and a fourth on the way, did not expect to get along, eat, dress, pay rent, buy fuel and light, on the Widow Dermout's small pension and on Hein's meager savings from his army pay? What plans had he for the future? Although we were all worried on that score, none of us felt like bringing up so prosaic and perhaps vexatious a question for fear of injecting a chilling note into the conversation and into the warm atmosphere of conviviality that reigned in the cottage. Even so, when Uncle Kees, as he got ready to leave, remarked that he probably could get Hein some work in Breda, Kees being one

of the commissioners charged by the Government with supervision over the work of restoring certain ancient tombs and
crypts in the Great Church of that city, Hein politely
declined and told us that his plans for the immediate future
were made.

Hein, it turned out, had bought a small parcel of good
land half an hour's distance from Gorcum on which he intended to do truck farming, peddling his produce from house
to house. Until his first crops, they would have to skimp
along on his mother's income. He had a cart already and
from a neighbor he was to get a couple of big dogs to pull
the cart. Oh, all would go well! Never fear! We were to
dismiss all worry from our minds. He, Hein, was young and
had strong arms. He could work night and day, if necessary.
By summer, when things started to grow, he would be in
business for himself. And when the bad weather came in
the fall, why, by that time he would have enough money to
put up a small stable on his plot and buy two or three cows
in the fall market and next winter he would be delivering
milk to his customers as well.

Hein was not downcast at all when he thought of the
future. He was full of hope and ambition. Yes, and Adriana
too. By summertime, she said, she would be able to help
Hein on the land with the picking and harvesting while old
Mrs. Dermout looked after the baby at home. Everything
was settled. By late autumn they would probably even be
able to move out of this cottage and rent a house with a
shop, where the vegetables and milk could be sold over the
counter. That would be her job.

"It sounds encouraging," said Kees as he walked home
through the drizzling rain, "but we should nevertheless
make it our business to drop in from time to time and keep
our eyes open. They can't live on Mrs. Dermout's seven or
eight gulden a week. There may be hunger and misery in that
house after the child is born."

And so indeed it came to pass. The baby was born, a
boy. They called him Dirk. But if Aunt Annabet had not
lugged her hampers of food and clothing through the
deserted streets at night, I'm afraid it would have gone

ill with little Dirk and his mother that winter. In the spring when Hein began to plow and plant, the rain came down in torrents for weeks on end. The summer was so wet that year that public prayers were offered for dry weather. Hein had no luck. The soil was saturated, drunk with water, as it were. Half of his crops were washed away. The potatoes rotted in the soil. Nor did Adriana make a speedy recovery from her confinement. She still looked worn and haggard when she went out with her husband to help in the picking and harvesting. There was no money to buy cows in the fall and the little stable they had built stood forlorn and empty, a pitiful reminder of their hopes and of their frustration when the snow began to fall.

We hardly recognized Hein one evening among the stevedores unloading a ship of grain by the Linge Quay. From a distance we watched him shoulder the heavy sacks in the hold of the ship, climb up a ladder, and walk along a narrow plank to the quay and into the warehouse. He staggered on his feet. Ary had learned that Hein actually did work night and day, as he had half in jest and half boastingly proposed on his wedding day. At nights he worked in the flour mill, where we saw him carrying the sacks. In the daytime he was splashing around in the mud on that miserable, water-soaked piece of land outside the town walls. How long could that last, how long could a man keep that up?

One day Mijnheer van Alphen drove up to the cottage near the Dalem Gate. Of course, all the neighbors ran out at the sound of the carriage wheels and the sight of the splendid equipage. Such vehicles never ventured into that quarter. The driver stood by the horses' heads and took off his hat when Adriana came out to greet her father. She looked thin and tired, and the emotional shock of seeing him made her clutch nervously at the neck of her simple cotton dress. Quite a few neighbors witnessed the meeting of father and daughter and heard every word that was said.

"Well, how long is this going to last? When are you coming home?" he said as he looked at her silently, startled no doubt by her careworn face and her humble appearance.

But as he spoke the cry of a baby was heard inside the

cottage and Adriana, half turning back, replied: "This is my home, Father! Won't you come in for a moment at least and drink a cup of coffee?"

"Is that man here?" growled Dirk van Alphen.

"If you mean Hein," she said, "no, he isn't home. He's out working. But Dirk is here!"

"Dirk?" he asked, looking up. "What Dirk are you talking about?"

"Little Dirk, your grandson, Father!" said Adriana, trying to smile. "Won't you come in and see him?"

"I have no grandson," said Mijnheer van Alphen, and added angrily: "Look here, Adriana, this can't go on. I can't leave my daughter here, in this damn . . ." He did not finish the sentence as he looked around and saw the faces of the neighbor women who had come as close as they dared to catch every word.

Adriana urged him again: "Do come in, Father, come inside!"

But her father shouted: "I will never set foot in that man's house, do you hear? That scoundrel, that lump of impudence, that dirty sneak! Never! By God, never in my life!"

"Hein Dermout is not a sneak," shouted one of the women in the crowd. "He's an honorable worker. You ruined him yourself, you brute, that's what you did when you took his job away from him. You ought to be ashamed of yourself. Brute, brute!" cried the women with full venom. "Get out of our street, you stinking tanner!" another woman shouted. "Why do you come here to poison our neighborhood?"

By now some men were sauntering up from the corner taproom.

"Come into the house, Father!" Adriana pleaded again.

He paid no heed and went on talking: "Why doesn't he go away to America, that man?" he shouted. "Tell him I will give him the money to disappear. Let him get to hell out of this town!"

"That's very kind of you, Father," replied Adriana, "but if he does, little Dirk and I will go with him."

Mijnheer van Alphen started at these words as if he had been struck in the face, and without another word walked back to his carriage. The men jeered at him as he rounded the corner. One drunken fellow picked up some horse manure and threw it at him through the open window of the carriage.

Every year, on the anniversary of Adriana's wedding day, her father returned to ask her to come home. Four years in succession he did that. The fifth year he did not need to ask her any more. Of that and of the events of the fourth year I cannot speak from personal knowledge, for I had left Holland myself. I heard the story from Willem van den Oever, the old policeman, when I returned to Gorcum for a visit shortly before Christmas in 1925. Uncle Kees had died, and I dropped in at the police station in the Town Hall to ask for certain addresses. We fell to talking about Adriana and Hein.

Willem told me that for a time things had gone from bad to worse with the Dermouts. A second child was born, a girl, a year or so after I left. Hein still worked his patch of ground, but did not manage to make a go of the vegetable business. He still had to fill in with odd jobs. Mijnheer van Alphen had grown old. His back was bent at last.

"You could tell," said Willem van den Oever, "that he was just a-wearying away for that girl of his. Many a night I watched him shuffle around in the neighborhood of the Dalem Gate and stand there looking up the alley where his daughter lived. When he heard footsteps, he scuttled away rapidly. One evening he recognized me and handing me a *rijksdaalder*, he said, 'Willem, old friend, do you know what it is to feel your heart turn to water?' Peering into the darkness, he asked, 'Willem, is that her cottage where the light is burning in the window?' I answered him, 'Yes, sir, that's it. You are not mistaken.' Then Mijnheer van Alphen said again: 'Go over there for me, Willem, will you, and shove this envelope under the door.' And then he walked away muttering to himself. The envelope contained money, banknotes, I'm sure of it, I could feel them," continued the policeman.

"Yes, you could tell he was a broken man. His clothes hung on him as on a flapping scarecrow. Do you remember how proud and dapper he used to step out? Well, all that was gone." Willem shook his head. "He slunk through the streets. People stood still to watch him. 'He's but a shadow of what he was,' they said, and that was the truth. He resigned his seat in the Town Council. He still went to his office every morning, but he never entered the factory. The foreman told me that the patroon closed the door of his office and just sat there staring out of the window, all morning, all day.

"Well, one afternoon," went on Van den Oever, "he comes down the Arkel Road from his factory a little before four o'clock on a biting-cold day. Let's see, it must be six years ago—no, it was seven years ago last fall. As he approaches the drawbridge there, you know, he sees a child playing on the edge of the bridge. The child was letting a paper boat trail in the current of the Linge River. Mijnheer van Alphen could see the child a long way off, because the road runs downhill toward the bridge. The child was leaning way over the railing. In alarm Mijnheer van Alphen shouted to the child. Startled by the cry, the boy slipped over the railing and down into the water. The current is strong there, as you know, Pieter," went on Van den Oever. "You fell in there once yourself, when you didn't come up to my belt here, remember?

"Well, Mijnheer van Alphen runs down as fast as he can and looking over the railing he sees the boy being carried off by the current and going under. There wasn't another soul in sight just then. He took off his overcoat and his jacket and plunged into the ice-cold water. He had to swim for it, but he caught the child as he went under. By then the current had carried them quite a way. We dragged them out about a quarter-mile downstream. The boy was unconscious, and we set right to work on him, pressing the water out of his lungs and moving his arms and legs.

"Mijnheer van Alphen just stood there and presently sent someone back to the drawbridge to get his clothes.

" 'Whose boy is it, Willem?' he asks me, casually.

" 'Don't you know?' I came back.

" 'No,' says he, 'Isn't he one of the Beekman boys?'

" 'That's not one of the Beekman boys,' I said, 'that's Dirk Dermout!'

"He didn't seem to catch on at first, but looked at me in a dull, stupid kind of way. And then his jaws start to tremble and he says in an agitated way: 'Willem, eh . . . is that, is that Adriana's boy?' and he turns his head stiffly in the direction of the child on the ground there.

" 'Yes,' I said, 'that's your grandson, mijnheer!'

"But he did not reply, he just groaned. Then he snatched up the boy and ran for all he was worth, to his home on High Street. Yes, and there we found him sitting by the boy's bed an hour later, still in his wet clothes and holding little Dirk's hand. I had gone to tell Adriana and she came along with me to her father's house. In the hallway we met Dr. Mendoza. He told us the child was fine, none the worse for his experience. But the old Doctor couldn't say much more. He swallowed a few times and walked out rapidly. I followed Mrs. Dermout up the stairs and outside the room we heard voices and stopped. We heard Mijnheer van Alphen say, 'And when you come to see the big wheels, Dirk, in the cellar of the factory, then there will be two Dirks, won't there, eh, you and I?'

" 'Yes,' we heard the boy say, 'two Dirks and one Hein, eh, Grandpa?'

"And then the old man again, *Ja, ja,* two Dirks and one Hein, that's right!'

" 'And Mother!' says the little boy. 'Oh, here she is!' Just then Mrs. Dermout and I stepped into the room. You can imagine the rest, Pieter!" said Van den Oever, now swallowing hard himself, like the Doctor, and taking a fresh bite of chewing tobacco.

"Did Mrs. Dermout go back to live in the big house?" I asked.

"Of course she did, and Hein too. He's the superintendent of the tanning factory now. You ought to call on them, Pieter. They're the kindest people in town."

I did call in the High Street that same evening. Old Dirk

van Alphen and Adriana themselves took me up the stairway to see young Dirk. He was sitting, doing his home work, in Adriana's room, the room where she showed Ary and me the photograph of Hein on Saint Nicholas Eve. Young Dirk told me he was in the second grade of the Gymnasium.

"Then you're starting to learn Greek," I said. "Do you still have Dr. Vossius?"

"Oh, yes," said Dirk. "But he's very busy now. He's writing a book on Ovid!"

BOOK II

Chapter I

ZEGER MOVES ON

ON HIS father's death in the autumn of 1915, Zeger van Rietvelt succeeded to the ancestral estates, which were then in a flourishing condition. In the month of June of the following year he married his cousin, the Freule Davina. He was twenty-one and she barely eighteen. There was a rumor current at the time that the marriage settlement involved certain financial considerations. But I do not see what they could have been, for both families were equally wealthy. Besides, it was a well-known fact that Davina's parents had given their consent, although she was still going to school, because their daughter and Zeger, it was said, had been lovers since childhood. In spite of this romantic aspect given to the marriage, the villagers of Rietvelt were quite positive in their affirmations, when I visited the neighborhood some ten or twelve years later, that the union of the two branches of the ancient noble family had by no means been a happy one.

Zeger's mother moved to The Hague after her husband's death and there Zeger followed her, leaving a manager in charge of the big farm. But he soon tired of life in the royal city and returned to Rietvelt. There he had the interior of the manor thoroughly remodeled and modernized in anticipation of his forthcoming marriage with Davina. All the old furniture that had served for generations was discarded. In the place of the small windowpanes of the manor house, huge steel-framed plate-glass windows were put in, a central heating plant was installed, a garage and an electric generating station were built. New lawns and flower gardens were laid out. Indeed, I scarcely recognized the old place when I passed by some years later.

After Zeger transferred the heavy burden of management that the Squire had cheerfully borne all his life to the shoulders of an estate superintendent, he seems to have found time weighing heavily on his hands. He grew listless and irritable, and in spite of an agreement that the manager was to have the exclusive charge and the sole responsibility in the direction of the vast properties, he found fault with nearly everything the new man did.

It was not surprising to learn, therefore, that within a year or so after his father's death no less than four managers had entered and left his service. It was then that Zeger discovered that the prosperous condition of his holdings—it was the time when Germany was in the deadly grip of the blockade and she bought, at fabulous prices, what could be spared, and more, of the Dutch crops—enabled him to indulge in whatever hobby he chose. The stocks and bonds in British armament firms and oil companies, which his marriage with Davina had added to his fortune, were soaring and made him one of the richest men in the country. Even if he should throw the money out the window by the handful he could not easily exhaust his wealth. He took up horse-breeding. There wasn't a horse meet or a race track in Europe at which Zeger did not put in an appearance. He kept a stable in Saint-Germain-en-Laye in France and one at Wannsee near Berlin. In the middle of the European war he rode in the military tournaments in Budapest, in Zurich, and in Maisons-Laffitte. He won a prize at the great international *concours hippique* held in Milan in 1918.

What had been a mere pastime soon became a veritable passion with Zeger. It left him little time to spend at home. Even when he returned for a brief time after a long absence abroad, he seldom remained indoors. People said that he had inherited all the restlessness of his grandfather. He cantered and galloped over the country roads and through the fields, and it was by no means an uncommon occurrence for him to ride out after dark. Neither rain nor cold nor summer's heat could keep that man quietly at home for a whole day.

He imported horses from every land under the sun, from Arabia, Morocco, South America, and I don't know what other strange places. It was as if plain, old-fashioned Dutch horses were not good enough for the Squire of Rietvelt, or as if horses were not obtainable at all in our own country. The exorbitant prices asked in that time of war for horses of any kind, let alone for the pedigreed thoroughbreds Zeger imported, and the enormous cost of shipping the animals to Holland by a difficult and of necessity circuitous route, did not deter him in the least. He had the money to spend and he spent it. For the sake of a rare and beautiful horse Zeger was willing to go to any length and spared neither expense nor trouble. He even managed to get hold of two magnificent stallions from Russia. They were of the hardy and high-tempered species bred by the Cossacks of the Don Valley, and they had traveled halfway round the world before they finally stood in the stable at Rietvelt having cost their new owner a good round quarter-million gulden.

When those two animals had become somewhat acclimated after that long and arduous journey, it was Zeger alone who rode them. He rode them mercilessly, as if he wanted to ride the life out of them, although they ran as well and as fast as any horse can run. But those beasts seemed able to stand any and every kind of punishment. There wasn't the faintest trace of a tremor discernible in their legs after the wildest chase. And this fact, strange to say, seemed to affect Zeger's nerves more than his brutal treatment affected the horses. It made him angry to see those horses after a long ride as fresh and unharmed as if they were ready to start again.

He behaved as if he were disappointed over their splendid powers of endurance. He wanted to master those two Russians, he said, break their arrogant and independent spirit and ride them until they should stand before him trembling, beaten and broken, begging for mercy as it were, and acknowledging his superiority and mastery. It was a peculiar thing with Zeger, and everybody in the countryside remarked upon it at the time, that mingled with his undeniable liking for horses there should have sprung up in him what amounted to a fierce hatred for those two animals he had brought from Russia at so great cost.

One of the two was a particularly high-spirited beast. The ruthless treatment that Zeger inflicted on it made its temper so fierce that the young Squire had great difficulty in remaining in the saddle when he rode the animal for some obstacle and the horse took it, however high or wide it might be, with the sparks flying from its hoofs. Between Zeger and that horse there raged a silent battle, a battle of nerves that started all over again with each new day. It was a question of who was the strongest and whose will was going to prevail. When Zeger came into the stable, or when he had the horse taken out and was ready to jump into the saddle, the Squire would turn pale with suppressed rage upon seeing the animal standing there with its nerves and muscles tense with expectation, ready to be put to the test. It pricked up its noble long ears at Zeger's approach. Its eyes sparkled and the red-gold skin gleamed with inner excitement. A thrill ran through its frame when the Squire swung himself into the saddle. It was as if the horse said: "Hold fast now! Hold fast, Zeger van Rietvelt, and let us see whose knees start to tremble first, yours or mine!"

And then Zeger, his teeth clenched and riding-crop in hand, would begin the test, and ride and drive like a madman, jumping fences, clearing ditches, racing like a possessed soul along the old hunting courses, thundering through hamlets and villages, never slackening his murderous pace for a minute but whacking the horse between the ears and driving the spurs into its raw flanks urging it on to still greater speed until the road over which he passed was flecked with splashes of foam and drops of blood. And so he would go on for hours and hours and day after day, riding like an insane person who imagines that he is pursued by some evil spirit.

Zeger's strength was pitted against that of the horse, until he began to feel that his forces were nearing exhaustion and he returned to the estate panting for breath and shaking in every limb. Then as the sweat-dripping animal was led away, Zeger would stand looking at it and swear: "Wait, you devil's spawn! Wait till next time. Next time I'll break your damned proud heart for you, see if I don't!" But the horse proved unbreakable. Its strength and will power were inexhaustible. And this resistance to his perverse passion tore and rasped at the Squire's nerves until he became an unapproachable wreck, snapping and cursing and yelling at everybody who came into his presence. In the end, it is true, the Squire did get the better of the horse, although it cannot be said that he conquered it in a fair and honorable manner. He stooped pretty low to have his way, and in doing so exhibited a depth of cruelty that was to be long the talk of the neighborhood.

One day Zeger had his estate workers place some logs alongside the old hunting course which ran between his property and that of Baron Wenselaar. On one side that course was skirted for several miles by a row of hedges and low wild-growing shrubbery. On the other side of the pathway lay a deep and dangerous bog. Peat had been dug there in olden days, but the workings had been abandoned and the holes had filled up with water and rotting vegetation. It was on the side of the bog that the logs were placed, ostensibly to mark off the swampy area, or at least to serve as a warning to passers-by not to venture upon the spongy surface, which was known to be full of treacherous patches of quicksand.

Along this trail Zeger came riding his magnificent Russian stallion one day at his usual reckless pace. He was homeward-bound and had been away all afternoon putting the horse to the test. He must have been in a furious mood, for he was seen by several persons to be lashing the animal with the ferocity of a lunatic. Maybe he was mad indeed; at least I cannot think of anything else to explain the senseless act he committed that evening. All at once he gave the reins a violent tug, turning the horse almost at right angles on its course. Checked in its headlong dash, the animal reared and plunged over the guard rail of logs and landed squarely in the soft, boggy soil. At once it sank away up to its belly and could not raise itself again. Zeger, although not unseated, hastily scrambled out of the saddle and, grabbing hold of the logs, pulled himself out of the bog onto the hard earthen pathway.

He was starting to walk away when he seemed to bethink himself. He returned on his steps, laid some of the logs over the soft ground in the direction of the horse, which was groaning pitifully as it struggled to release itself from the sucking quicksand, and then, taking his riding-whip, started to lash the helpless animal across the eyes. He beat and beat till the sweat poured down his face, and all the time he was laughing in a raw, unnatural way. Men working in the fields on the other side of the hedgerow saw and heard him. At one moment Zeger tore off his jacket and flung it into the pathway, and then he resumed his insane lashing until at last only the horse's head was showing above the surface and the dying beast sank away into the bog. Then only did he pick up his coat and walk home. From that day on, I was told, his irascibility subsided and he became his usual affable self again. He had conquered.

It was around this time, that is to say some six or eight months after his marriage to the Freule Davina, that Zeger took to visiting a brother nobleman of his in the vicinity, a certain Count Frans Terwillen, who was, as I recall him vaguely, a likely enough young fellow at first sight and in fact as handsome a man in appearance as the Squire himself, although so much darker of countenance that he might well have been called swarthy. He had a good property, this Terwillen, and he also bred horses; only, being of a more practical turn of mind than Zeger, he did not breed them for the race tracks. As to his morals, the less there is said about them the better. The universal opinion in the county was that his history was not to be touched except with a pair of tongs. Among the common churchgoing people he was considered definitely beyond the pale. Everyone knew that he was an inveterate gambler, a man who scoffed publicly at religion, and that he had been mixed up in some scandalous affair with a married woman in his youth. At Terwillen's house, a rambling old manor that stood alone and forsaken near a bend in the flint-colored River Linge not far from the village of Asperen in a flat, clayey meadow,

rather dirty-green as if depastured partly by geese, and near
which there was also one of the outlying forts of Gorcum's
defense system, the two friends met to play cards.

Of course they were not alone. The Terwillen manor
had for a long time been the headquarters for the younger
elements of the rural nobility, a gathering-place for idle
moneyed young men who, if they cannot be called the scum
of mankind, are nevertheless the foam, drifting by on the
surface without a clear destination, without principles and
without ideals. Terwillen was a bachelor and did pretty
much what he liked. I knew him only by sight. To me he
was always the pink of politeness, but my Uncle Kees, who
had done his portrait, judged him a high-going individual,
one who was watching his time and diligent to seize all business opportunities in spite of a certain air of nonchalance
and carelessness.

Before long the two friends were sending their carriages
to Gorcum in the evenings to pick up some of the younger
officers of the garrison and other military men who were
temporarily detached to put in a stage of practical work at
the fort in the neighborhood of Asperen, and who had no
place to go at night in that dreary and Godforsaken country where the lights went out at nine o'clock. Sometimes
these men stayed at House Asperen over the week ends, and
at such times Zeger was not seen in Rietvelt for days. And
it wasn't only card parties that were held at Terwillen's
house. Fashionably dressed women from The Hague and
Rotterdam could be seen on Saturday descending from the
afternoon train in Gorcum and stepping into carriages bearing the Terwillen and Rietvelt crests. These women left
again on the noon train on Mondays. Who were they? Well,
the servants said they were not of the nobility, in spite of
their fine clothes and feathers. Heaven knows who they
were, or how men like Zeger and the Count had ever come
to make their acquaintance.

What went on at House Asperen on those week ends did
not, of course, long remain a secret in a rural community
where the very walls of the houses had ears and where
flunkies and coachmen and valets of the various estates con-

stantly met in taprooms and kitchens to gossip and carry tales. I do not think a more sordid mass of eavesdroppings, kitchen ashes, and floor-sweepings was ever got out of a gentleman's household than came from House Asperen. If the stories of the servants are to be credited, the place became nothing less than a brothel. The champagne and Schiedam gin flowed there in torrents. Hadn't Piet Harte himself, the veteran with the cork leg, who sometimes accompanied his young master to Terwillen's house, told how he was summoned to the salon one evening and ordered to keep the phonograph running with American jazz records? And how he had seen there a number of girls from The Hague in the condition of our first parents, yes, and in that condition sitting on the laps of the officers, or running around in the room holding wineglasses in their hands, and how one of them in Piet's own presence executed a strange, sensuous dance on the hearth rug right in front of the fire while the room was darkened. It had put Harte in mind of the days when he was stationed as a soldier on the Island of Bali. "Only those Balinese girls," said Piet, "at least wore a girdle or something, and no man could touch them." And what Piet had seen with his own eyes was not all, nor was it the worst by any means. The Terwillen servants knew far more. Piet did not miss the opportunity to drink up heartily himself when he went along with the Squire, and he was usually sound asleep somewhere in a hayloft or a stable long before the orgies of his master reached their climax.

That Piet did not exaggerate was evident from a certain photograph that went the rounds in Gorcum at the time, a photograph showing the whole company of men and women at the Terwillen mansion standing stripped naked in the garden. That picture had been taken, it was said, on a balmy Sunday afternoon at a moment when the bells of Asperen's church tower called the faithful to worship. One of these photographs, falling under the eyes of the commanding officer of Gorcum's garrison, had led to the issuance of an order to the younger officers to avoid Count Terwillen's company. That is how the scandalous goings-on at House Asperen really became public knowledge, for the order was published in the officers' messroom in town.

I cannot say through what torments and pangs of regret the Lady Davina went when she learned of her husband's debaucheries. In that case, too, our information rests for the greater part on the reports and the gossip of servants. One thing is certain, however—six months after the wedding day her marriage was hopelessly on the rocks. And considering the circumstances it must be owned that little else could have been expected. Davina was a mere child when she married Zeger. She had been carefully brought up; that is, she had been meticulously shielded from coming to a knowledge of good and evil and had spent most of her adolescent years in finishing schools of one kind or another, at home or abroad. She was not only a child, she was youthfully inexperienced. She knew nothing of the world beyond what she had read in old-fashioned romantic novels that were carefully selected for her. Of love she knew even less. She hardly knew Zeger. She had accepted him as a matter of course, as something self-evident, as one accepts a birthday present. She unconsciously assumed that life with him would be but a prolongation of the pleasant brief vacations she had spent at Rietvelt manor from time to time in the company of her parents. Nothing had prepared her for the disillusions that followed.

When she was left alone after her wedding day and her parents and the guests had departed, she suddenly looked into the void. All at once life was meaningless and empty. Before she fully realized that anything was amiss events started to pile up so that she scarcely had time to take account of the situation in which she had been thrown or to discover at which point things had gone wrong. Zeger treated her as a child from the beginning. For a time he was endearing and affectionate, but he soon tired of her simplicity and her lack of worldly sophistication. To him the childish prattle of love's sweet nothings was a game, a diversion, a pleasant pastime; to her it was reality. Although they were not far distant in age, Zeger had already lived too much to accommodate himself to Davina's innocence and naïveté.

He flew into an uncontrollable rage when he caught her playing with dolls one day. He was genuinely astonished when he learned that she wept when he went off on one of his horse-buying expeditions, and that she dreaded to be alone in the big old house. The creaking of the old beams in the night, the tapping of the deathwatch beetle, the gnawing of a mouse behind the wainscoting, threw her into a fright that did not leave her till the light of morning crept through the curtains. He listened politely and with an amused smile when she recited poetry to him, and at first he joined heartily in the fun of taking up a play and dividing the roles and answering each other as if they were actors on the stage. Once he found it amusing; the second time he was bored. When Davina proposed the game a third time, he asked her if she had gone crazy.

Ary or Jetze could have told Davina that Zeger had never taken delight in any quiet intellectual pursuit, that he detested music and pronounced theatergoing the rankest nonsense. Zeger wanted amusement and stimulation of another kind; he had to be up and doing, racing his horses, playing cards till all hours of the morning, tearing across the Continent, never staying in one place more than a day and then off again by boat or train. When Davina wished to surprise him once and told him to leave the room and not re-enter until she called and he found her upon his return dressed up as a nun, he roared with laughter. But when she repeated the performance the next evening and came out of her dressing-room in the costume of Mary Queen of Scots and declaimed Schiller's verses, Zeger tore the gown off her shoulders and asked her brutally when she would have done with that foolish schoolgirl kind of make-believe.

In a few months' time husband and wife were quarreling openly. Zeger's angry voice, swearing coarsely as if he were among his grandfather's troopers, could be heard coming through the open windows in the evening. Then the workers on the estate doused the lights in their cottages and sauntered up closer in order not to miss a word and stood listening under the elm trees near the big house till the storm of words blew over. Davina's maid, after helping her undress, came downstairs to join the others and told of her mistress's tears and of the callous disregard of the master, just sitting there and smoking his pipe and badgering his wife with questions as to when she would go back to her father and mother to be nursed and pampered.

The servants agreed that he was tired of her. He was always growling or short-spoken in her presence and seemed always itching to be away. There were violent scenes at the dinner table, too, with the Lady Davina, whose figure showed plainly that the Rietvelt dynasty would not be extinguished, pleading with the Squire not to go to Asperen every evening and he replying that he wasn't a child that must be kept indoors after dark or a nursemaid to watch over a nervous pregnant woman. Then there would be a loud banging of doors and a few minutes later the Squire riding off full-gallop in the direction of his friend Terwillen's place.

Ary told me later that Davina's parents came from The Hague one day quite unexpectedly and made an attempt to persuade Zeger to mend his ways, pointing out to him his unreasonable, irresponsible, unheard-of behavior in leaving a gentle, sweet girl to whom he was married but a few months to her own devices and terrors night after night. That was the time Zeger broke into a most violent tantrum. He covered his in-laws with a burst of vituperation and curses, ran out of the house, and did not return until he had been notified that they whom he called the meddlers had departed. Davina, it is said, then and there decided, with her parents' approval, to leave her husband as soon as her child should be born.

With the restrictions placed on the officers' movements by the commanding officer, attendance at the gatherings in House Asperen fell off sharply. Zeger, too, did not visit his friend as frequently as before. Instead, he began to spend some of his evenings at the home of the Baron Steeven Wenselaar, who lived next door to him—that is, Wenselaar lived on the next estate; the mansions themselves were a good two miles distant from each other. The Baron Steeven Wenselaar, it will perhaps be recalled, was the invalid whose wife, according to Zeger's grandfather, was some fifty years younger than her husband. She was the lady upon whom the Dowager Amelie Ten Eyck spied through her binoculars when Ary, Jetze, and I were guests at the Rietvelt manor and who was seen to be wearing a new fur jacket that day. The Baron Otto's remark about Steeven Wenselaar's age was of course a gross exaggeration. To have been fifty years younger than her husband would have made the Baroness only fifteen. In fact she was well into her thirties when Zeger made her acquaintance. It is true that she appeared much younger. She had retained a certain girlish slenderness that was rare enough in the Holland of a quarter-century ago when married women, either through neglect or by design, early abandoned all pretenses to youthfulness.

Besides being an exception in having guarded a supple figure, the Baroness Marie Wenselaar had an extraordinarily attractive face and affected a certain rather foreign elegance in dress and manners. She had copper-colored hair and red-brown eyes, and long black eyelashes that gave her eyes the appearance of a pair of chrysanthemums. But the most fascinating part of her features was her mouth. Its light-red lines, bent up slightly at the corners, gave her face an expression both of gentleness and of will power. Her laughter had a ring of suppressed sensuality. She had a way of staring at a person or an object—it may have been merely the effect of her petaled, doll-like eyes—as if she were constantly astonished. Her voice was low and *troublante*, as the French say, with a slight hoarse undertone such as young girls of school age not infrequently have.

Zeger met her one evening as he rode out to Asperen for dinner. The brief twilight of a wintry day had just given way to a night that promised to be black and stormy. The wind whisked the snow off the hard frozen road in small, powdery clouds. Zeger was proceeding at a canter, dressed in his short fur coat, with his head bent forward over the horse's mane. As he passed the mansion of the Wenselaars, which stood a good way back from the road at the end of a double row of elms, his horse shied so violently that he was almost unseated. He came to a stop with a curse. Looking around and trying to discover what might have been the cause of the animal's sudden fright, he noticed a dark figure moving among the trees of the avenue. At once he wheeled and spurred his horse in that direction, shouting imprecations at the person whose stealthy approach was the cause of his inconvenience. A woman's voice answered him, and it suddenly dawned on him that he might be speaking to the Baroness Wenselaar, which was indeed the case. He dismounted at once and apologized for the rudeness of his language. She laughed her low, mocking laugh at his fears that a would-be burglar or highwayman might be prowling in the Wenselaar grounds. "Steeven would like nothing better," she said, "if only to fire off one of the rifles he keeps in his sitting-room. He always complains that nothing ever happens around here to break the monotony of life. He can scarcely move about, it's true, but I think the report of a burglar on the prowl would almost surely make him forget his pains."

It was freezing weather. The wind came with a sharp, cutting force over the bare fields. The Baroness started to walk back toward the lights of the mansion in the distance. Still somewhat perturbed about his boorish and unreasonable behavior of a moment before and desirous to efface the recollection of it, Zeger was suddenly all affability and charm. He walked back with the Baroness, leading his horse by the reins. He inquired about Steeven Wenselaar's condition and expressed regret that he had not found the time to call on a neighbor who had been a dear and lifelong friend of his father's. She explained her presence outside at that unusual hour by saying that it was her custom to take a vigorous stroll up and down the avenue before dinner every day, no matter what the weather. She asked him where he was bound when her sudden appearance halted him. When he mentioned his friend Terwillen's name, the Baroness asked with that peculiarly disturbing laugh whether the Count was really the devil incarnate rumor made him out to be. She had heard, of course, of the gatherings in Asperen that had led to the commanding officer's sensational order, and she felt highly amused at the thought of this gentleman ordering his officers about as if they were the inmates of a young ladies' boarding school.

For a moment they stood silently at the foot of the short flight of steps leading to the entrance of the mansion. The snow, caught in the draft that blew around the rambling corners of the old house and its dependencies, whirled in spirals around their shoulders. Zeger's horse pawed the ground impatiently and he stroked its muzzle soothingly with his gloved hand. As he began to make his adieus the Baroness looked up sharply at the door for a moment as if she heard someone approaching from the inside. In the same instant the full light of the lanterns that burned on either side of the stairway fell on her face. It was the first time that Zeger could clearly distinguish her features.

A mumbled exclamation of surprise escaped him before he could check himself. Her eyes were like two still lamps in which burned a dark flame. She was quick to notice his agitation, and an amused smile over his boyish inability to hide his emotions flitted over her lips. But before he could say another word, a lackey, attracted by the sound of voices and by the scraping of the horse's hoofs, threw the door wide-open. The Baroness made a shivering gesture and said that they had walked much slower than was her custom on her evening promenades. She pressed Zeger to come inside, if only to warm himself for a moment and to say a word of greeting to the Baron. Zeger was easily persuaded. He threw the reins of his horse to the lackey and walked up the stairs with her.

"Steeven!" she called out as soon as she stepped into the hall. "Steeven, guess whom I have just captured!" Zeger thought that her voice had suddenly undergone a complete change. It was no longer low and caressing as it had been a moment before, but high-pitched and with a forced note of cheerfulness in it. The Baron Wenselaar was in the sitting-room on the left of the hall. He was lying on a pile of cushions in a reclining chair near the fireplace, in which roared a huge log fire. Thick plaids were spread over his legs. As Zeger entered the room, the Baron raised himself on his elbows, adjusted his pince-nez, and stared over their rims. Zeger walked to his chair with outstretched hand.

"By all that's holy," exclaimed the Baron, "if it isn't

Zeger van Rietvelt, my own neighbor! Well, well, who would have thought it? Good evening! Good evening! This is indeed a surprise. Where in the name of heaven did you capture this rare bird, Marie?" He turned to the Baroness, who had shed her heavy coat and scarf in the hall and who now followed Zeger into the sitting-room. Zeger looked around at her while still shaking the Baron's hand. She wore a mauve muslin dress that clung to the curves of her figure. Zeger saw that in walking her knees lightly touched her skirt.

The Baroness explained to her husband the circumstances of her encounter with Zeger. She laughed merrily as she told of Zeger's fears of a highwayman prowling on the estate. Still speaking, she sat down on a sofa facing her husband and crossed her legs. Zeger looked at her furtively. But the Baron talked with the loquacity of persons who are often alone.

"You have neglected us terribly," he said to Zeger, wagging a thin bony finger at him. Zeger took a seat by the Baron's side. "I do not think we have seen you since your wedding day. It's an outrage, really, when you know that Marie and I are eating our hearts out here with curiosity." He began to ask questions about the Rietvelt estate and about the horses, but without giving Zeger an opportunity to reply.

"Is that one of your famous thoroughbreds I heard outside there just now? Hell's bells, I am going to get up to see it, Marie," he said to the Baroness, "tell Andries to bring in my wheel chair. God, I haven't seen a good horse since my accident! But I tell you, my boy, you ride them too fast. I hear you going by at nights and I say to myself he rides like the devil." . . . And how were Zeger's mother and Davina? The Baron jumped from one subject to the next with the erratic inconsequence of one burning up with curiosity and excitement.

"I hear the population of these Netherlands is to be increased soon, eh?" and he laughed. "Capital, my boy! Capital! The more the merrier. It's not a bad breed, that of the Rietvelts." He laughed again. "Incidentally, that was a

wise move on your part to put a manager in charge. That's
what your father should have done years ago. Many times
I advised him to get a good man. I said to him: 'Arnout,
you are working yourself to death. The estate is too large
for you.' But he wouldn't listen. The Squire always wanted
to do everything alone. What a man he was! When I come
to think of it, I don't expect we will ever see the like of him
again. Still, he might be alive today had he listened to my
advice."

And how about that *concours hippique* in Berlin where
Zeger had won a gold medal in the jumping tournament?
"Why didn't you come in to tell me about it?" went on the
Baron. "I was itching to congratulate you. God! we in
Holland haven't the chance so often to celebrate a victory,
you know. Marie, did you ring for Andries? Will you have
an apéritif, Zeger? It's a little too late for tea, I think.
Marie, why don't you ring for Andries and tell him to bring
me my wheel chair?"

The Baroness poured tea. Zeger got up hastily to help
her roll the teatable closer to the fire. He thought he heard
her sigh when his fingers lightly brushed the sleeve of her
dress. The Baron rang a hand bell and ordered the servant
to bring in some more wood. When Zeger had resumed his
seat and the Baroness looked up from the teatable to ask
him about the amount of sugar for his cup, Zeger noticed
that the dark shadows under her eyes gave her face a touch
of sadness. Her cheeks had lost the rosy tint they had had
outside. He felt a wave of sympathy welling up in his heart
for the woman. The Baron talked uninterruptedly. He urged
Zeger to stay for dinner. But the young Squire said he could
not possibly stay, as his friend Terwillen was probably even
now waiting for him and he had still a good six miles to go.
"You'll be there in no time," replied the Baron, "the way
you ride."

After pouring the tea the Baroness sat down by Zeger's
side. She rested her hand on the arm of her chair, which was
quite close to Zeger's chair. He did not look at her.

"Frans Terwillen," said the Baron, "is a tremendous
show-off. He likes it to be known that he does not care a

rap for public opinion and that he is a first-class lady-killer.
The more scandals the better. But it doesn't amount to a
hill of beans. I don't believe a hundredth part of what I
hear. It's all show and pretense. Still, Frans is a good boy
at heart. The trouble is the rascal has too much money. He
doesn't know what to do with it, so he gambles. You ought
to tell him, Zeger, that I still play a good hand and that
Marie trims me regularly. That ought to tempt him.

"Besides, he owes me a visit for simple Christian charity's
sake. Tell him that. Tell him that we are dying of ennui in
this house, and that we do not think the goods of this world
are divided justly, with us having all the boredom and he
all the gaiety in his neighborhood. Tell him I want to share.
I am a socialist." The Baron laughed and the Baroness
stared silently into the fire.

The Baroness saw Zeger to the door. A stable boy
waited at the foot of the steps with his horse. As he bent
over to kiss her hand, she said to him in a whisper: "Come
soon again! Real soon, do you hear?" Zeger looked into her
eyes and murmured weakly that he was ready to obey her
every command. Nevertheless, it took him weeks before he
called again on the Wenselaars. And when he finally returned, he did not come alone; he brought his friend the
Count Frans Terwillen. Now I do not know whether Terwillen was there by the desire of the Baroness or merely
because of Steeven Wenselaar's half-jocularly expressed
desire to see "the rascal." The fact is he came. For a time
the two friends were regular dinner guests at the mansion
and stayed for a quiet game of cards in the Baron's sitting-
room afterward. This happened once or twice a week, sometimes a little oftener.

There was nothing unusual or out of the way in this.
Neighbors visited each other that way all over the district.
How else would they have passed the long winter evenings?
But then gradually the entire situation changed. Zeger and
Frans Terwillen brought others of their friends. Oh, none
of those gamblers and revelers who had formerly carried
on so scandalously at House Asperen. But young squires of
the neighborhood and officers and young bankers from Gor-

cum with their wives and women friends, all highly respectable persons, one may be sure, and members of the best families. The Baron Wenselaar would not have mixed socially with anyone below his own class. He might be helpless and an invalid, but he still had authority enough to draw the line as to who came to and what went on in his own house.

Before Christmas the Wenselaar mansion had become the gathering-place of a whole crowd of gay young people and the parties of the Baroness were the talk of town and county. One night it was a musicale, the next evening a dance or a festive dinner. There was always something going on. From five or six o'clock in the afternoon onward, almost every day there was a steady procession of carriages and automobiles up the drive, and throughout the evening passers-by on the highway could see the windows of the mansion brilliantly illuminated and drivers and grooms and chauffeurs walking with lanterns in their hands between the drive and the dependencies, stabling the horses or bringing them out for departing guests. Wenselaar House was as busy as a beehive. And quite a change from former years!

The Baron Wenselaar, who was known as a touchy, moody old hermit who shunned the company of his fellow men and who had for years been nailed to his chaise longue by the fireplace with a weak heart and a diseased spine, in perpetual pain and agony, really dying a lingering death, one might say—that man had suddenly turned into the most affable and generous host for miles and miles around. It looked almost like a miracle. If it wasn't a miracle, people said, there was certainly some mystery involved. Steeven Wenselaar, who had outlived the Baron Otto and the Dowager Amelie and even the Squire, Zeger's father, and so many of his contemporaries, was keeping open house.

Of course people understood that it was not he, but the elegant Baroness with her French manners and her doll's eyes who had so long been kept a virtual prisoner by the invalid's side, who had at last broken her bonds and who was the real animater of the flurry of social events in the aristocratic circles of the district. The Baron himself

admitted as much. What could he do? he would ask. "Half
my back is gone! My legs are turning to stone. All I am
good for is to look on as Marie amuses herself." He had
given her carte blanche, he said, to break the monotony of
life at the manor by whatever means she saw fit. And money
was no object, for Wenselaar was as wealthy as the Rietvelts, or Terwillen for that matter. And so she had started,
first with Zeger and Frans and then gradually extended
the number of her guests, step by step, until her house was
filled with visitors from one week end to the other. Why,
the Company of the Free Blowers of Gorcum, the symphony
orchestra under the direction of old Beethoven Bis, had
performed for the Baroness on the occasion of her birthday
ball, and a small jazz orchestra from Gorcum was in regular
attendance at the manor at least one night a week.

Now I do not know of these happenings from direct
personal experience and observation, for I was no longer a
resident of Holland when they took place. Of course I do
know the topography of the so-called Land of Arkel in
which those events occurred as well as I know my own
pocket, for I lived there eighteen years and I went over every
inch of the ground—I might well say many times. I had an
opportunity to familiarize myself thoroughly with the
history and the lore of all the old families, the manors, the
estates, the ruins, as well as the rivers, brooks, and roads of
the district, when, still a gymnasiast, I was honored with an
assignment "to write a monogram of historical, cultural, and
archaeological interest" on the subject of the remnants of
the Arkel period in the environs of Gorcum for a local historical society of which my Uncle Kees was the recording
secretary.

Of what took place at the Rietvelt and Wenselaar manors
during the few brief years of my absence, I learned first
of all from my friend Ary Brandt, who had become a pastor
in the interval and who kept a close watch on all that happened in our old native polder. I saw him frequently up to
the time when an impenetrable curtain was drawn over
Holland and over the greater part of Europe by the brown

marauders of Berlin and everybody and everything in my fatherland was blotted from view for six long years. Before that Ary never failed to keep me informed when I visited him, and sometimes in his letters to Paris, as to what was going on. I also met Zeger van Rietvelt again, but only once, for a brief moment and under particularly tragic circumstances. Most of all, at least about the present subject, I gathered from Dirk Mensert and Bernt Sas, the two villagers of Rietvelt who were involved in the case of the desecration of a grave, which, it will be recalled, had agitated public opinion in our district considerably some years before.

Those two fellows no longer resided in the village of Rietvelt, but a short distance outside, in a hut thrown together from odds and ends, planks, saplings, and cast-off building material they had managed to pick up here and there. The roof consisted of tin cans flattened out on boards over which lay a thick blanket of moss. The cabin stood on the edge of a small forest, or rather near a cluster of a hundred or so oaks and beeches, for there are really no woods that can be dignified with the name of forest in the whole length and breadth of the Land of Arkel. A swift-running brook, the so-called Willem's Vliet, coursed through the wooded plot on its way to swell the waters of the Linge River. A wooden bridge, actually a mere row of planks, without railing or protection of any kind, joined the Rietvelt and Wenselaar properties at this point.

The highway was half a mile distant. In the rear of the cabin, two hundred yards from the cluster of trees, ran an old hunting course, which Squire Arnout had still used but where Zeger seldom set foot after the incident with the Russian horse. That wooded plot was part of the Crown domains, a sort of no man's land. Dirk and Bernt had no right to live there, of course, for it is the curious destiny of all Crown lands, it seems, to remain forever fallow, uninhabited and unencumbered. It was royal preserve, in other words, wasteland. Dirk and Bernt had put up their habitation there because they had to live somewhere. Zeger van Rietvelt had ordered them off his property and the cottages in the village they had rented formerly had long since been occupied by others.

They eked out a miserable existence, for employment of any kind was out of the question for the two former jail-birds. When they returned to Rietvelt after finishing their sentence, they found that everyone shunned them. They were as poor as church mice. Even in summertime during the harvest when labor was often imported from Belgium and Germany, Squire Zeger's instructions were precise and irrevocable: the two friends were not to be taken on, not even temporarily, not for a day or an hour. All the other farmers in the vicinity slavishly followed the Squire's example. The poverty of the two men prevented them from staying in the village and they were not permitted to set foot on the estates. So they had, in desperation, squatted on that plot of Crown land. There they were tolerated, it is true, but the least infraction of the law, they had been warned time and again, would mean another stretch in jail or relegation to the colony for vagabonds at Veenhuizen. How did they live, then?

Well, they were quite cheerful and frank about it—they poached and pilfered and begged. Once a week they jour-neyed to Gorcum and stood in line before the building of the Reformed Consistory, where loaves of bread were given out to the needy. But there it was a question of first come, first served. They were not always on time. Other days they were unceremoniously elbowed out of the way as aliens and inter-lopers by hungry native Gorcummers. For the rest they snared a rabbit or a hare occasionally, they fished in the Linge and in the canals or called at the kitchen doors of the farmhouses and manors in the neighborhood to ask for charity. "There are still some good Christian people left, Pieter!" said Dirk to me when I visited their cabin one day late in the autumn of 1931.

I did not doubt it. But although Dirk was, superficially at least, quite cheerful about it and he and Bernt appeared in the best of health in spite of their getting on in years, I gathered soon enough that theirs was nevertheless a most uncertain and even hazardous existence, ostracized as they were by the community of the respectable, hungry half the time, in constant danger of being evicted, and on top of that at the tender mercies and churlish whims of rustic gendarmes who could act as arbitrarily with them as they pleased, quite sure of being upheld by Squire Zeger in any eventuality connected with the two vagabonds. No, theirs was certainly not an enviable lot. These two men, I ruminated, were expiating heavily that silly crime of lifting Dirk's wife from her pauper's grave and laying her in a decent sepulcher. It is true that through my Uncle Kees' intervention and that of other people their sentence at hard labor had been reduced to a mere six months. But once released from prison they were social outcasts for the rest of their lives. That was stiff punishment! "We are on our good behavior night and day," said Bernt, scraping the ashes from his pipe and shaking his head.

At night, too? Yes, the poaching and most of the fishing had to be done at night, as even the water in the canals, brooks, and rivers was leased and parceled off into private fishing preserves, and woe to the man who trespassed! They had become real night owls, hunted animals, hunting and hunted at the same time, on the alert like watchdogs every step of the way. The nocturnal landscape was as familiar to them as the old road to Gorcum was to the average wayfarer in daylight. They knew every path and hedgerow, every ditch and puddle and nook and cranny, of the neighborhood and where to take shelter at a moment's notice behind clumps of bushes and shrubbery at the approach of footsteps that might always be those of one of the men of the law on his nightly rounds.

Of course, Dirk was saying, on those nocturnal wanderings they frequently passed over Baron Wenselaar's property. They could not avoid it. And they could not help noticing either that a big change had come to the formerly still and solitary mansion, what with all the bustle and activity, the coming and going of people at all hours of the night. In the rear of their hut, from the old hunting course right to the carriage drive of House Wenselaar, extended a stretch of perfectly flat grazing land. On bright nights, by stepping off the wooded plot of the Crown domain they could clearly see the lights of the manor like a row of tiny jewels dancing in the branches of the elms in the avenue. Without going outside they could hear the clatter of the horseshoes and the rattle of carriages and equipages as their ironbound wheels left the dirt road and struck the cobblestoned pavement of the highway.

They always knew when something was going on at the mansion. They had been quite near the place, too, some evenings and seen the guests leave, Count Terwillen, Squire Zeger, Captain Folette, and their ladies. Oh, yes, these people had stepped into their carriages within a few yards, within earshot, of Dirk and Bernt. No, it wasn't that they had been drawn by curiosity. What concern was it of theirs what the ladies and gentlemen at House Wenselaar did do or did not do, or who they were? Indeed it was much safer to keep out of sight, not to be seen by the big folks, not to draw their attention at all. It might have disagreeable consequences to be discovered at night on the property. Suppose Squire Zeger spotted and recognized the two ragged prowlers! Wouldn't he be annoyed and pass word to the gendarmes? You could be sure that he would take steps right the following day. And then it might go hard with them.

No, it was on their way back from inspecting their rabbit snares near Hoog-Vuren one night that they had passed quite close to House Wenselaar. There was a good long rabbit run there near the big swamp. Perhaps I remembered the spot, Dirk asked, near the little ruined church? On their way back, while crossing the avenue of elm trees leading to House Wenselaar, which was full of carriages, the doors of the mansion were suddenly thrown open and a whole company of ladies and gentlemen emerged. They were talking and gesticulating and some of the men were singing. They must have had a gay time. Kind of strange, Dirk thought, how the old Baron could stand all the noise and that so often, he with his pains and moans. Dirk knew him quite well from the days when he himself was the official lamplighter of Rietvelt and repaired watches as a side trade. In those days he went once a week to wind the clocks at House Wenselaar. Yes, he knew the Baron as well as the old house, every nook and corner of it in fact. For there were clocks and pendules in every room. That was one of the Baron's hobbies, clocks, clocks of all kinds, foreign and outlandish freaks, some of them. Dirk remembered quite well. It wasn't so many years ago, after all.

He had been summoned into the Baron's sitting-room, too. Yes, that had happened more than once, either to receive payment for his services or to talk about some clock or other that was running fast or slow, because the Baron was a stickler for accuracy in his clocks. It was an obsession with him. He lay awake at night, he told Dirk, listening to his clocks ticking all over the house, and if one of them, either upstairs or downstairs or in the outer wing of the manor, was so much as a second slow or fast, he would know about it and he would send for the repairman immediately the next morning. The Baron wanted all his clocks to strike the hour at once, all in unison. He tolerated no irregularity in any of them, not by a fraction of a second.

He was rather a hard, exacting man that way, always fussing about those clocks of his. And still, not really a man at all, you might say. There wasn't enough left of him to call him a man. He was a mere bundle of bones with a wrinkled yellow skin wrapped about them. All day and all night he lay there in his chair by the fire, groaning and twisting. Every move cost him untold agony. Sometimes he screamed with the pain and then that wicked foreign woman, the one with the glassy bead-eyes, said Dirk, would come in to rub his legs and to soothe him with her talk. It was pretty hard to imagine how such a man, a wreck of a man really, who was dying a slow death, had suddenly become so fond of company and of gay crowds that he filled his house with them almost every night. It wasn't reasonable.

"But that's not what I wanted to tell you," said Dirk. "The Baron Wenselaar is dead and gone now a long time. What I wanted to tell you about is that winter of the tragedy, now thirteen years ago. It was in November that we began to notice things. Bernt and I came home late one night. Snow had fallen all day and the going was hard. We were walking along the highway when we suddenly heard the sound of hoofbeats behind us. The loose, woolly snow muffled the sound so much that the rider was almost upon us before we could slide off the dike road and hide behind a hedge. Of course," said Dirk, "it was Squire Zeger who rode by there. Who else could it have been? He was the only man who rode horseback in the Land of Arkel. He was going full-gallop as always and was soon out of our sight and hearing. We continued our way home and we built a fire of peat and blocks of wood as soon as we came in, for it was cold. We were getting ready for bed when Bernt says to me: 'Did you hear that?' 'Hear what?' I asked.

" 'There it is again,' he said. And now I heard it, too. 'Sounds like the bridge creaking,' I said. 'Somebody is going by.' 'That's what I thought,' says Bernt. I was talking of the small wooden bridge there over Willem's Vliet" explained Dirk with a wave of the hand.

" 'Who'd be passing at this time of night?' I wondered, thinking that it was perhaps Izak the policeman on our trail, following our footsteps in the snow, or another of the gendarmes. I went to the door and looked out. 'Come here,' I whispered to Bernt, 'come and see who goes there.'

"It was one of those white nights—you know, Pieter, no moon, but a pale shroud of light in the sky. The ground was white with snow. To us two, accustomed as we were to moving around in the dark, everything was as clear as daylight. There was a man going by. And there couldn't be a shred of doubt as to the man's identity. It was Mijnheer van Rietvelt. It was the Squire.

" 'Where can he be going at this hour?' I said to Bernt. 'It must be after two o'clock. He's going in the direction of House Wenselaar.'

" 'He must have forgotten something,' said Bernt, 'for he had just come from there when we saw him passing by on his horse on the highway.'

" 'Don't be foolish,' I said. 'Hasn't he his servants to send if he has forgotten something? Couldn't he wait till tomorrow? Look, he is striking out for the back of the manor. He is avoiding the carriage drive. He's standing still now. He's looking around. He's afraid of being followed. That man is bent on mischief or my name isn't Dirk Mensert,' I said to Bernt. 'Let's see what he is up to!'

"Well, we put on our coats and we went out," Dirk continued. "We made a wide detour while keeping our eyes on the dark figure in the snow. He went, as I said, to the rear of the mansion. With the stick he carried, he struck a blow against a tree and waited a moment. We could see a door open near the kitchen. There was a feeble ray of light for a second and then the Squire disappeared inside. We walked a little nearer to the manor and went right through the orchard, in fact to the back of the house, still giving the place a wide berth, you understand, because I didn't want our footsteps to run too close. And there we stood still for a moment."

"Do you know the Wenselaar manor?" Dirk asked me.

"Only from the outside," I said. "I have never been inside."

"I see," he went on. "You know, then, that there is the old tower which stands to the north of the main building. That's really the oldest part of the place. They say it's the only thing that remains of the fortress that stood there hundreds of years before."

"Yes," I said, "the tower is all that remains of the original castle. The rest was blown up by a band of retreating Spaniards in the year 1584, the year the Prince of Orange was assassinated."

"Was that the year?" asked Dirk. "Yes, I remember now learning at school about it. That was the year when the good Prince was murdered at Delft by Balthazar Gérard. The murderer was sent by the Jesuits, wasn't he, Pieter?"

"No, not by the Jesuits," I said. "He was sent by the King of Spain!"

"Well, that's the same thing," said Dirk. "They were all in cahoots that time to murder us. They got the Prince all right; they shot him, the good man. They say the little children wept in the streets when he died."

"That's true," I said, "and the little birdies didn't sing for a whole year!"

"Is that true?" asked Dirk. "I never heard that about the birds. Did you learn that at school, Pieter? Or are you joking?"

Bernt burst out laughing.

"Now then, about the old tower . . ." Dirk resumed his story.

"You're not going to tell me that it's haunted, I hope," I interrupted him.

"Sure it's haunted." He nodded with a laugh. "All those old places are haunted. It's the ghost of an old lady that is said to be walking around in the Wenselaars' tower at nights. The servants wouldn't go near the place for love or money. They all sleep in those rooms above the stables, two or three hundred yards back of the manor, all of them that is except that flunky called Jacques, who is a Frenchman and who came to this country with that wicked woman when she married the Baron Steeven. He was her bodyguard and confidant. He followed her like a dog. Even when she went shopping in Gorcum he went along and sat on the box of the carriage with the driver. He was around all the time. But of the phantom I never saw any trace—nor anyone else, you may be sure. That's all poppycock, of course, and old wives' tales, stuff to frighten children."

"But it's very useful," spoke up Bernt suddenly, "very useful to have a ghost around when you don't want to be disturbed, isn't it?"

"It certainly is," went on Dirk. "People imagine that the entire tower was deserted, that nobody ever went in there, that it was just an old forgotten ruin. But they are wrong. There are four or five stories in that tower and a stone staircase. There is at least one large room on every story. From the manor itself you can get into the tower through a low gallery that starts at the end of the entrance hall. That takes you to the foot of the staircase. There is a carpet on the steps and every room in the tower is perfectly well furnished. The room on the second story is a huge bedroom. There are fireplaces in every room, and clocks of course.

"That's how I came to know about the place. I went there every week for years to wind those clocks. I had a good look around then, because nobody ever came to disturb me there. The servants would have been scared to come in and the Baron was too crippled to climb the stairs. Once in a while that French lackey would walk in when I was busy with a clock and ask me if I would be long. He would sneak up on me on those thick rugs and stand there before me all at once. Sometimes he startled me, but I was not afraid of him. I was doing my duty and doing it honorably. He needn't be afraid, I used to tell him, that I would carry anything off. Besides, that would have been impossible. Nothing but heavy old furniture in these rooms, Pieter, cupboards as big as this cabin and armored suits and hundreds of swords and flintlocks and pikes on the wall. Quite a collection, just like a museum. I suppose it was worth a lot of money.

"Well," he went on, "as Bernt and I stand there that night in the snow looking at House Wenselaar, just after Squire Zeger has gone inside, what do we see? We see a light passing those narrow slits of windows on the staircase of the tower. We didn't see any human figures. That would be impossible, for those windows are too high in the wall for anyone to reach without a ladder. All we saw was a light and two shadows following each other closely. They did not go higher than the second floor, but on the windows of the rooms on that floor the curtains were drawn closely. So I said to Bernt here: 'There you are! Now we know what is going on. Let's go home. It's not a good place to hang around.'

"I had a feeling right then and there, right from the beginning, I mean, that something dreadful would happen. I could feel the evil of the place. It scared me, I am telling you frankly. 'That wicked woman has our Squire in her power,' I said to Bernt when we got home. 'And over there in House Rietvelt is Lady Davina waiting for her child to be born. God grant that she never discovers what her husband is up to in the dead of night!'

"Of course," said Dirk, holding a warning finger, "it wasn't any business of ours, what the Squire was doing. It would have cost us as much as our lives almost, you might say, to have spoken about what we had seen. If any gossip had come to the ears of the Squire and it had been traced to us, we would have been out of our hut in no time, out on the dike and nowhere to go. The Squire would have seen to that. He has no mercy, and especially not with us. So we kept it strictly to ourselves, what we had seen that night and what we saw the next night. 'It's not profitable to eat cherries with a lord,'" said Dirk, quoting an old Dutch proverb.

"An hour or so after we returned to our cabin, we heard the Squire crossing the bridge. Bernt got up and looked out of the window. 'Yes,' he says, 'there he goes. He will be home in a quarter of an hour, just before the farm hands get up for the milking. He thinks nobody has seen him.' The next night he was out again—the Squire, that is. But that time he came on horseback. He left House Wenselaar and returned there within the hour. He just rode around on the highway to give the other guests the impression that he was going home and then promptly went back by way of the short cut. The two of us were fast asleep when we heard the rubadub of a horse's hoofs on the planks out there.

"The first night we saw him, I figure, he must have gone on foot merely to explore the trail. The second night he knew the short cut sufficiently to go on horseback. That short cut was his secret. At least so he thought. We heard him pass almost every night. Sometimes it was one o'clock, sometimes two, sometimes three, and about an hour later he'd pass by again homeward-bound. That went on right into December.

"And then one night—it was Christmas Eve, I remember it as well as yesterday, although it happened nearly thirteen years ago—there was a big affair at House Wenselaar. The whole yard was filled with sleighs and horses and automobiles and you could hear the bells jingle and jangle on the highway, back and forth, one load of visitors after the other. They stayed late that night, too.

"About two-thirty the Squire passed our hut on horseback and struck out for House Wenselaar by way of the old hunting course. We didn't even look out, we were so used to it. But his passing woke us up and we lay there talking for a while, Bernt and I. About a quarter of an hour went by and we had grown silent when Bernt roused me and said: 'Dirk, there's someone at the bridge, and it isn't the Squire.' Bernt had got up and was standing by the window looking out in the direction of the Willem's Vliet.

"I was out of bed in a jiffy and joined Bernt at the window. I looked. 'Yes, there's someone there,' I said. We opened the door cautiously to have a better look, because the window was covered with a layer of frost. And there, would you believe it? there was a woman. She was going up and down the planks and stamping on them here and there with her foot, as if wanting to assure herself how strong they really were, or rather how weak. Well, they were pretty bad, weather-beaten and rotted. Heaven knows how long that bridge had been there without anybody's ever applying a fresh coat of tar or nailing down those boards properly. It wasn't hard at all for the woman to pry one of them loose, tilt it on its end, and let it plunge into the creek below. We could hear the crash on the ice and the water gurgling through the opening. We stood petrified. What could we do?

" 'Whoever she is,' I said to Bernt, 'she is preparing a deathtrap for the Squire.'

" 'But don't you see who she is?' he says. 'It's a pregnant woman . . . that's the Lady Davina!'

"My breath caught in my throat," went on Dirk. 'Good God,' I said to Bernt, 'Mevrouw van Rietvelt! She knows about it, then, that her husband takes this short cut at night. She knows everything.' What were we to do? I didn't know. We watched her a little longer. She had difficulty in prying a second plank loose. She was tearing frantically at the end. We could hear her groan and gasp as she tugged and heaved with all her might. It was an ice-cold night, too. I think the thermometer hadn't been so low since that year when the Merwede froze over solid.

" 'That woman will hurt herself,' I said to Bernt. 'We had better show ourselves or let ourselves be heard somehow, if only to scare her away. If she keeps on like that she will drop with exhaustion. After she goes we will have to watch for the Squire and stop him. We can't let him kill himself. We'll have to warn him. If he rides as wildly as he usually does, he will go right through those holes and break his neck. We can't have that on our conscience, too.'

"At last she had a second plank loose. A third seemed to come away easily. She looked at the damage she had done and walked off like a person in a trance. We also came nearer and looked at the holes. There were indeed several planks gone, and there was no doubt about it: anyone venturing on that bridge with a horse would surely have an accident. It was growing darker, too. Snow began to fall as we re-entered the cabin. We lit the lamp and sat down to wait for the Squire. He couldn't be long. It was a quarter after three. And sure enough, we may have sat there twenty minutes or so when we heard the stamp of a galloping horse on the old hunting course. We ran to the door and shouted: 'Halt, halt, the bridge is out! Halt, halt!' But the rider did not pay the slightest attention. He heard us, of that I am sure, and he saw us too, for we had run right out into his path. But he just whipped up his horse and went thundering by. The instant he struck the bridge the entire structure collapsed. His horse's feet were caught in the holes and down he went, taking all the planks with him.

"We ran to the water's edge. We could hear the horse struggling in the broken ice. We called out: 'Are you hurt, mijnheer?' But, by God, there was no answer. Bernt ran back for a lantern and we set to work trying to lift the unconscious man to the shore. He was lying head-down in the water.

"We tried to pull him out by the legs but his hands were tangled in the reins and it was hard to loosen them because the horse, which also lay half-submerged in the ice, struck out with its forelegs each time we came near. The animal could not quite raise itself and it was plain from its anxious winnowing and groans that it had suffered serious injury.

Still, we weren't thinking of the beast then, you may be sure, we were only thinking of the man. I stood in the water up to my chest and held up his head so that he wouldn't drown while Bernt cut the straps with a knife. In the end we got him out and laid him on the snow.

"As we put him down I almost tumbled over with surprise. The light of the lantern fell on his face and I saw that it wasn't the Squire at all. It was Count Frans Terwillen from Asperen. He was dead. His forehead was bashed in and my clothes were covered with blood from holding him up. How he got there at Willem's Vliet at that late hour, and why he was riding as if all the hounds of hell were after him, I guess will always remain a mystery. Nothing was brought out about that at the investigations that followed and took all winter and all the next spring.

"But to continue," said Dirk, "about what happened that night before Christmas. Just as I stood there and Bernt crouched on his knees bent over the Count trying to stop the flow of blood from his forehead with chunks of ice, we heard another horse come galloping toward us from the distance. I flew up and started to swing my lantern like a madman. Presently the second rider of that night came into view. And this time it was Squire Zeger. He reined in his horse and stood still.

" 'What's up?' he asked angrily.

" 'The bridge is down, sir, and there has been an accident. Count Terwillen has been killed.'

" 'Who?' he asked as if he did not understand me.

" 'The Count Terwillen, sir,' I repeated. 'His horse fell on the bridge and he was thrown headfirst into the creek.'

"Squire Zeger dismounted. I held the lantern while he looked down on the dead man's face. Then he walked to the bridge and taking the lantern out of my hand, he held it at arm's length to look down into the water.

" 'How did this happen, Mensert?' He turned to me.

" 'Someone removed a few planks out of that bridge an hour ago,' I told him, 'and when the Count came riding up, his horse stumbled and its fall brought all the rest of the structure down.'

" 'You saw that?' he asked. 'I mean you saw someone remove the planks?'

" 'Yes, sir, I saw it. We both saw it,' I said.

" 'Then why didn't you warn the Count?' he asked.

" 'We did try to warn the Count,' I said. 'We tried to stop him. We yelled at him to stop. But he went right on.'

" 'Who removed those planks?' he asked again.

" 'I cannot tell you, sir,' I said.

" 'You cannot tell me? What do you mean? Can't you tell, or won't you tell?' He stood right in front of me and held the lantern almost in my face.

" 'I can't tell, sir,' I said.

" 'You mean you do not know the identity of the person who removed the planks?'

" 'I cannot say at present,' I replied. 'Please excuse me, I am too upset.'

" 'Idiot, god-damned fool that you are!' he yelled at me. 'Don't think that we won't be able to make you jailbirds talk! Don't think that, you scoundrel!' He advanced on me threateningly and held his fist under my nose. 'What were you two doing around here at this hour anyway? I must say it looks very suspicious. A bridge is tampered with, a gentleman is killed, and two well-known criminals are caught on the spot, one of them with a knife in his hand.' He pointed to Bernt, who had just picked up the knife with which he had cut the horse's reins. 'What more do we need?' said the Squire. 'The case is as clear as crystal.'

" 'But we live here, sir,' I said to the Squire. 'We were not here illegitimately.'

" 'What do you mean, you live here?' he snapped at me.

" 'We live in that cabin back here, that cabin in the woods over there,' I told him.

"He took a look around and then, coming close to me again with the lantern in hand, he asked: 'How long have you been there?'

" 'Several years, sir,' I told him.

" 'Several years, eh? Were you here all this winter, too?'

" 'Of course,' I said. 'That's where we live. That's how

we came to be witnesses of what happened here this night and . . .'

"He did not let me finish. 'You have no right to live here!' he cried. 'It's royal preserve, that piece of woodland.'

" 'I know, sir,' I said. 'We have no right to live anywhere, really, but we thought seeing that Her Majesty probably doesn't mind if two of her poor subjects . . .'

" 'Shut your mouth,' he said. 'You have no decisions to make. You are trespassing. We will see about that. This time, I think, we'll get rid of you two packs of vermin for good. I think we have you properly now, murder and trespassing. Stay with the body,' he told me, 'till I fetch help.'

"He mounted his horse and rode off. There we were in a fine fix. I said to Bernt: 'We will have to tell them who tampered with the boards. I didn't dare tell the Squire that it was his own wife. He wouldn't have believed me. He might have killed me in his anger.'

"We could still hear the horse groaning in the ice and making efforts to raise itself, and we were shivering with the cold. My clothes froze as stiff as boards on my body. Pretty soon the Squire came back with Izak, the policeman, the manager of the Rietvelt estate, and several of the farm hands. They loaded the body on a cart and Izak shot the horse, and then he told Bernt and me to follow him. When we came to Rietvelt village he locked us up in the jail of the municipal building. He told us we were held at the disposal of the royal procurator, but he didn't say a word more. And then we really started to shiver with the cold in our wet clothes, and shiver for other reasons, too.

"Well, to come to the end of the story, Pieter," said Dirk, "we weren't kept in jail very long. 'The Lord remembereth them that sit in darkness.' " Dirk piously lifted his cap as he quoted from Holy Writ, and Bernt lifted his.

"The second night after the accident the Lady Davina died in giving birth to a son. She was in horrible pains, it seems, for many hours and they got all the doctors of the neighborhood, including the old Jewish doctor from Gorcum, the man with the strange name."

"Dr. Mendoza," I said.

"Yes, Dr. Mendoza," answered Dirk. "He's the greatest maternity doctor in the Land of Arkel. He never lost a baby in all his years and he brought thousands into the world. He saw at once that Lady Davina's pains were not normal birth pangs, that she had done something or other, inadvertently or otherwise, to bring on the labor. He talked with her a long time and he saved the child. She herself refused to be saved, I understand. When she saw her husband return that night and she inquired what the noise of the shot was she had heard, it appears the Squire told her that Terwillen had been injured in an accident at the Willem's Vliet bridge. She asked the Squire if he was dead and when the Squire nodded, she just turned her head to the wall and said: 'I killed him!'

"I don't think," went on Dirk, "that she really wanted to kill anyone. She just wanted to teach her husband a good lesson. But when she learned that her act at the bridge had cost another man his life, she was so shocked that she lost the strength and the courage to go on living. In fact that is what she told Dr. Mendoza. She told him everything, how she had watched her husband go to Wenselaar House night after night and how she had decided to take revenge, how she found the bridge over which he rode every night and how she had loosened the planks and prepared a deathtrap for her husband.

"That saved us, too, that she told the Doctor all this. For the Doctor knew that we were held on suspicion and he came to the jail himself the next morning early to set us free. He put us in his carriage and drove us back to our cabin. On the way he asked us some questions and we told him what we had seen. We did not have to testify in any of the investigations. The Doctor's word was enough. But, as I said before, they never found out what Count Terwillen was doing there that night riding like a fury. Nobody ever found out where he came from or where he was going. I guess that's the Squire's secret, don't you think so, Pieter?"

There is not much to tell about Zeger van Rietvelt and

what there is to say yet about him will of a necessity be of a rather unpleasant nature. The end of him, as a collaborator of the enemies of our fatherland and a purveyor of victims to the Gestapo, is the saddest episode in his career. That he came to his treasonable acts is inexcusable, but it lay in the fatality of things and becomes understandable when the circumstances are taken into consideration. I will not be his judge here, for we cannot know the secret courses of the human mind.

The death of his young wife left no deep or lasting impression on Zeger's mind. Predictions that the shock of it and the consciousness of contributory guilt in the matter would cause the Squire to reconsider his conduct, fill him with remorse, and bring him to mend his ways were not fulfilled. Sometimes a violent experience serves as a turning-point in people's lives, as an awakening and an incentive to take stock before continuing the journey of life. But that did not happen in Zeger's case. Davina's death was more of an annoying interruption in the ordinary course of affairs on the estate, it seems, than a cause of spiritual disquiet and sorrow to him. It is true he went to church a couple of Sundays to hear Dr. Satyn, but that did not last. He went into mourning, too. The livery of the house servants was changed from green to black and the carriage horses wore a ribbon of black crape on their headgear, but that was only for a year. Long before the year was over, as a matter of fact only a few weeks after Davina's funeral, he resumed his visits to House Wenselaar and to the beautiful Baroness.

Davina was forgotten. It can be said perhaps that they had not been long enough together for an enduring affection to grow up between them, but the assumption that they had been lovers virtually from childhood, which was the consideration alleged by Davina's parents in giving their consent to an early marriage, was refuted almost from the start by the way in which Zeger neglected his cousin. Her death and Zeger's fribbling behavior after her death showed conclusively that their union had been one of convenience, an affair of family interests to which Davina was sacrificed and which, insofar as Zeger was concerned, meant little more than a profitable business deal. Even her father and mother were shocked to learn upon visiting her tomb in the churchyard of Arkel a year after her death that her husband had not once returned to the grave since the funeral, that it remained unadorned, and that no funds had been set aside for its upkeep.

When old Baron Wenselaar died in the early spring of 1921 and his wife, the enchantress Marie, shortly thereupon gave up residence on the estate and moved to Brussels in the company of her keen-eyed French valet, Zeger seems to have been thrown off his balance for a moment. Whether the rumor is true or not, that Zeger had offered marriage to the lady and also that he had been accepted, and what's more, that the banns had already been published, I cannot say for certain. There is no doubt, however, that for a time he acted as a badly disappointed and deeply injured man. He stormed and raved to anyone who would listen to his furious denunciations of the departed couple that he would overtake them, that he would administer to the treacherous Frenchman the treatment he deserved, mutilate him properly, and bring back the Baroness dead or alive. He did indeed make inquiries as to which road they had taken, in what hotels they had stopped on their way to Belgium, where precisely they were living, and several times seemed actually on the verge of starting out after them.

People said they thought he was losing his mind, so violent and sinister a mien he had in those days. It was his mother, who had been apprised of the crisis in her son's life by the estate manager, who hastened to Rietvelt from The Hague and who succeeded in bringing her son back to his senses. She convinced him that he had no claims on the Baroness, that she wasn't worth troubling about in the first place and that she had all along used him as a stopgap and a plaything while waiting for her husband to die and inherit his wealth for the sake of her French lover, from whom she had never been separated. Zeger saw the whole depth and length of the woman's intrigue at last and gradually recovered his composure.

On his mother's suggestion he came to reside in The Hague with her, for the second time in seven years, but as on the former occasion he soon tired of life in the Residence. He set out for a long trip that took him as far as the Indies and the scenes of his father's military exploits in Achin. When he returned after a year he purchased the estate of Count Terwillen near Asperen village, had the house renovated, and moved in. He had had enough of Rietvelt manor, he said; he never wanted to see the place again. If he had been able to acquire House Wenselaar also, he added, he would have burned it to the ground and blotted out its memory.

In Asperen he took up his dead friend's hobby of farming and raising dray horses for the Belgian market, but he also became interested in various industrial undertakings in the neighborhood of Gorcum, particularly in an old iron foundry, the dilapidated condition of which, both physically and financially, seemed to indicate its early collapse. With Zeger's investments, the factory was restored and expanded into a modern steel plant. A huge sawmill was installed on one side of the steel mill and on the other a cement factory that stretched the whole length of the road from Gorcum to Arkel. A copper-refining plant came next. Then a sugar refinery, which after that of Souchez in France is one of the largest in the world. The green slopes of the River Linge disappeared under the dust and ashes of cement-grinders and coke ovens. Gorcum was being industrialized at last after being an agricultural center since the tenth century. Coming events were beginning to cast their shadows before them.

Under the false slogan of freedom of enterprise—false because it is a mere screen behind which men struggle for the power to dominate and exploit—capitalist industrialism, penetrating into the most obscure corners of Europe, began drawing those places and the peoples therein along with the rest of the Continent toward the next military cataclysm, which was to follow as naturally and ineluctably in the wake of unbridled industrial anarchy as night follows day. Zeger now flew over the roads in a low-crouching Vauxhall car that had been specially built for him by a

British firm on the model of those swift machines that patrolled the English and Scottish coastal regions during World War I.

He was the chief animater, the spirit and the driving power, behind the industrial expansion in the district. He was weary, he said, satiated up to his neck with the dullness and the self-satisfied smugness and drowsiness of the inhabitants of the Land of Arkel. Their archaic manners and lack of initiative and imagination, their resignation and slowness, made his gorge rise whenever he looked out of the window. Gorcum? Zeger would exclaim. Gorcum, that was just a nice little antique shop, full of romantic and sentimental interests, no doubt, but ages and eons behind the times. The people who lived in that shop were mummies and museum pieces. Were these the sons of Jan Pieterszoon Coen, the conqueror of Java and of the Water Beggars, those heroic buccaneers of the seventeenth century? Why, the Gorcummers had not changed their mode of life since the days of Waterloo, while the rest of the world forged ahead and prospered. They were asleep, like Rip Van Winkle. They were in a rut of crushing monotony, scarcely aware they were alive at all.

How did they imagine Holland had once become a Great Power, anyway, sweeping all enemies before her from the seven seas and founding a huge colonial empire? Did they think all this was achieved by dreaming? Did our fathers perhaps sit with their hands in their laps listening to dull fundamentalist sermons when riches were to be garnered, when foreign lands were to be conquered and enemies to be driven out? No, they buckled their belts and ventured forth to face the storm and all adversaries. They were not old wives, but men. They went through with it, whatever they undertook, come hell and high water, as that certain merchant of Amsterdam once told the States General who reproached him with delivering gunpowder to the Spanish enemy. "I will sail my ships through a hell filled with devils, Your High Mightinesses, if there is a chance of profit in it." That's what he told them! Wasn't that the spirit that made Holland great?

Well, he, Zeger, he was going to bring that spirit back.

He was going to put some new ideas into the heads of those rustic and stolid Gorcummers and Arkelers. He was going to wake them up. He was going to change and revolutionize their lackadaisical mode of life by showing them enterprise and daring and how to take risks. He remembered Ary Brandt at the Gymnasium insisting that in the long run the economic situation controlled all the other situations, religious, intellectual, social, romantic, and sentimental. That was why he was going to reform the Land of Arkel economically. He would start by teaching the people efficiency. He liked that word, which he had picked up in America and for which there is, thank heaven, no precise equivalent in the Dutch language. When he pronounced it, *effeeciencee*, he clenched and shook his fists so that the burghers of Rietvelt and Asperen thought he was talking of some newly discovered enemy. Effeeciencee, wasn't that another variety of those monstrous Bolsheveekee or Fasjeestee? They would nod their heads slowly when they heard Zeger talk about efficiency, and then cautiously take a step backward from the gesticulating young Squire and say that his grandfather, old Baron Otto, was just like that, always ready to fight.

Yes, Zeger was out to change the Land of Arkel from top to bottom and from one end to the other. Using a word of Jan Steen, who put some live geese into a huge pot of boiling hops in his brewery one dull day in order to hear them cackle and scream, the young Squire said frequently that he, like the great painter, would "bring a bit of liveliness into the brewery." Just wait and see!

And if the truth is told, he did change the face of things. It was he who prevailed upon the Ministry of Defense to withdraw the ancient restrictions that forbade within a five-kilometer circumference of Gorcum the erection of any building or structure that would offer a visible target to an approaching enemy. Gorcum had walls, a triple set of them; let the enemy's artillery hit them, if it could, but let nothing else be touched. That was the rule drawn up toward the close of the Eighty Years' War, around the year 1638, I think. Like the walls, that rule still stood solidly, braving the centuries. As an invitation to the dance it had been followed with scrupulous monotony by Prussians, Frenchmen, and Spaniards, each in their day, as testified the façades of many buildings that were pockmarked with cannon balls.

Many attempts had been made in the course of time to change the mind of the Dutch High Command on the subject of the building regulations, but to no avail. These gentlemen demanded a line they could defend, or rather that Napoleon or William the Silent could have defended. They had not yet learned to think of offense and defense in terms of airplanes and tanks which would ignore their ridges and earthwork bastions. Zeger had no difficulty in The Hague. His name opened every door. Before the third gin and bitters the Minister of Defense scratched his head and saw the light. His Excellency, in fact, had long since recognized the uselessness, the archaic folly, of that old regulation. He would promptly remedy the situation, that went without saying. In the mechanized wars that announced themselves more distinctly every day, one might as well build outside as inside the town walls. What difference did it make, ha, ha?

Zeger erected a six-story office building of steel and concrete and glass, a triumph of the modern Dutch school of architecture. It stood right outside the Arkel Gate on a plot of land that formerly belonged to Hein Dermout. There was an elevator in it, and from the top story, which Zeger turned into his private office, he could see the Merwede River in the distance and he could follow the Linge River up its course as far as Arkel village. The buildings of the steel plant, the sawmill, the cement factory, and the sugar refinery as far as the eye could reach lay at his feet as it were. In that building all his multifarious interests, agricultural as well as industrial, were brought under one roof.

But that was not all. Zeger made a trip to London and sold a block of shares in his steel plant to a British armament trust. Then he went to Berlin and to Essen on the Ruhr and did the same there. That was international cooperation for you, he used to say laughingly to his friends at the club, where he appeared regularly around five in the afternoon for an apéritif and a rubber of whist before speeding out to Asperen for dinner. Yes, that was the brotherhood of man cemented by steel, and Holland in a perfect humanitarian role of intermediary between England and Germany!

And the old shipyard on the Merwede River, that chaotic, sprawling collection of black, weather-beaten wooden sheds and rain-sodden shanties about a mile out of town in the direction of Dordt, where since time immemorial they had hammered together punts and buoys and smacks and flat-bottomed luggers and other light craft of that sort for the fishing and commercial trade, that old tumbledown eyesore of a place, who would believe it? Zeger acquired that, too. Now, what in heaven's name did he want with that? Hadn't he enough as it was to keep him occupied? What else had that restless man up his sleeve, and where was he going to stop? Foolish questions these, really, insofar as Zeger was concerned, who did not even bother to answer them. He was forging ahead, always on the go, always unpredictable, and always on the lookout for new enterprises and new conquests like another Alexander or Caesar.

Nobody could tell where Zeger would stop. Just as he had done in the case of the dilapidated old iron foundry, he changed and overhauled and renovated everything at the wharf. He rased the old structures, put up modern buildings and hangars, and installed amazingly intricate and expensive machinery, which he imported from abroad. There were some engines, I am told, as big as locomotives and of a shape and a design such as no one in Gorcum had ever seen. In a year—no, in far less time, in six months perhaps— the site of the old shipyard was unrecognizable. The municipality ran a fine broad concrete road to the new plant to replace the old muddy path that zigzagged along the outside foot of the dike and was inundated half the time when the tide was high. And then Zeger began to turn out trawlers and tugs and turbine boats.

His first big order came from the Chinese Government, for a set of enormous dredges to clear the Yalu River of sandbanks and other obstructions. Zeger's men themselves

hauled those huge dredging machines down the Merwede
and Meuse rivers to Rotterdam and then from the Hook
of Holland clear around the world, through the English
Channel and the Gulf of Biscay, around the Cape of Good
Hope—for the machines were too broad for the Suez
Canal—all the way to China. That was a feat of engineering and navigation of the first magnitude and for a long
time was the talk of the industrial world in both England
and Germany. Holland was coming back, they said, yes,
and leading the way. And in China it was Zeger's men, too,
who did the work of dredging. It was said Zeger's contract
with the Chinese Government ran into tens of millions of
gulden. And even before the job was finished there was a
new contract with the Soviet Government for dredges to
clear the navigation of the Lower Volga and then with the
Government of the Argentine to deepen the harbor of
Buenos Aires.

What a time that was! Gorcum became known all over
the world. How ridiculously old-fashioned now seemed the
sleepy little town of six years before where only the soft-
sweet tinkle of Sint Jan's carillon broke the stillness of
morning! Now factory whistles screamed and you could
hear their shrill wail all over the Land of Arkel. And what
bustle and animation in the streets! Busses were running in
and out to the neighboring villages and along the rural
dikes to the new industries. Zeger certainly had rejuvenated
the district. His name was on everybody's lips. He was again
to all intents and purposes the Lord of Arkel, like those
forefathers of his who sleep in their marble tombs in the
Great Church. Big electric arc lamps hanging from steel
cables that stretched from roof to roof across the principal
streets had replaced the old gas lampposts. There were
scores of new shops, yes, and a department store, owned
by the general holding company of which Zeger was president. There was scarcely an undertaking of any consequence
in Gorcum or in the Land of Arkel in which Zeger did not
have a finger, or more often, a whole hand.

The brand-new milk pasteurization plant on the High
Street with its spotlessly white tiled floors and walls, and

the luxurious restaurant and pastry shop next door, which attracted so many customers—they were his. The new rural credit bank and the insurance company? It was Zeger who set them up in business. The Excelsior Grocery Corporation, of which one branch shop was soon opened in every quarter of the town and in a dozen of the villages of the neighborhood, that was Zeger's idea and his property. He hit upon the idea one day; a month later the grocery corporation began to function. It was always that way with Zeger. With that man execution followed the conception of a plan in a flash. He did not hold long-drawn-out conferences and confabulations with his associates, nor did he know anything about a policy of caution and watchful waiting. It was either yes or no with Zeger and no hesitations whatever. If an opportunity presented itself, he seized it. More often he created the opportunity, too, for his keen instinct for business was never asleep. One thing followed the other as naturally as elephants on parade.

Zeger endowed the municipal hospital with a hundred beds and equipped the old institution, which dated from the Middle Ages and which some still called by its medieval name of Pesthuis, with a modern surgery. This, incidentally, had become quite necessary because of the accidents that occurred at the various factories. There were now more accidents in a month than there were formerly in ten years. The two new surgeons from Amsterdam were Zeger's appointees. They were brilliant young men who knew what to do when a badly mangled body from one of the plants was rushed into town. They were not at all like the bonesetters and accoucheurs who had hitherto looked after the health of the community in their easy-going, fatherly way.

Zeger was elected to the board of regents of the orphan asylum. He had his representatives in the Town Council, not official of course, but men devoted to his interests. He even had an observer in the Consistory of the State Church. Zeger was kept au courant with everything that went on.

He insisted on receiving a regular report on the sermons that were preached, after one of the ministers held forth one Sunday on the case of Nebuchadnezzar, the Chaldean

monarch standing on the roof of his palace surveying his
wealth and exclaiming pridefully: "This is Babylon the
great that I have built," and then told how the kingdom
was taken away from him and he, the King, lost his mind
and went among the beasts of the field crawling on all fours
and eating grass like them for seven long years. The minister, it is true, had not once pronounced Zeger's name, but
to these who had ears to hear the allusion to an empire-
builder vaunting his power and wealth was obvious enough.
That sermon had been the talk of the town for weeks on
end. Now such a minister was a troublemaker or a potential
troublemaker of the first water. Such a man would, if allowed to proceed in that vein, disturb the wholesome, amicable relationship between capital and labor that Zeger
prided himself on having established and which he considered the very basis of his success. He was not going to
tolerate the surreptitious dissemination of class-war doctrines in the community, not even in sermons by ministers
of the State Church, who, he remarked, ought to know
better in the first place and who ought to know for one
thing on which side their bread was buttered. Zeger demanded a report on the man's sermons and succeeded in
having the Consistory warn the Pastor to watch his step.

He wanted reports on church attendance, too. He liked
to hear that there was a good attendance at the services.
It is true he never set foot in church himself. He didn't
care, he said, for a religion that based itself on the doings
of dishonest Jewish cattle-dealers in the far-off land of
Canaan. But he liked it nevertheless when it was reported
of certain of his employees that they were assiduous church-
goers. Such men could count on his protection and favors.
Zeger kept an eye on everything, not only on his vast industrial enterprises and on the movement of the world's markets, but on such seemingly insignificant details as the moral
health of the community.

The influx of strangers into town and county had begun
to change the habits of the citizenry. There were theatrical
performances, a night club, if you please, several cafés
chantants where artists from Amsterdam entertained with

off-color songs and salacious dancing. People were staying up later than formerly, walking in the streets, looking at the brilliantly lit shops and eating meals at midnight in the restaurants. There were all kinds of stories going the round about young folks, apprentices at the factories and soldiers and shopgirls and maidservants, wandering out into the dark, into the shrubberies along the river's edge and there carrying on shamelessly. Zeger financed the establishment of a so-called Midnight Missionary Society, which sent out men armed with flashlights to spy out the dark corners in the environs and to lay charges of harlotry against the girls if they were caught in the act. Zeger was not going to have any laxity of morals in his domains. That was not the way our fathers had become, etcetera, etcetera, etcetera. The fathers were Zeger's models, or rather he made them the models, whose conduct, as he imagined it, was to be emulated in every respect.

Yes, Gorcum had become a different place and the envy of many another town in Holland twice its size. Where else was there such a building craze and such a bustle? Who, do you think, built those new settlements, those clusters of villas and long lanes of charming cottages outside the town walls? Each house had enough land for a flower garden and a vegetable plot. Beauty was combined with utilitarianism. And plenty of fresh air! Wasn't it Zeger, too, who wanted to tear down the old gray schoolhouses in town, including the Gymnasium, and rebuild them outside the town walls in the new quarters, right in the open with big playgrounds around them for the children? Is it surprising that in addition to being the richest man in the realm next to the Sovereign he was also the most popular for miles and miles around?

People were earning money by the fistful. The town was full of strangers: workers, technicians, engineers, buyers, clerks. One even heard foreign languages spoken in the streets, in the taverns, and in the moving-picture show that Zeger brought to the old lecture and music hall after tearing out the antiquated interior and enlarging its seating capacity with a gallery of comfortable leather seats in the place of the old benches. Room had to be found for all these new-comers. The three or four old hotels were wholly inade-quate to take care of the men and their families who milled around in the narrow streets, giving the town the perpetual atmosphere of a holiday. Zeger built a hotel, a modern establishment with bathrooms and a banquet hall and all the modern appurtenances. But some of the most respectable old houses, too, the fine old mansions on the High Street, were subdivided into apartments or were turned into room-ing houses and pensions. Some of the oldest families did not turn up their noses at making a little money by taking a paying guest or two.

It was indeed an era of prosperity that had dawned, and it was all due—nobody would deny that—to Zeger's initia-tive, to his dynamic spirit of enterprise. He was really a remarkable man, a man of genius, you might almost say. Such a man by rights ought to sit in the parliament, be one of the framers of the laws of the country, a man who had made a success of his own business and who had shown that he knew how to tackle affairs. A man with practical sense, not one of your politicians or lawyers, or ideologists and dreamers who imagine that the moon is made of green cheese and who think that the rainbow's end can be reached merely by talking and debating. Would Zeger represent the parliamentary constituency of Gorcum, which comprised not only the town but the Land of Arkel and the Land of Altena across the Merwede in Brabant Province as well, and in addition some extensive polders in Gelderland Province?

He could have the position for the asking. Nobody would have dared to oppose his candidacy except perhaps some no-account socialist or grumbler. A nonpartisan committee, or rather a committee composed of representatives of all the major parties, came to offer him the post. He was urged to stand at the next general election on a forthright nonpar-tisan business platform and to work in the parliament for a business administration for the whole country to take the place of the old party system with its sectional interests and fractionalism. Oughtn't a country to be united? Shouldn't all citizens have a common ideal and common aspirations? Their interests were identical, were they not? Then why quarrel and debate and argue and vote and disturb the rhythm, the even tenor of things, by holding elections every so often that frequently turned into occasions for bitter recriminations and strife and disunity? Zeger took the request under advisement. At the same time he allowed the delegation to carry away the impression that he was not averse to political honors.

He was then nearing forty, a handsome man who still had that head of silken pale-yellow hair which fell in a shock on his forehead and which he shook out of his eyes by a curt, instinctive gesture. He was gracious of manners, although a little brusque and short-spoken at times when in the midst of a business deal or when someone or something contravened his plans. He ruled his little empire with a gloved hand, but in that glove was a fist of iron, and everybody knew it. It was not safe to contradict or to go counter to the ideas of the Squire of Rietvelt. He brooked no interference. He was the nobleman to his finger tips, courteous, well-spoken, generous, and pleasant. But there always remained something in Zeger of the spoiled rich man's child. He sulked and scowled when things did not go his way or when he encountered opposition.

He not only sulked, but he grew petulant and fell into tantrums of rage. He roared and raged and stamped his feet and beat the table and frequently, in an access of fury, smashed whatever object lay nearest at hand. At such moments he was very much like some overgrown pouting and pampered child, overfed on a diet of cake, whose every whim has always been indulged and to whom suddenly a sugarplum or a new toy is denied. For days on end he would sulk along, taciturn and palefaced, unapproachable, nourishing his grudge, flying off in a new rage at the slightest incident, taking everything in ill part and growling or shouting his orders to servants and employees in a rude voice, hoarse with pent-up anger. Then it was the old Zeger who had come back again, the insufferable snob of school days, sudden and quick in quarrel, heedless of the sensibilities of others and downright contemptuous of the lesser breeds in his class. These were the traits in his character which had kept him a friendless individual all his years.

Of course there were plenty who courted his favors, who fawned upon the mighty man, who worshiped at his feet and willingly submitted to every sort of indignity so long as the master had privileges and sinecures to dispense, sycophants, flatterers and lip servers who received his every word as a pearl of wisdom, who laughed in an exaggerated way at his jokes and quips. But to say that there was a single man or woman who loved Zeger for his own sake would be an untruth, sad as it is. Time had not tempered his soul with the slightest admixture of tolerance. He was harsh, imperious, unfeeling, and but seldom relaxed in a gentle smile. It is true that nobody but the irrepressible Ary Brandt had ever ventured to point out the evil traits of his character or remonstrate with him for his haughty and callous behavior toward others. He had had his own way from his childhood days, always pampered, always a child of fortune, his every command obeyed, his every fancy and caprice satisfied. There was something forbidding in his nature, something frigid and unbending that repelled a friendly, heart-to-heart approach. And it was one of those tantrums into which he flew occasionally that was the cause of his downfall.

While he plunged head over heels into all sorts of business ventures, Zeger was also very much preoccupied with something quite apart from that. He fell in love. It would perhaps be more appropriate to say that his eyes fell on a certain girl and that her appearance pleased him so much that he wanted her. That would indeed be fitter, for no more than Zeger was himself loved by man or woman was he capable of truly loving anyone else. He saw the girl and, Scripturally speaking, lusted after her. He wanted her the instant he saw her. And what Zeger wanted he usually got, whether it was a fine horse, a factory, or a beautiful woman to amuse him. She lived in the village of Asperen, where also stood the mansion that had belonged to Count Terwillen and which Zeger now owned and occupied.

He noticed her one morning in the late summer of 1933

as he drove by in his sports car. She was hanging some washing on the line by the side of a cottage that stood at a sharp bend in the road where it turns into the highway that goes from Asperen to Gorcum. She looked up for an instant from her work at the passing automobile. He was pulling on his gloves, and slowed down somewhat at the bend of the road. He was driving himself, as he generally did in the morning, and the chauffeur sat in the back of the tonneau. The hood of the car was folded back, for it was a brilliant morning. The air was soft and yet fresh and laden with the perfume of hayfields and clover and cornflowers. Zeger glanced back at the girl, but she had resumed her work and paid no further attention. He called back over his shoulder: "Who is that girl?" The chauffeur said she was the daughter of a small farmer, a man Karel Bouman by name, one of Zeger's tenants.

"Bouman?" Zeger called back. "That little hunchbacked runt, you mean?"

"Yes," answered the chauffeur, "that's her father. Her name is Martha."

"Martha? It's a marvel what jewels lie hidden in these manure piles of villages," said Zeger. "Martha, eh? Well, well!"

He did not continue the conversation, but all day the girl's eyes were before him, and in the evening he slowed his car again and drove by the cottage at a snail's pace, looking into the yard and into the windows, but without catching sight of her. And so it went every day, in the morning and at night, Zeger slowing down to a mere crawl, trying to catch a glimpse of Martha.

Zeger's conduct must have been quite embarrassing to the girl and her parents, who could not help noticing the Squire's sudden and ostentatious interest in their house and farmyard. They were simple and humble folk, rather shy, slow of speech and self-effacing by nature and circumstances, but not so backward as not to be aware which of the occupants of their cottage occasioned the Squire's exaggerated attentions. They knew their daughter Martha was beautiful, that she had the kind of warm and exotic beauty which so

strangely stirs the blood and the imagination of the phlegmatic Dutch. They knew it so well that they had kept
Martha at home in Asperen and had not sent her into
service in town as was done in the case of so many girls of
her station in life.

The Boumans were Dutch and yet, in a sense, they were
not Dutch at all. Both husband and wife were of Spanish
descent. And not only they, but nearly all the inhabitants of
that village of Asperen, were of indubitable alien origin. It
should perhaps not come as a surprise to the student of history to encounter foreigners or persons of foreign descent
in a country that for centuries has been a haven of refuge
to the persecuted and proscribed of other lands, and I would
not mention the matter here if it were not that the case of
the people of Asperen was indeed exceptional and that it
goes a long way toward explaining Zeger's infatuation for
the girl Martha Bouman. For whereas the others, Spanish
Jews, Bohemian Hussites, French Huguenots, English Puri-
tans, Portuguese Catholics, and so many other refugees, were
gradually assimilated and were in the course of time completely integrated in the body social, leaving hardly a trace
of distinctive corporate existence, these villagers of Asperen
still lived, to all intents and purposes, in a little world apart.
They constituted a block of strangers in the midst of the
well-nigh homogeneous ethnical population in our district
and in the kingdom as a whole. If it were permissible, one
might be tempted to speak of a tiny island of Hispanidad in
a human sea of Dutchmen.

They were strangers, not strangers in speech, in manners,
or in religion; nor were they, of course, in the least discriminated against insofar as civic rights were concerned.
The second-rate citizen simply does not exist in a civilized
country like Holland. They were strangers in looks, in their
physiognomy, and in the way they kept themselves apart
from others. Asperen was a little ghetto. There was something outlandish, too, something exceptional and even startling I always thought, in the dress they affected, particularly
in the brilliant hues of the costumes of their womenfolk,
which contrasted so sharply with the sober, somber, and

almost mournful tone of the rural dress in general vogue in our parts. An Asperenaar and especially a woman from Asperen was always recognized as such in the streets of Gorcum, at the market, and in popular assemblies. Their faces gave them away.

Some held contemptuously that the people of Asperen were mere gypsies who had strayed our way from the Hungarian plain and who upon seeing that our land was good had settled down to an agricultural mode of life after wandering back and forth over the length and breadth of Europe for ages making their living as tinkers and horse-traders and from whatever they could gain by pilfering and robbery. But that was a mistaken notion, and a slanderous one to boot. The Asperenaars were not gypsies, they were pure Castilians. Their descent had been traced and their origin scientifically established by reputable historians, one of them being H. A. van Gogh, a nephew of Vincent the painter, and another, a seventeenth-century scholar, the famous Abraham Kemp, to name but two of the erudite who have pored over the Asperen people's antiquarian lore and who have extracted some readable, illuminating books from the interminable rubbish heaps of manuscripts on deposit in the Dutch museums.

How did they, then, the ancestors of these Asperenaars, originating as they did in the sun-drenched fields of the Tierra di Campos in the heart of Castile, ever come to take up their abode in an unfriendly water-soaked polder in an obscure nook of Holland? Was it by choice? And how did they come to do this at a time when Holland and their country, Spain, were locked in a desperate, ferocious struggle in which no quarter was either given or asked? For it was in the course of the Eighty Years' War that they made the change, and they made it voluntarily, not by any means as refugees or outcasts or as stateless wanderers.

Here is how events came to pass. In the fateful year 1572 there lay in Asperen a small Spanish garrison. It was probably a mere detachment of the larger force stationed in Gorcum, which was strongly held by the Duke of Alva, being a fortress city and the key to a vast populous area. Gorcum, after Brielle and Dordt, was one of the first towns to throw off the Spanish yoke and come out for the Prince of Orange. The Calvinists rose against the Spanish garrison, massacred the troops to the last man, stripped the churches and monasteries of the paraphernalia of the Roman Catholic cult, and dealt very harshly with the clergy. They imprisoned the parish priest, one Leonhardus Veghel, a man known for his piety and learning, and fifteen of his associates, clerks and monks, and, with sadistic joy, forced the nuns into marriage with some of the most disreputable characters of the town. Upon the demand of Lumey, Scigneur of Treslong, one of the patriot commanders, a man with a reputation for savage cruelty, the captured clerics of Gorcum were shipped to Brielle, where upon their refusal to abjure the mass, they were done to death in an unspeakably brutal manner. These fifteen or sixteen clerics were canonized in the course of time and are known in the annals of the Roman Catholic Church as the Martyrs of Gorcum. To this day pilgrimages to their common grave in Brielle are undertaken by the faithful.

Other monks were massacred on the spot in Gorcum, in spite of the earnest remonstrances of the Prince of Orange. As a boy I was present, or at least I came running in a hurry, when workmen in the course of laying down the pipes and tubes for the new lighting system by gas were reported to have come upon a tunnel in the neighborhood of the former cloister of the Minor Brothers and, following the tunnel, upon a huge iron door that was bolted and locked. Broken down, the door revealed a stone stairway on which lay the skeletons of some seventy men. These bones were subsequently identified by crucifixes and rosaries and some altar vessels as those of the inmates of the monastery to which the staircase in question gave access. The tunnel itself had been used by the monks as a passage from their cloister to the Great Church. Whether these men had taken refuge on the subterranean stairs while the Calvinist mob ransacked and looted their building or whether, as seems more likely when regard is given to the bitter temper of the sectaries, they were purposely locked up in their dungeon to perish there, could not and cannot be ascertained.

From Gorcum the revolt and the anti-Catholic fury soon
spread to the neighborhood. The Geuzen, or Beggars, who
were the partisans of that day, gathered before Asperen,
which they knew to be one of the villages where the
Spaniards were entrenched. They were on the point of going
over to the assault when something occurred that gave an
entirely new and unexpected complex on the situation. A
citizen of Gorcum by the name of Teunis Vermeer, who was
the leader of the band of local patriots, decided to recon-
noiter the village before launching the attack. I have the
story from his faraway descendant, also a Teunis Vermeer,
who like his ancestor was a printer and book-publisher in
our community and who allowed me to examine the chronicle
of his forefather's exploits as it was written in the front
pages of the family's Staten Bible.

Teunis the elder entered the village to spy out the lay
of things and to find out the exact spot in which the Spaniards had concentrated their forces. Once inside Asperen, he
fell in with some patriots who informed him that the commander of the troops, the Spanish Captain Don Fernando
di Teruel, had just been converted to the Calvinist faith.
The case is rare, I will admit. Teunis Vermeer felt the same
way about it, and he rightly demanded some elucidation. He
was told that the man, Don Fernando di Teruel, had fallen
in love with one of the local girls and had, in honorable
knightly fashion, asked her hand in marriage.

The girl's father, however, had made it the sole condition of his consent that the Captain forswear the Church
of Rome and all its works and become a true believer.
Instead of handing the father over to the Inquisition or
dealing summarily with so obvious an heretic, as would have
been Don Fernando's right under that royal Spanish decree
which condemned all the inhabitants of Holland to death
regardless of their religious affiliation (the theory being
that there could not possibly be any mistake made, since
God would know His own anyway on the Day of Judgment)
—instead of that, the gallant Captain accepted the condition. A Dutch girl, in his case at least, was well worth a
mass, and all the masses in the world. Now would it be

just, Teunis Vermeer the elder was asked, to slay the Captain with the rest, the righteous with the unrighteous? Shouldn't the Captain be called out and warned or put in a safe place while the patriots dealt with his men in the usual Geuzen fashion, cut off their ears and noses before hanging them and quartering their bodies? Don Fernando, husband of a Dutch woman and member of the Church of God in Asperen, surely did not deserve such a fate.

Teunis was convinced. The Captain was fetched. The situation was explained to him, and to everyone's astonishment he suggested that his men too be given an opportunity to save themselves by faith, so to speak. He volunteered to put the proposition to them himself. Since no one could speak Spanish sufficiently to enter into a theological disputation, the Captain was considered the logical man to undertake this missionary role, and he went off. He soon returned with the happy news that his men, a hundred or so in all, I think, had seen the light and were ready to embrace the new religion. Teunis went back to the partisans camped outside the village, the dominies were sent for, and the Spanish troopers were rebaptized upon their acceptance of the Augsburg Confession.

The crisis would have been over and done with and solved in a most amicable and edifying manner had it not been for the local parish priest, a certain Father Jan Jansen, who came boldly out of hiding to denounce his former colleagues in the priesthood—the Calvinist dominies of Gorcum—just as they were engaged in sprinkling the baptismal water on the foreheads of the Spanish troopers. Jansen was not allowed to finish his excoriations and anathemas. He was seized and without further ado carried to the top story of the tower and there hanged, face downward, tied securely to the knocker of his own church bell, so that his head was swiftly reduced to a bloody mash when the partisans and their newly found friends and coreligionists started to pull the ropes in joyous celebration of "God's mighty deeds done this day to the parish and people of Asperen." That was in the year 1572, in the glorious month of May.

Those Spaniards, then, so curiously converted en masse, remained in Asperen. They settled there. They realized that, having become Protestants, if only to save their lives, and having participated in the murder of a priest and in the iconoclastic furor that followed Father Jansen's death in the neighboring parishes, they could scarcely return to Spain or rejoin the main body of Don Alva's troops in the Netherlands. The Iron Duke would scarcely have had the patience to listen to their explanations, and the officers of the Inquisition with the Spanish Army would have seen to it that short shrift was given them. Most of the men therefore followed their commander's example. They married Dutch girls, produced children, bought land, acquired some riches and comforts, and in the course of time their offspring completely forgot the sunny land of Castile, the King with the hang lip in the Escurial, and the religion of their fathers. Most of them changed their names, too; Teruel became Terwillen, the ancestor of Count Frans; Camposino became Bouman, meaning farmer, one who tills the soil. They were Dutch by nationality as much as any native son of whatever stock, but not Dutch in looks. The Spanish strain predominated throughout the centuries, chiefly, I think, because of the high percentage of intermarriage among the descendants of Don Fernando's converted infantry.

Martha Bouman, the girl who attracted the Squire's attention, was a member of that strange, self-communing clan. In her the Spanish features were preserved to a remarkable degree. Her skin was olive-colored, her eyes dark and fiery, and her body lithe and sinewy, sensuous and feline —altogether a most attractive young woman. No wonder that a connoisseur like Zeger, who had drunk deeply of the cup of the mercenary Lubentia in Paris and a hundred other places where love is for sale, felt moved and disturbed at the sight of her. It must be said that she was indeed worth looking at, as it is worth looking at a painting by Velásquez or El Greco. Only Zeger soon discovered, to his chagrin, that unlike a painting, Martha could not be had for love or money: she was not for sale and she was not for hire.

She was betrothed to a young man of her own tribe and

community, a certain Wynant Monshouwer, a boy as swarthy
of features and as Spanish-looking as she herself. In the
case of Martha and Wynant, Zeger was knocking his head
against a stone wall, and as occurs inevitably when a man
persists in flinging himself against a rock, he knocked himself out. His passion for Martha, suddenly conceived, fever-
ishly nourished, and ruthlessly pursued, ended by plunging
him into crime, into murder, and into prison.

The denouement of that career of fuming vanity and
cold, self-indulgent calculation came with startling swiftness.
The bubble was about to burst. Sometimes life does pay its
debts as well as death, and does it more promptly. At first
Zeger seemingly could not get it into his head that the girl
would have nothing to do with him, that she feared him, in
fact, as if he were the Evil One incarnate. He could not
imagine anyone's ignoring him or passing him by with contempt. All his life he had been used to flattery and servility
in others and to seeing his merest whim gratified. Why
should a mere country girl be different from the rest? He
attributed Martha's lack of response to his attentions to
shyness, to an awkward, pouting, bucolic modesty. Ah, those
peasants, shrewd they were and coy, full of tricks and
dodges, but the game was worth the candle in this case!

It amused him to hunt on an unfamiliar terrain. After
his many experiences when favors had been heaped in his
lap, it gave his jaded senses a thrill to stalk and still-hunt
and maneuver this delectable bird, to shoo and drive her
step by step until finally he could close the trap upon her.
How long would it last? How long could she resist when
Zeger brought his full power and ingenuity to bear? But
Martha did not look upon the flirtation in so lighthearted a
manner. She knew quite well that in the Squire's eyes she was
as a bright new toy upon which his fancy had lighted for a
moment, and that if she surrendered she would be cast off
disdainfully as soon as the novelty wore off. What happened
to young girls of the so-called lower orders when they fell
into the hands of their so-called betters? That was an old
story, as old as the story of Hagar and Ishmael. Moreover,
there was her loyalty to her betrothed, to Wynant Mons-

houwer, small, insignificant farmer though he was and not to
be compared, of course, with the Squire in influence and
wealth. But can a humble and pure love that has ripened
through the years of childhood and adolescence into death-
less affection be swept aside at the word of command of an
intruder, however mighty and self-asserting he may be?

When after some months of futile endeavor Zeger's
passion made him impatient and he swore in his overwhelming conceit that he would have Martha Bouman dead
or alive, he overshot the mark. It is true that he had always
been able to acquire what his heart desired—money, women,
property, the world's applause and honors. How many
opponents had he not crushed in his unbridled hunt for
profits and power? He had forced his rivals to the wall, he
had ridden roughshod over their rights and human sensibilities and later cast them aside as squeezed-out fruit. And
now a mere slip of a girl with her crippled old father and
a boorish yokel of a fiancé were in league against him. A
laughable combination really, when he came to think of the
powerful alliances he had attacked and brought low in one
fell swoop. Yes, he would show these peasants a trick or
two if they persisted in their obstinacy. Why, before long
that girl would come crawling to him on her knees. She
would beg him to take her and offer herself freely without
any strings attached. See if she wouldn't! It would be fun
to hear the tune that girl would sing when the screws were
put on her father and on her friend, and with every wrench
those two would have the life squeezed out of them.
Wouldn't she come running then and cringe at his feet?

He had spoken to Martha twice. One morning he had
the good fortune to see her waiting at the bus halt. He
stopped his car, invited her inside, changed seats with the
chauffeur when she blushingly accepted, and drove her to
Gorcum. Then he told her what he wanted of her frankly
and bluntly, in a businesslike fashion, without reticences
or false modesty, as was his wont. He promised her God
knows what, a reduction in the rent on her father's land, an
outright freehold, a house of her own in Gorcum or anywhere else she desired, a trip to Paris, money, clothes, a

good position for her boy friend. What else did she want? Martha remained polite but stedfast in her refusal. He took to sending her flowers and presents. But the gifts were returned to the mansion without a message or a word of comment.

He summoned her father and talked with him of the plot lying next to old Bouman's farm on which the man had had his eye for years but could not buy because of the exorbitant price the Squire demanded. Bouman brought his daughter with him the evening he was called to the Squire's. Zeger offered him the parcel of land free as a gift. The peasant was struck speechless. But when Zeger named his condition, bluntly again, and unabashed, that Martha remain at the mansion that very night, the old man turned livid with anger and fumbled for his knife. The gesture made Zeger laugh heartily. But a moment later he swore, too, flushed with humiliation, that he would have her come what may.

He became sick with desire and exhausted one expedient after the other to get the girl in his power. Nothing availed. He wrote letters to her, imploring her to have mercy, to forgive his past rudeness and indelicacies. He said he had come to love her truly and he offered her marriage. He renewed his promises. He flattered her and cajoled, and when that did not help and he received no reply, he made a threat. He would ruin her father and her fiancé and drive them dishonored out of the community. "If you do not heed my entreaties," he wrote, "I will kill you. I cannot bear the thought of anyone else holding you in his arms." That threat of death weighed heavily against Zeger when the time came.

That year of 1934, at the fall fair in Asperen, which was really a minor kermess with a merry-go-round, a wheel of fortune, shooting galleries, and numerous other amusements and attractions, but where they also held an exhibition of agricultural products and on the last day there was run off a program of trotting and wagon races, bareback riding, and jumping, Zeger had entered a few of his sleek and heavy Brabant horses. Toward four in the afternoon of the last day of the fair, he turned up himself to watch the final sports events. He was taken to the judges' stand, shook

hands with the farmers assembled there, lifted his hat to
the crowd in the grandstand, and was given a program to
follow the entries. His cattle, he was pleasantly informed by
the presiding judge, had, as was usually the case, carried
off most of the prizes in the final judging, which had taken
place that very morning. The matter left Zeger rather
indifferent, for his only interest lay with the horses. That
old passion had not entirely left him.

He watched the farm lads and the young farmers ride
into the arena, salute the judges, and then gallop by, one
after the other with a small stick in their right hands with
which they were to tilt at a ring that was loosely held in a
spring mechanism attached to the outstretched arm of a post
standing directly in front of the elevated judges' booth. The
man who succeeded in detaching and spearing on his stick
the most rings in a series of rapid turns around the field
was of course the winner. That man happened to be Wynant
Monshouwer.

Following the ring-tilting came a trotting event. In a
vehicle of extremely light and almost flimsy construction,
consisting of no more than a couple of wicker seats above
four thin wheels and a whippletree, a contestant would take
his place with his woman by his side and then make the
horses go through their paces. The extra passenger was
taken along to ensure the proper balance to the feather-
light, fragile contraption. It required great skill, experience, and a pair of extrastrong arms to pull the affair off
properly, for the horses were to trot as fast as possible, yet
they were never to canter or to gallop, nor was a whip to
be used in driving them to their highest speed. A galloping
horse, if the animal broke its trot only for an instant, dis-
qualified its owner at once. Again Wynant Monshouwer
was one of the contestants in this event, and for his partner
he had brought along none other than the beautiful Martha.

From his vantage point Zeger had a good opportunity
to observe Martha at leisure as her carriage drew up at the
starting-point just below the judges' stand. She wore a
dark-blue dress with a girdle of wine-red silk to which was
fastened a small bunch of flowers. Her smooth dark hair

was held back by a velvet ribbon of the same color as the girdle. It was tied bow-fashion at her neck. In her ears were a pair of large gold rings, and she did not wear a hat. Wynant sat slightly forward with his back straight and taut, holding the reins as the horses pranced and impatiently pawed the soil. The dinky was painted a brilliant pink and through the spokes of the wheels boughs of green myrtle had been woven. The horses had red and blue ribbons tied to their headgear. A murmur of delighted admiration zoomed through the crowds on the grandstand at the sight of the handsome equipage and its young occupants. Martha smiled and revealed her snow-white teeth. Here and there people burst into handclapping and there were shouts of encouragement and admiration for Monshouwer. "You got the best-looking horses and the best-looking woman there, Wynant. Let's see what you can do!" One of the judges turned to Zeger to remark upon the splendid appearance of the carriage nearest the stand, which was Martha's, but Zeger replied only with a curt nod of the head. His eyes were fastened on the girl.

They were off. Wynant Monshouwer won both the first prize for a perfect trot and the *prix d'honneur* for the splendid appearance of his entry. As soon as the winners were announced Zeger left the judges' stand to mix with the crowds. He was looking for Martha. He found her standing by a refreshment booth talking with some friends. She was in the company of her father and mother. Wynant, the fiancé, who had gone off to stable the horses, joined the group just at the moment Zeger approached. The Squire congratulated the young farmer on his victories, and an embarrassed silence ensued. He bade the men cover themselves, for they had taken off their hats when he came near and were still holding them in their hands. Wynant thanked the Squire curtly and spoke a few words to Martha. They were about to walk off when Zeger stepped forward and, bowing to Martha, complimented her on her appearance. "I have never seen you look so well," he said, "and I wonder if you will not give me one of those flowers in your girdle as a memento of this day."

Martha did not know what to answer. Was the man insane, or what? Had he no feelings whatever, writing her those insolent, threatening letters only a few weeks before and now acting as if there wasn't a cloud in the sky? She laughed a little and was starting to turn her back on him when Zeger took her gently by the arm and, swinging her around, begged once more for a flower. But then Wynant stepped up and with a face as pale as death he said to Zeger:

"I'll ask you to keep your hands off, Squire!"

"Give him a flower, Martha," said her father. "He's our Squire and means no harm by it!"

"No," replied young Monshouwer, "she's not giving him anything, damn his soul to hell." He looked fiercely at the Squire, who calmly lit a cigarette, and sneered: "I see, I see, the Spanish blood is up. We'll soon be drawing our knives, I suppose."

The peasants did not say a word, but Martha seized her fiancé's arm when she saw his fists clench and unclench and that his teeth were clamped together with suppressed rage. Zeger walked off with a shrug of the shoulders.

Half an hour later Wynant and Martha were driving home in their sulky. The sun was setting and there was a tang of frost in the air. From the fairgrounds to Asperen was a good three miles along a straight dirt road on the side of which ran a deep ditch, a small canal really, but not wider perhaps than five or six feet, just wide enough for a punt to pass. Beyond the ditch lay farm land. On the edge of the ditch grew clusters of knotted pollard willows. Wynant and Martha were silent. The encounter with the Squire had spoiled the day's triumphs and joys completely for them. Wynant was afraid, now that he had affronted the Squire so boldly, that the disagreeable incident at the fairgrounds would not be the last of it. He said so to Martha in a low voice and shook his head. She did not reply, but laid her hand on his arm.

At that instant they heard the sound of an automobile klaxon behind them and Wynant instinctively tightened his hold on the reins. The horses had pricked up their ears, nervously affected by the hooting horn. Wynant knew at

once, of course, that it was the Squire's automobile which
was coming up behind, for there wasn't another private
car owned by anybody for miles around. The hooting signified that the Squire wished to pass. But that was impossible.
The road was too narrow for two vehicles to move abreast.
Unless Wynant urged his horses into the ditch, the Squire
would have to remain behind until the next road crossing
was reached where Wynant could pull out to give leeway.

What happened now occurred in the twinkling of an eye,
in a flash almost, much quicker than it takes to tell. The
Squire's klaxon was heard. Martha looked around for an
instant. The Squire's low-built, swift roadster was perhaps
a thousand feet behind them. Wynant urged on his horses
to reach the side road as quickly as possible to let the Squire
pass. The animals shot forward with a bound and broke
into a gallop. But now the Squire's klaxon wailed like mad
in a continuous, frightening, shrill yell. Wynant had all he
could do to keep the horses under control. Martha crouched
low, holding her man tightly clasped around the waist. There
was nothing else in that flimsy vehicle to seize hold of, and
to let go of Wynant for an instant would have thrown her
out.

The sulky flew over the road, the wheels scarcely touching the ground. The horses' necks were stretched out
almost horizontally. Their ears lay back on their necks and
their madly tearing hoofs flung large clots of dirt into the
faces of the occupants. Wynant stood with one foot on the
whippletree. His other leg was bent double under him in
the wickerwork of the seat. He was swaying to and fro like
a ship caught in a hurricane. But still he lashed the horses
on to greater speed with the loose ends of the reins. The
Squire's horn howled on in a frantic, insane wail behind
them.

The horses were in mortal terror and could not have been
brought to a halt even had Wynant tried. The Squire was
driving them mad with his hellish siren. Wynant said later
that he felt that his only hope of escape lay in reaching the
side road. The ditches on either side of the way prevented
him from turning aside. To have stopped would have

meant instant death for all. For the Squire was coming full-speed. The distance between the roadster and the sulky was growing shorter every second. Zeger's head was bent over the wheel and his eyes were grimly riveted on the vehicle ahead. Homegoing pedestrians later testified that Zeger seemed intent on catching up with Martha and Wynant. To them it seemed a race they witnessed, a mad, horrible race. Terror-stricken, they stepped aside. Some jumped right into the water to be out of the way of the swaying and roaring automobile.

Still the Squire's horn wailed. Martha and Wynant could hear the crepitating rumble of the motor right behind them, like the moan of a tigerish animal bent upon snatching hold of them. The Squire showed no intention of slowing up. Wynant shouted to the horses. He whipped and lashed them. He yelled at them frantically while Martha, her head buried in his lap, lay trembling by his side. Just before they reached the crossroads the crash came. Zeger's crouching machine, snorting like some strange armor-nozzled, pre-historic monster, struck the carriage squarely in the rear. The wheels were flung to splinters. There was a scream. Martha was thrown clear across the ditch, where her head struck one of the stumpy willow trees. The horses were plunged into the water and Wynant lay by the side of the ditch, head downward. Zeger's car was barely scratched, and its heavy wheels crunched over the broken fragments of the sulky. At the crossroads a few yards beyond he drew up, looked around at the wreck and the prostrate human figures, and calmly drove off in the direction of the mansion.

Zeger had said that he would have Martha alive or dead. Now his wish was fulfilled. There she was, the girl who had smiled so engagingly only an hour before at her folk in the grandstand, a pitifully crumpled form lying against the trunk of a clipped tree, her blue dress soiled with mud and the white foam from the horses' mouths, her face distorted with the panic of the last few moments, her dark, dilated eyes wide-open as if still staring at the galloping death that had overtaken her. When they picked up the body they had to wrap her poor head, for fear that it would come apart in their hands, in a blanket hastily borrowed from one of the buggies that lined the road behind the wreck all the way back to the fairgrounds. Wynant Monshouwer had both legs broken and remained a twisted, painfully limping cripple for the rest of his days.

That was the upshot, the brilliant climax, of Zeger van Rietvelt's high-going career. At least so it seemed for the time being. But there was more to come, more of the same sordid character, things even more abominable. These things, it is true, did not happen immediately, not until a short interruption, not until a short pause lay behind, and not until the putrid fermentation of the social system, after spreading much malodor, came to fruition in the black pestilence of fascism. First Zeger would yet have some time to think over the road he had traveled, the wrecks he had strewn along his path, the pain and the heartbreak he had caused, the hopes he had extinguished, all the ruthless sacrifices to his selfish ambitions. Not that the years of imprisonment' brought him to another view of life or that correction tempered his soul to gentler ways. To the contrary, those years in prison embittered him with their poison, they made him more cynical and more unendurable than he was before. They set him scheming for revenge.

Revenge on whom and for what? Revenge on society, on his fellow men, on his brother Hollanders? For what? For having gravely injured him, for having broken off his career and for contravening his plans. When Ary Brandt insisted that I come along one day to visit our old schoolfellow in that circular prison house in Haarlem which had been built from the steel and cement turned out by his own factories near Gorcum, Zeger spoke of himself as of a badly injured man, as a victim of a scheming cabal of radicals and lawyers, an innocent victim of an inconceivably ungrateful, unjust, and sordid world. We found a much-enduring man, but a man who assured us that he still had his trump card to play.

Zeger's trial did not come off till two years after the death of Martha Bouman. The case went from one postponement to the other. There were investigations and counter-investigations, verifications and checkups by an entire

corps of lawyers and experts who went up and down the
countryside measuring distances, interrogating witnesses,
digging up old records and land titles. The baptismal, birth,
and marriage certificates of the dead girl and her parents
were examined. The experts sniffed and snuffled for some
irregularity, a date wrongly entered, a name misspelt, a
seal, a stamp, one little hieroglyphic figure missing in one
of the documents, as if it were the Boumans who had been
in the wrong by daring to be born into this world at all and
breathing the air that blew over the great Squire's estates.

An order was issued to investigate Martha's and
Wynant's little savings accounts in the post office. There
was a great deal of ado about a trip Martha had made
with her teacher and schoolmates to Nijmegen in the summer vacation several years before. Where, answer yes or
no, where had that girl obtained the money, the three florins
and fifty cents for the railway fare required for that great
journey? What did they not investigate? An autopsy was
performed two months after her death to determine whether
Martha had not perchance been drinking heavily that day
at the fair in the company of her fiancé and thereby had,
perhaps unwittingly but effectively nevertheless, contributed
to the cause of her own death. Weren't there witnesses
who affirmed that she had been extraordinarily gay and
happy, as if she anticipated some event, some thrill, some
adventure at the close of that day of the horse races?

Everybody was questioned who had ever had but the
remotest acquaintance with the girl: the pastor, the doctor,
the neighbors, the rural police, the photographer, the midwife. Who knew what might turn up if one kept on stirring,
on what interesting clues one might stumble, maybe some
indication of mental aberration or a neglect to have the
tonsils removed, or—appetizing hope!—a sexual irregularity, a love affair with a soldier boy or a farm hand?
Incriminating evidence that would have been, surely, something for the lawyers to build a defense on for Zeger.

I doubt not that in the end they would have questioned
the horses, if it were not for the fact that these animals had
been shot out of their misery and that their carcasses had

long since been sold to the chevaline butcher in Gorcum. That possible bit of evidence had been eaten and thoroughly chewed and digested and gone into the bloodstream and muscles of the hungry proletarians. Nothing was found to incriminate Wynant Monshouwer or Martha's father and mother, except that they were there, existing, that they lived and breathed, and that the old man had once made a gesture as if he were going to draw his clasp knife in Zeger's presence.

The affair stirred the community greatly. Everybody took sides. Everybody had an opinion. Attorneys with heavy briefcases went up and down between Zeger's offices and the bureaus of the highest *instantie*, that is, the Department of Justice in The Hague. No effort was left unmade to save the Squire, benefactor of the people. In the end, some officer of the law had nevertheless to be dispatched to request Zeger to present himself on such and such a day at such and such an hour before the Court in Dordt. Zeger had been at liberty all the two years that had elapsed since his crime. He had almost forgotten it. At the fall assizes in 1936, he was sentenced to three years' imprisonment. A Jewish attorney who was a socialist, representing the Crown, demanded ten years. The defense claimed mitigating circumstances and suggested that the two years of waiting for the trial, two years of mental torture for the defendant, be graciously deducted from the sentence.

And so Zeger went to the jail in Haarlem one day, he traveling first class while the policeman in civil clothes who was to conduct him to prison sat in the third-class coach. And there we found him, Ary and I, in 1938, wearing a gray prison suit. He was a little thinner, but otherwise the same old Zeger. He talked for a quarter-hour of current affairs, for he was allowed to read the newspapers. He predicted that there would be a big war in Europe before many months had passed.

"Next year," he said, "it will start. That fellow Hitler is the God-given leader Europe has needed for a long time. He is going to straighten things out a little. To begin with, he will get us the Baku oil fields back. That's as certain as tomorrow's sunrise. Deterding and Colijn are supporting him, and every decent businessman in the land. It's a pity we haven't a man like Hitler here in Holland. He's a genius. That man certainly has shown how to put labor in its place! God, if we could put an end to all this democratic twaddle in Holland too, what a day that would be!"

Not a word of regret or contrition came from his lips. Zeger eyed us a little suspiciously. Perhaps he was afraid that we would bring up the past. But we listened in silence, shook hands with him when the guard signified that our time was up, and wished him good luck.

Outside the prison I said to Ary: "I didn't know we were to get the Baku oil fields back. Did we ever own them?"

"Don't be so naïve," replied Ary. "You can smell them all over the place. Every second bourgeois in Holland has Russian bonds or stocks that have been made worthless by the October Revolution. Wouldn't you like the man who promises to redeem those bonds at full value and maybe a little better?"

Chapter II

ADRIANA LENDS A HAND

THERE they were at the Arkel Gate: the first detachments of the German Army marching and riding into town for all the world like our own artillerists and pontooners coming home from a week's field exercises on the heaths and moorlands of a neighboring province. Not once did the head of the German column take the wrong turn at intersections and road crossings or even hesitate about direction. The German guides who walked in front seemed to know every detail of the city's topography as accurately as if they were native-born boys who had all their lives dwelt in our midst. The Bavarian band played the old familiar tune of "The Good Comrade," the same tune our band played when the regiment returned from maneuvers and all the boys and girls, and many adults, turned out to welcome the garrison back.

But the enemy marched through empty streets. Nobody had ventured outdoors to watch the German procession. The shutters were up and the blinds drawn before the windows of all the principal houses and shops on the route of march. Nothing was heard but the blare of the band, the crash of cymbals and the roll of the drums. When the music stopped, commands rang out in that exasperating, metallic-voiced shrillness of the Prussian *Paradeplatz*. The sound was as sharp and menacing as the snap of a whip. Then came the heavy, weighty tread of a mass of men marching in step and the rumble of wagons, kitchens and caissons. A slight drizzle was falling. The gray tarpaulins covering the engines of war gleamed in the soft, mother-of-pearl light of an evening in May.

All the normal activities of daily life had come to a standstill. Trains had stopped running. Schools were closed. The farm lands were deserted. Industries had ceased operation. The very windmills in the polders stood still as if paralyzed, like men holding their arms above their heads to ward off the blows of some unseen titan. People sat in their homes huddled around the radio listening to unfamiliar announcers' voices gloating over Holland's woe.

Your government has fled, they heard. Your army is a panic-stricken mob streaming south in chaos. . . . Your cities are burning. . . . Your ships are sinking at their moorings. . . . No power on earth can resist the German Army. . . . *Achtung! Achtung!* Anyone found transporting specie or currency notes will be summarily executed. . . . The *Wehrmacht* is animated with the friendliest feelings toward the kindred Teutonic people of the Netherlands. We come not as conquerors but as liberators to free you from Anglo-Saxon plutocracy and Jewish internationalism. . . . *Achtung! Achtung!* Funds should not be withdrawn from the banks until further notice. . . . To be found on highways or rural roads will be considered activity designed to hamper German military operations and is punishable with death. . . .

Occasionally a thin, far-off voice from France or from across the Channel, half-drowned in more powerful ether waves and by the deafening roar of the *Luftwaffe's* squadrons, which were constantly overhead, would attempt to whisper encouragement: The army in Zeeland Province is counterattacking. . . . Help is coming. . . . The British are re-forming their lines. . . . The Corps of Marines, after a superhuman effort at Rotterdam, is joining the regular forces in the islands. . . . At one time a clandestine station told of a Captain Jetze Sissingha taking a group of high German naval visitors on a trial run in a brand-new Dutch submarine found in the harbor of Ymuiden and then deliberately scuttling his craft when ten miles out to sea. Some listeners may have remembered the son of the pastor of Loon and the capers he cut with the girls in town when a gymnasiast.

At another moment hearts were buoyed up with the announcement of a gigantic British air fleet about to attack the blitz columns pouring through Holland. But then the rasping voice of the new announcer at the official broadcasting station would cut in with sneering references to Viscount Gort's ridiculous little army running faster than the German armored cars for the port cities of France. . . . The British are leaving their Allies in the lurch. . . . The Belgians are ready to give up. *Achtung! Achtung!* Burgomasters and local officials in the Netherlands must remain at their posts. Desertion will be punished with death. . . .

For two days Gorcum had been an empty city. By order of a fool or a traitor its inhabitants were ordered evacuated to the Province of Utrecht. Fourteen thousand persons, the old, the young, the lame, the halt, the blind, started out on the roads leading northward only to be halted by dispatch riders at the Lek River telling them that the Germans they were fleeing in the south were but a few miles to the north. The pitiful exodus made an about-turn. Death was everywhere. The road back was bombed incessantly and without pity. The guns on Gorcum's ramparts and in the outlying forts were still firing in the direction of Brabant when the first German patrols were within a stone's throw on the opposite side of town.

After the fall of the principal fort to a regiment of paratroopers who trained the nozzles of their liquid-fire spouts on the defenders and burned them to a green-hued crisp, the cannon on the ramparts grew silent and Colonel Hubert van Vredenburg, himself seriously wounded, following instructions of the Commander in Chief, gave the order to hoist the white flag on the Citadel. The town of Gorcum with its elaborate triple ring of defense works, fortifications, strong points, bastions, broad rivers and canals, of which our official history books and military manuals frequently spoke as "the key to the Fortress Holland," was in German hands.

As with the key so it went, alas, with the door and with the whole house. The national defense collapsed much quicker than the German High Command in its most optimistic calculations had dared anticipate. "Holland in ten days, Belgium in a month," became Holland in five days, Belgium in a week. The friends and Allies of whom the Government had told the people vaguely but repeatedly, without ever identifying them, as bound to come to Holland's aid in the hour of danger, failed to put in an appearance. In the selfsame hour that the *Wehrmacht* crossed the frontiers, the Dutch Air Force ceased to exist. It was caught asleep on the ground in spite of warnings that Göring would strike at dawn on the morning of the tenth of May and then would obviously try to repeat what he had already successfully accomplished in Poland and Norway; that is, destroy the airdromes and aerial equipment in the very first hour of hostilities. Pursuing the myth of strict neutrality that kept the Dutch Government from making a common stand with the Belgians and the French even after Holland and the other two countries had been attacked by the same enemy, it never occurred to the authorities to fly their three hundred planes to France to join the Franco-British force. That too, I suppose, might have been cited by Hitler as a breach of neutrality.

Like everyone else, the members of the Cabinet had for nearly that whole year, which corresponds roughly with the epoch of the so-called phony war, watched the Germans mobilize on the country's borders. Three times in succession they had seen the *Wehrmacht's* swiftest columns emerge from the defenses of the Siegfried Line in the vicinity of Aachen and make straight for a point where the borders of Holland and Belgium meet. A high-school boy of average intelligence could have foretold Their Mighty Highnesses of the States General that Germany's opening attack would be designed to drive a wedge between the Dutch and Belgian armies in order to engage and destroy them severally.

When the thrice-repeated threat did finally materialize, the Government refused pointblank to have the General Staff enter into conversations with the Belgians and the

French. Holland was still neutral. When the Germans struck at the spot that they had unmistakably indicated, the Dutch Field Army was found to be concentrated in an entirely different region. The Navy could not prevent the landing of German troops on the North Sea coast from barges and transport vessels sailing down from the direction of Hamburg and Emden, because half its effectives were absent convoying boatloads of gold to England or conveying leading politicians and their hangers-on to safety.

All the illusions about the might of Holland's tanks, the perfection of the artillery, the quasi-miraculous efficiency of the so-called water-line defenses, the splendor of the modernized Navy and the rest of the military paraphernalia on which successive governments of jonkheers, imperialists, and other half-brothers of fascism and authentic directors of oil and rubber trusts fed the nation for years —all these illusions were suddenly shattered by the reality. When the Dutch people saw the military defense collapse in a few hours, they lost heart even before being put to the test. When confronted with the only conceivable military force in the whole world that might eventually have turned into a direct military threat to Holland, the Dutch Army proved as useless as an umbrella in a shower of robot bombs. Yet to keep this military establishment afoot generations of Dutchmen had poured out their sweat and treasure.

I will not deny that the Dutch Army might have withstood an aggression by the Danes, the Swiss, the Belgians, or the Andorrans, but it so happens that these states at no time showed the least hostility toward Holland. When it came to facing the *Wehrmacht*, the existence and potential threat of which was the sole raison d'être of the Dutch Army, our legions might as well not have existed at all. They melted away like a flurry of snow on a spring morning. One need not be a Clausewitz to have foreseen what happened. We foresaw it as clearly as if it was an event of past history when we were boys debating the evils of militarism at school. The Dutch Army was no match and never could be a match for the *Wehrmacht*.

Knowing all along that Holland could never raise and equip an army strong enough to resist Germany for a single day, and there being no other Power extant in the whole world harboring evil intentions against the realm's territorial integrity, why did the Dutch Government have an army at all? Why hadn't it disbanded the Army as a useless luxury and an outworn anomaly long before, as Denmark did, and confided the people's safety to treaties and covenants of international guarantee? It may be objected that a Germany on conquest bent would not have respected the sanctity of such treaties and that the Reich, invoking the principle of military necessity, would have overrun Holland as surely as it overran Denmark, which had indeed disbanded its army. But this is only saying that Holland would have succumbed in either case. What is the difference?

The difference is that Holland would have had clean hands and a clean conscience and that her honor as a Christian nation would not be stained with the blood of her own children needlessly sacrificed in May 1940. The difference is that the land of Grotius and Erasmus, Spinoza and Rembrandt, small as it is, would have set the world a great example in breaking the vicious circle of armaments and counterarmaments that produced World War I and World War II and which will produce World War III before we have reached the half-century mark. The abstract principle of national honor that the statesmen have invoked in justification of the four days' war was and is as safe from German aggression as Prime Minister Gerbrandy's predestination doctrine. Holland's honor is safe in the hands of her artists and scholars, her scientists and men of the spirit. It can never be represented by imitation Junkers, trust magnates, and the oppressors of Indonesia's millions.

I confess that for the day when Holland was attacked by the German Army, a day which I had announced a year before it dawned, I had dreamed of a man arising with a heart too large for Holland who would have the courage to say to his countrymen that the talk of their politicians' neutrality had been a lie, that the Dutch Government through its diplomats and statesmen, who alternated between the boards of directors of Royal Dutch Shell, Batavia Oil, and the administration of the country, had been up to their necks in the international plot to destroy the Soviet Union, and that the whole scheme having miscarried now, there was no profit and no honor to be gained for the nation and for humanity by continuing to play the game of blood and guile, the game of imperialism—a man who would have said: This is not for you and me: This is the Devil's own work. When a Dutch minister dares speak so and the Dutch public applauds his speaking, then the nation will be glorious, and her praise, as Elizabeth Browning says, instead of exploding from within, from loud civic mouths and functionaries, will come to her from without, as all worthy praise must, for the good she has fostered, and the lives she has saved. . . .

When the Germans had installed themselves with that efficiency which they displayed everywhere else and which made one often think of the magic skill of Barnum & Bailey's men in fitting together the most heterogeneous material in a few hours' time and producing order out of chaos, Mijnheer van Alphen could hardly bear the sight of his own tannery. That he was obliged to turn out shoe leather for the enemy's vast and growing armies and thus indirectly to contribute to German military successes and to the oppression of individuals and nations who were as much the victim of Nazi aggression as the Dutch, was something that rankled and seethed in the old merchant's mind. He was not a man of many words, but those who knew him intimately were aware that he felt his position as a humiliation and a crime. It weighed on his conscience and made him feel a traitor. Still, what else could he do? To have closed his factory would simply have led to its seizure by the Nazi authorities, probably to deportation for the workers to some slave camp in the Reich, and, who knows?—to imprisonment or even death for himself as a saboteur of the German war effort.

"If I am to suffer or die," he said one night at dinner to the members of his family, "I will not suffer or die for anything I have refused to do, but for something that I have deliberately done." That was the young Dirk van Alphen speaking again, the man who had never been conquered in his life except by his daughter Adriana, the same resolute stubborn Dutchman and patriot who would not knuckle down to anybody. Dirk Dermout looked sideways at his grandfather. He could see by that grimly determined face now grooved with a thousand tiny wrinkles that the old man was in earnest. "They are not going to prevail," Mijnheer van Alphen spoke up again. "Never," he added, striking the table with the flat of his hand, "never, do you hear, never will we submit. We'll break their damned necks first."

Yes, it was bad enough to be forced to collaborate with the enemy. But that wasn't the worst. The worst was that representatives of the Gestapo had been stationed in the leather factory. That was altogether unbearable. The sight of one of these inspectors of the German *Arbeitsdienst*, the Ministry of Labor, walking around in the Van Alphen plant, snooping and ferreting in all the nooks and corners, poking his nose into the account books, or with that typically German air of supercilious condescension toward people regarded as a lesser breed giving the workmen their orders, criticizing their lackadaisical, sullen behavior and the slow tempo of their work, or making suggestions for speeding up things and for making changes in the administration— that was too much. It made Dirk van Alphen's blood boil. When one of these uniformed efficiency experts spoke to him, the old man deliberately averted his eyes. He could not look the fellow in the face. Not that he feared the German. He was afraid of himself, afraid to let himself go, afraid that he would explode in a burst of pent-up wrath. He kept his hands in his trousers pockets so as to hide his clenched fists.

The old gentleman was so worked up that his friends feared an explosion of his held-in irritation and wrath. There might be an incident any day. You could feel the storm gathering. Hadn't Dirk van Alphen answered back one of these blood-and-soil philosophers who was lecturing him on the rank of the Nazis as *Edel-Germanen*, Teutonic blood nobility, and on the possibility of the Dutch people being elevated by a long and arduous process of education and training to the same exalted position as their thorough-bred High German brothers—hadn't he answered him with the question: "This scoundrel Mussert, I suppose, is already a full-fledged *Edel-Germane*, is he?"

That the German official had not grown angry over this reference to the head of the Dutch Nazi Bund and chief of Dutch quislings was because he mistook Mijnheer van Alphen's word for a question of inquiry and solemnly proceeded with his explanation of racist doctrine. The Dutch, he said, and the other Teutonic, Nordic, and Saxon tribes, such as the Danes, the Flemings, the Norwegians, and perhaps even the Finns and the English, being of the same or nearly the same blood as the noble *Herrenvolk*, were ultimately destined to share in the good fortune of the master race. As to the Poles, the Jews, the Russians, and suchlike *Untermenschen*, they were simply to be exterminated and blotted out for the good of mankind. It would be a measure of racial prophylaxis, of self-preservation for the *Herrenvolk*, to get rid of those Semitic and Slavic simians once and for all. They were the curse of the world, the greatest hindrance to the forward march of mankind under the direction of the superior race. But the Dutch were to be treated leniently, he added reassuringly to the astonished Mijnheer van Alphen, who was hearing the racial nonsense for the first time in his life from an authentic apostle of the doctrine.

"Leniently?" asked Dirk van Alphen. "Do you call the bombing of Rotterdam a lenient measure, thousands of men and women buried under the ruins of their homes in ten minutes' time and that after the commander of their country's army had surrendered?"

"Oh, the bombing of Rotterdam, that was a mere incident, a sort of object lesson to the Dutch people, a warning for them to collaborate faithfully with the New Order. *Ja, ja,* one mustn't take such things too seriously." Besides, the damage would soon be repaired. It would in fact have been repaired long before if it weren't for those damnable English. With their bombing operations over a friendly neighborly country like Holland—what an outrage really,

what abject inhumanity that was!—they were likely to
interfere with building operations. "Churchill is such a
fool," the German said. "If only he would realize what the
Führer has in mind. The Führer doesn't intend to harm the
English in the least."

"But you just told me what the Führer has in mind," said
Mijnheer van Alphen. "He only plans to kill off a hundred
million human beings or so. How long do you think it will
take you fellows to change the world?"

"*Nu*, a hundred years or so, perhaps less," the German
official thought. "We have just started. We are on our
way."

"On your way out, you mean," came back Mijnheer van
Alphen.

"Herr van Alphen," the German said pompously, "I
hope you will not make me wish that our *Luftwaffe* had
bombed some other localities besides Rotterdam." But Dirk
van Alphen had already turned on his heels and was gone.

Conversations and verbal encounters of this sort were
fraught with extreme danger. One could never know how a
particular German, perhaps some undercover sleuth of the
Gestapo out to detect incipient rebellious thought or "evil-
intentionedness," as it was called, would take Mijnheer van
Alphen's satirical references to persons high in the Nazi
hierarchy. How many Hollanders lost their lives or were
peremptorily shipped off to languish and often perish in
German concentration camps for a mere incautious word—
for an epithet mumbled at the address of the Führer or one
of his domestic or alien bonzes, for a phrase of frank criticism of the regime of terror—is hard to say. There is no
doubt that their number runs into tens of thousands.

Trouble between Dutchmen and their oppressors often
started in a seemingly most innocent way. Not infrequently
it had a personal basis. The Dutch are a people of frank
speech and manners who do not hide their opinions, as they
say, under chairs and benches. They are terribly emphatic.
They are not easily riled or quickly excited, but once aroused
they never let go. They are reached by depth of sentiment
and not by words, however sonorous. The Dutch tried to

hide their feelings, but they did not always succeed. If looks and glances and ironic smiles could have killed, Holland would have become the tomb of the German Army and of the Gestapo.

There were no open battles, at least not during the first years of the occupation. The Dutch terrain does not lend itself to the kind of guerrilla warfare that was waged so long and so successfully in countries like Norway and Yugoslavia, where bands of franc-tireurs could retreat and plan new sorties and attacks from the comparative temporary safety of almost inaccessible mountain ranges, from hidden crags and well-nigh impenetrable forests. In Holland nothing is hidden; everything—houses, roads, rivers, cities, and hamlets—lies exposed to the four winds of heaven. A dog could not move across one of those flat polders and meadows without drawing attention to itself. Hence at the start there was little so-called underground activity. The people seemed stunned by the magnitude of the disaster that had overtaken their country. The inexorable might of the German repressional apparatus that moved in on them seemed to stagger them.

There was so little open resistance at first that the Germans were led to believe that the Dutch were the first in Europe to have acquiesced wisely in the inevitable, that the sons of the irrepressible Water Beggars were the first to be tamed and that they would in the future turn out dutiful collaborators in Hitler's scheme for the transformation of the European social order. All three top Nazis, Seyss-Inquart, Anton Mussert, and Josef Terboven, at one time or another went so far as to broadcast to the world their entire satisfaction with the peaceful and harmonious integration of the Dutch nation in the New Order.

Of course, there were a number of genuine, spontaneous collaborators in Holland, men who liked Hitler because of his social philosophy and the forthright, resolute manner in which he translated his theories into action. Some of the most ancient and honored Dutch names were stained with the moral blight attaching to the ruling class, which always in the most decisive moments of history places its class in-

terests before those of the nation and of humanity as a
whole. France had them, Belgium had them, Norway and
Yugoslavia had them, as well as Britain and America. Why
should Holland, an imperialist power of the first rank, not
have them too? The class struggle is an ever-present reality.
It is not something that's merely preached by Marxists. The
Marxists only constate its existence and work for its ob-
literation. The bourgeoisie practices the class struggle. How
can it be otherwise? Jesus said long ago, Where a man's
treasure is, there shall be his heart also. That word of the
Lord's is at the same time the simplest and the most profound definition of the class struggle and of the materialist
interpretation of history.

With some Dutchmen belonging to the haute bourgeoisie
—bankers, industrialists, oil and rubber barons, landed
Junkers, some leading military men, and even some ministers of the Gospel—their treasure lay with Hitler and the
things he stood for. To them the Führer was the barrier
against Bolshevism, the guarantor of the capitalist social
order, the enemy of democracy and its legitimate eldest
daughter, the social revolution. Hitler had crushed the
social revolution in the Reich during those six awful years
that the pontiffs of public opinion so readily overlook—the
six years 1933-39 when he exterminated the vanguard of
the greatest, most progressive, and most valuable social-
democratic movement in Europe from which for half a
century had issued all the energy, the theoretical justification, the financial support, of all the causes of freedom,
enlightenment, and progress on the Continent, and which,
if Hitler and his international backers had not intervened,
might well have given Germany the basis of what is today
considered a decent and civilized life. The Führer destroyed
that movement root and branch because so long as it existed
he could not train an entirely new generation of Germans
for the total war he envisaged.

With that Hitler, and those particular policies of his—
rearming of the Reich, killing the Jews, proscribing free
thought, exterminating labor leaders, scholars, and men of
independent mind—our Dutch ruling class, no more than

the ruling classes of France or Britain or America and the lords of the famous "free press" ever found the least fault. They never even protested. Worse, they applauded and encouraged him until the man thought that he had the world's backing when he finally did the thing for which he was purposely brought upon the scene: attacked the Soviet Union, whose crime, in the eyes of that international clique of big cartelists, was that it had put an end to their class struggle in having successfully withdrawn one-sixth of the earth's habitable surface and two hundred million human beings from experiencing the benefits and blessings of their system of free enterprise: exploitation, periodic depressions, racial tensions, one crisis after another and war and war again.

Mijnheer van Alphen was not one of these. Like most men of his generation, Dirk van Alphen was hopelessly confused on the subject of social warfare. He believed the bourgeois journals who deny the existence of the class war and who actually wage it in so saying. Problems arising between capital and labor should be settled by the parties involved, not by a foreign government and least of all by armed force and violence. He did not, as Zeger van Rietvelt did, look upon Hitler as a sort of friendly enemy, a savior of capitalist loot. He considered him the enemy of his country. Like many another businessman, he left not faction, he was left by it. He detested the Nazis and all their works wholeheartedly. That is why his daughter Adriana grew anxious as she learned of the ever more frequent tiffs between her father and the Gestapo men at the plant, so that in the end she persuaded him to stay at home and leave the running of the factory to Hein Dermout, her husband.

But then Hein got into trouble himself. Or rather not Hein in the first place, but Dirk, Mijnheer van Alphen's grandson, who had been home in Gorcum since the closing of the University of Leyden by order of Artur von Seyss-Inquart, the Nazi Governor-General of the Netherlands, because of the spirit of defiance and "evil-intentionedness" shown by both students and professors. For the time being young Dirk was doing some clerical work at the factory, assisting in the administration, keeping accounts, and when the occasion arose serving as interpreter between the German overseers and the workers.

Inasmuch as the Van Alphen factory was to become the scene of a series of incidents related to the struggle for liberation, something perhaps should be said at this point about its location, its interior, and its mode of operation. It stood outside the town walls a short way, a little more than half a mile in the general direction of the village of Arkel. In my youth it was still the only building in the fields beyond the ramparts that was tolerated by the Department of National Defense. For reasons of high strategy, as has been said before, no structure of any eminence was for a long time, for many centuries, permitted to be reared in the immediate vicinity of the important Fortress Gorcum. That an exception had early been made in the case of the leather factory was probably owing to considerations of popular hygiene. The odors emanating from stacks of rawhides in various stages of putrefaction must have been too much even for our not-too-particular ancestors, who had their open sewers running through the streets.

Of course the building was put up several hundred years before the date of this chronicle and I do not precisely know what argument, if any, was invoked to keep the tannery outside the walls. If I cling to the smell theory, it is because I recall hot summer evenings when the aroma pervading several streets well inside the town nearest the Arkel Gate and nearest the Van Alphen factory was by no means that of roses of Kasanlik. After Zeger van Rietvelt's industrialization mania, the Van Alphen factory no longer stood alone. It was but the first of an endless row of buildings stretching along the Arkel dike road which parallels the Linge River: the cement factory, the iron foundries and the steel mill, the sugar refinery, and still other industries, all the way up to Arkel village itself.

The Linge River runs from north to south, enters Gorcum near the Arkel Gate, and bisects the town into an upper and a lower section before falling gently into the broad bosom of the mighty Merwede, which flows from east to west in the direction of Rotterdam and the North Sea. Higher up, the Linge is but a bucolic stream, draining farm lands, rolling past fine rural estates, and it is navigable only to small craft, flat-bottomed, horse-drawn barges, tugboats, and the like. It was the stream where the young ladies of Gorcum used to go boating and rowing on summer afternoons. Many an idyl ripened to love in the shady landing-places along the shores planted with pollard willows.

The ancestors of the Van Alphens, the builders of the factory, had dug a canal starting about a mile to the north of Gorcum. The canal connected with the Linge River, captured its waters, and after a wide semicircular curve rejoined the same river about a quarter of a mile above the town. The factory sat squarely across this canal. A system of sluice gates controlled the flow of water. A dam some twenty feet high just above the factory produced the falls that operated the machinery of the plant. It was an old-fashioned arrangement, no doubt, but provided a cheap source of motive power.

The factory itself was a substantial structure, built for the ages, two stories high of red and yellow brick. It was none the worse for its three hundred years, the Van Alphens always having kept their property in perfect repair. The most interesting part of the place was the basement where the gigantic wooden wheels turned, creaking and thundering with a deafening roar and splashing the water into foam-crested waves. There was a whole system of wheels, large and small, interlocking with each other and connected by shafts and furiously winding spindles through the ceiling with the hammers on the main floor. By approaching the factory from the town side and going along the banks of the canal, you could enter that wheel room in the basement and watch the spectacle unobserved by any of the employees. I did it many times when a youngster and remember being chased off the property but once.

Those hammers on the main floor beat the oil into the leather to make it supple. Others crushed the hides into tanned leather. It was a noisy business, and men working in those rooms had to shout at the top of their voices when they wanted to make themselves heard. In other rooms on the main floor were large stone kilns and metal tanks containing acrid-smelling chemicals and fluids in which the leather in various stages of preparation lay soaking and stinking.

It was in the hammer room that the first serious incident occurred, shortly after closing time on an afternoon in July 1941. Most of the workers who were left were in the act of tidying up, changing to their street clothes in the locker rooms. Many had already joined those from the other industrial plants who were streaming homeward along the road. A German supervisor, a man named Karl Meltzer, an unbearable pompous ass with a strong dosage of the superman mentality, who had shown himself particularly harsh in his dealings with the workers on a number of occasions, had left earlier in the day. Now he suddenly returned. He came racing through the Arkel Gate in his Mercedes car and, noticing the workers going home, stopped several groups with a shouted order to go back at once to their place of work. The workers shrugged their shoulders, acted as if they hadn't heard or hadn't understood, and calmly continued on their way home. Meltzer alighted at the factory gate, ran into the office, a small detached building, looked around for the manager, Hein Dermout, and not finding him, rushed out again into the factory. In the now silent hammer room he came upon Dirk Dermout in conversation with Hendrik Petersen, one of the foremen. The two were busy repairing some machinery. Another man was below in the wheel room passing up a rope through a trapdoor in the floor.

The German ordered Dirk to have the workmen brought back immediately in view of a rush order for an extraordinarily heavy supply of finished leather that had just come by telegraph from the supreme Commissariat Department. Dirk replied that the men had left and that it would be almost impossible to bring them back at that hour. Couldn't the execution of the order be delayed till tomorrow? What was the rush?

"Don't you understand?" snapped the German. "*Jetzt geht's los gegen Russland. Die grosse Stunde ist gekommen.* We're about to attack Russia. The supreme hour has struck. We need boots, boots, and still more boots to kick those Asiatic swine back into China or into the Pacific Ocean. This is a top priority order, don't you see! Go out at once and get those men back!"

"Where d'you think you are, in the barrack square at Potsdam?" asked Dirk quietly.

"I am where I am," the German screamed back. "I am the one who commands here and no one else."

"Since when?" asked Dirk.

"Do you refuse to obey an order of the German Army, Herr Dermout?" asked the Nazi, his face purple with rage. As he spoke he reached for the revolver in his belt.

Dirk shrugged his shoulders. "Pipe down, man," he said. "Hitler isn't barefooted yet, is he?"

The German whipped out his gun and pointed it at Dirk's breast. "Now," he said, "you will come with me, you damned Dutch pig." And turning to the foreman, he added: "Call the Gestapo station and tell them I have a prisoner for them."

The foreman, who had been kneeling down looking through a shaft into the wheel room, slowly rose to his feet. As he brushed the sawdust off his trousers he called casually through the trapdoor: "That's all right now, Simon. Let her go!"

Immediately the rumble of the big water wheels going into motion could be heard and all the big hammers in the room slowly rose in the air. The German looked around startled.

At that instant Dirk lunged forward and knocked the man's chin up with a blow of his fist. Meltzer staggered on his feet and grunted. He blinked, but he still held the revolver in his hand. The foreman plunged forward too, seized the German around the waist, lifted him bodily from the floor, and smacked him down on the huge flat table. The hammers were coming down with regular rhythm. Without a moment's hesitation, the foreman pushed the

German's head to a point where a hammer blow struck him square in the face.

"That's one who won't go to Russia," he said quietly as he picked up Herr Meltzer's pistol.

The worker named Simon came up through the trapdoor, looked at the dead German, and asked: "What do we do with that?"

"Slide him into the hole," said the foreman. "The rats are as hungry as we are."

"Take off his coat first," said Dirk. "I need it. We can't leave his car standing in front of the plant here. I'm going to drive it into town."

Herr Meltzer was stripped of his uniform and a moment later dumped like a sack through the trapdoor into the Linge Canal.

"Sir," said the foreman to Dirk, "you better make yourself scarce. This is not going to be a joking matter to the *Moffen*, you may depend on it. Put on gloves before you touch that automobile."

Dirk waited till dark, changed into Meltzer's uniform, hid his own clothes under the seat, drove the car into town and out through the Chancellory Gate, then in an abandoned stretch of marshland near the Merwede's edge changed back into his own clothes and, leaving the car slowly sinking in the swamp, walked back home.

Dirk told his parents and grandfather at dinner what had happened at the factory.

"You're sure no one else was around except Petersen and Simon?" asked Hein. "What about the night watchman?"

"Simon engaged the watchman in conversation while I drove off the car," said Dirk.

"Did the body sink?" asked Grandfather van Alphen.

"I couldn't tell. We never even looked."

"We'll have to go over and make sure," said the old man. "The body can't stay where it is. If it floats, they'll find it tomorrow. If it sinks, they're bound to go dredging in a few days when Meltzer is missed. Once they are convinced there's . . . a . . . mystery involved, they'll leave nothing untried to unravel it. The body is bound to turn up sooner or later downstream or near by. It'll be all the same. That is, unless we do something about it now."

"But we can't bury the body," remarked Hein. "How can we get it out of the water, out of the factory, without someone noticing?"

"The body should stay in the factory," said Adriana.

"There's no room for burial in the factory or near it," said Hein.

"I'm not thinking about burial," said Adriana. "We'll drop it in one of the kilns, cover it with hides, and let it dissolve in the brine."

"It won't dissolve in brine. Brine would rather preserve it."

"No, but it will dissolve in potassium cyanide," said Adriana. "We have to get busy right away."

"I'll get Petersen," said Hein.

"You'll stay right here at home," came back Adriana. "Neither you nor Dirk is going to be seen leaving this house this evening. In fact I'm going to make certain that you are seen here at home. Call the military commander, Freiherr von Schwabenfels and ask him over for a party of whist. Get Zeger van Rietvelt, too, and a few others. Let them think we have changed our minds, that we are admirers of Hitler. But get them here."

"But what about the body?" everybody asked.

"I'll take care of that myself tonight after our guests have left," said Adriana. "Only I want Grandpa to call the watchman while I'm at the factory and keep him here at the house until I have done the work."

"But, Mother, you can't be thinking . . ." began Dirk.

Ah, that Adriana! The courage she had, the fearlessness of that woman! What trials and terrors did she go through in shielding those she loved! Now that the war is over and the specter of fascism driven off the scene for the time being, one hears so much of what the men did, of the valor of our soldiers, of their almost incredible achievements under murderous fire and in hazardous circumstances seemingly inextricable. We have learned very little of the role of our women under the brown terror. Yet after the liberation of the Netherlands I had received up to the beginning of October 1945 fifty-nine letters from all parts of Holland, from men, women and children, friends, relatives, and some perfect strangers, and I must say that I have not ceased marveling at the display of courage in the face of a monstrous tyranny on the part of humble and timid women of whom one never would have thought that they would dare venture outdoors at all. Many did things as brave as Adriana, indeed. The performance of some borders on the incredible and the fantastic, although in writing about their own contribution they mention it in the most casual way, as something self-evident and perfectly obvious.

Alone, Adriana went to the factory that night. She avoided the royal road of the main streets and the Arkel Gate. At that last point she was bound to be seen by the sentinels and would most probably have had to show her identification papers. No, she slipped out of the back door of the big house on the High Street, followed the narrow alleys between gardens and back yards, and after making a wide detour slid down the earthen walls of the ramparts. Then, following the banks of the Linge Canal, she entered the wheel room beneath the tannery in the same way we boys used to get in when we wanted to have a look at the wondrous machinery. The night watchman, she knew, was absent from his post and would remain with his old patroon until she returned.

Stumbling and falling a dozen times, tearing her clothes and bruising herself severely, she finally crawled through the last tunnel of that molehill of passages, manholes, and conduits, and only then switched on her electric torch. She had reached the wheel room. She wasn't long in locating the body. It was in an upright position, standing up in the water, as it were, right in front of one of the motionless big wheels. Meltzer's head was slowly bobbing up and down as his body was rocked by the rhythm of the waves. An involuntary cry escaped her when she noticed that Meltzer's eyes were open. Could he be alive? The thought must have flashed through her mind that moment that if he were indeed alive, she would have to kill him right there and then for Dirk's sake. I doubt not that she would have been capable of it. But Meltzer was dead. The eyes were fixed and glassy, staring unseeingly at the shadows her figure threw on the whitewashed walls of the vast underground room.

She placed her torch against the wall, pulled on a pair of rubber kitchen gloves, took one of the hooked poles from the bracket on the wall, and started to pull the body toward the bank of the canal. When it was dancing and rubbing against the wall, Adriana knelt on the narrow quay and reached over. But the short wet hairs made the head slip through her fingers. She tried a few more times with no better result. She then realized she would not be able to raise the body except by getting into the canal herself and pushing it up from below. Quietly she undressed and slipped into the cold water next the corpse that danced away from her as if it were playing a game. The body was still with rigor mortis. Adriana, treading the water, hugged the corpse around the knees and after a struggle in the course of which the dead man slid from her grasp again and again, she finally lifted him onto the quay. But the heaviest part of the work still lay before her.

To lift that unwieldy and unyielding mass to her shoulders and carry it up the stairs to the tankroom was something that would have taxed the strength of a Hercules. Adriana had always been an athletic woman and was robustly built, but she was fifty years old or thereabouts. No matter how she tried, she could not raise the inert object from the floor. As long as the body was in the canal, the buoyancy of the water had helped her. Now the weight paralyzed her arms. She hesitated for a moment, wondering if it would not be better to send her husband and son to the factory early in the morning before the workmen arrived and have Hein and Dirk do the rest of the job. But no, neither Hein nor Dirk must be seen. They mustn't be seen by anybody. Not the slightest opening must be allowed to implicate them in the killing of Meltzer.

Adriana got dressed and dragged the body to the foot of the stairs. And then began the ascent, the most arduous and most heartbreaking part of the night's work. The stairway was a narrow spiral shaft with sufficient room for just one man to go up or down. Step by step she drew and pulled the body up. Three or four times the stiff, unbending burden became wedged between the wall and the steps in that narrow tubelike passage so that Adriana had to jerk and heave and even kick it loose. At last it was done. The body was upstairs. She doused her lamp and felt her way to the first tank. Then she went back and dragged the body over the floor, raised it inch by inch against the tank, and finally heaved it over the side. She did not step back quickly enough to avoid her clothes being splashed with the evil-smelling concoction in which the leather lay soaking.

She sank exhausted against the wall. Suddenly a flash of her lamp revealed that the man's wet underclothing had left a trail from the head of the stairway to the tank. She wiped the floor thoroughly dry with some jute bags she found lying in a corner. Then, plunging her arms into the adjoining tank, she pulled out three inordinately heavy moisture-soaked cowhides and slid them into the container that held Meltzer's body. He was covered. Once more she wiped the floor, and then began the homeward journey, crawling back through the slime-covered water of the tunnels, wading across the oozy moats before the town wall, scrambling up the ramparts, and sneaking into town dodging the patrols who did not miss even the alleys and back yards on their nocturnal rounds. At last she was back at her own garden door and fell into the arms of her waiting husband and son.

"It's done," she said simply as they carried her upstairs. "You can tell Father to let the watchman go back to his job."

Of course the absence of Herr Meltzer was noticed the next day in official quarters. But it did not immediately produce any anxiety on his score. Those Nazi *Herren* knew each other and their missing colleague too well to be alarmed. They snickered amongst themselves, putting forth conjectures as to which Dutch girl or woman could be having the honor and pleasure of Red Karl's presence.

Only when three days had passed and Meltzer still hadn't

shown up do they seem to have begun to worry. After that it took perhaps another week before the sleuths established the fact that the missing supervisor had last been seen riding toward the factory at eventide. From that point, however, they lost all track of him again. They arrested the foreman, Hendrik Petersen, and the night watchman. They put these two men through twenty-four hours of grueling questioning, beating and torturing them, yet failed to get the slightest clue as to the whereabouts of their vanished colleague. Then they began dredging the canal and the Linge River, which showed, as Mijnheer van Alphen remarked, that they were on the right track, or nearing it at least, and that their suspicions centered upon the tannery and its environment as the scene of the crime. A few days later they were positively convinced that there was foul play involved in Meltzer's disappearance when one of their experts, having taken a young prostitute for a walk in that deserted and swampy part of the Merwede's shore, accidentally came upon Herr Meltzer's abandoned automobile.

Then the Nazi rage knew no bounds. A score of the most prominent citizens were immediately seized as hostages at their homes and lodged in a coal shed behind the King William barracks. These men, who hadn't the slightest knowledge of the Meltzer affair, were informed that if the mystery of the supervisor's disappearance was not solved within a week, two of their number would be executed at the expiration of that term and two more every week thereafter for so long as the man's unexplained absence continued. In addition the local Gestapo, reinforced by a squad of fiends from the neighboring city of Dordt under the command of a certain Hauptmann Birker—who had won his laurels in terrorizing Moravian peasants and who was known in that country as the Butcher—began a systematic search of every house and building in the community.

A detachment of these silent green-uniformed individuals would suddenly drive into a given neighborhood, close off the streets, and arrest every male inhabitant in the roped-off quarter from the age of sixteen up, and of course any man who happened to be found walking or at work in those particular streets. The arrested persons were loaded in trucks and driven to the local *Sicherheits Polizei* headquarters, whence, after undergoing a few days of questioning, bullying, and hunger, they were shipped off to labor camps in the Reich. Many of these razzias took place in the middle of the night when every citizen could be expected to be home. The sound of the motortrucks suddenly roaring into a street or a district, the sharp commands ringing out and the clatter of the hobnailed boots on the cobblestones, became one of the most dreaded aspects of the occupation. That was the terror raging at night of which the psalmist speaks, the silent pestilence that flieth in the darkness. Men would rush to the roofs or into cellars or some secret hiding-place in their homes to escape the searching parties. Often to no avail, for the Germans are thoroughgoing in whatever they undertake.

Indeed they left not a nook or a corner untouched. They went about tapping walls, ceilings, and floors for sliding panels and loose boards, pouring burning oil down the chimneys, and even descending into wells to inspect their walls. Houses were often reduced to wreckage by these searchers as they battered down partitions and hollow-sounding cupboards and as they simply dumped household material out of the windows in order, as they said, to have more room for their investigation. On the queer theory that each act of depredation and terrorization was bound to increase the Dutch people's respect for the German name, everything went with military precision; the more damage done the better. The effect, of course, was the very opposite: it only served to deepen loathing and detestation for a nation turned into brutal marauders.

The arrest of the hostages threw the Van Alphen family into deep consternation. What were they to do? Hein and Dirk Dermout continued to go to work in the morning and behaved as if the disappearance of Herr Meltzer concerned them only remotely. This was thought to be the best way to avert suspicion. Besides, the testimony of Freiherr von Schwabenfels, the local military commander, and of Zeger van Rietvelt that they had spent the better part of the evening of the labor supervisor's mysterious vanishment as guests at the big house on the High Street, and that they had there been in the presence of all the members of the family, was taken at its full value. Zeger gave his personal assurance that the Van Alphens themselves were not implicated in the affair. Their attitude toward the occupying power was perfectly correct, he said. They were sincerely collaborating and setting an example in the community in establishing friendly relations between Germanic brothers who were at last standing together under the Führer's illustrious leadership to make a new Europe and a new Holland.

Even so, after supper at eventide the Van Alphen family withdrew to the old merchant's room, to discuss and weigh every angle of their predicament. They were in a sore quandary. Mijnheer van Alphen said he could not bear the thought of the authorities carrying their threat of executing two of those perfectly innocent fellow citizens into effect on the following Saturday while he remained an inactive bystander. Should someone then go to the Gestapo and make a clean breast of it all, explain Meltzer's death as purely accidental? What good would that do? Would that save the hostages? Would the confession be believed? Wouldn't the *Sicherheits Polizei* ask the question why, if Meltzer's death was an accident, the body had been hidden, why it had been stripped of its uniform, why such extraordinary precautions had been taken to remove all traces of a simple accident? Why hadn't a physician been called, and why had Meltzer's body not been allowed to lie where it fell until the police arrived? And then that ugly wound on the forehead. How could Herr Meltzer have fallen on his back on one of the tables in such a position that his head was like a piece of iron on a smithy's anvil in the path of a descending hammer?

They realized that they could never explain Meltzer's death away as an accident. After all, the Germans were not fools. Nobody would believe that Adriana had made the body disappear. That would seem altogether incredible. The Van Alphens were in distress and time was pressing. The public execution had been set for three in the afternoon on Saturday. The relatives of the condemned men had been notified. What to do? For Dirk Dermout to give himself up would, of course, mean death. And would that set the men free? Wouldn't the Germans rather seize the opportunity of an eventual confession to stage a mass auto-da-fé, as they had done in so many places, to make the population cower? One thing was certain. The Gestapo would not easily accept a young man's explanation of his having acted in panic in covering up all traces of an accident. Moreover, that Dirk should sacrifice himself—of that Adriana wouldn't hear. She would rather go herself, she said. But even then, if she confessed, her son and husband would still not be safe. They would at once be apprehended as material witnesses.

Dirk was in favor of collecting a few resolute men in the gardens adjoining the King William barracks and on the night preceding the scheduled execution make an attempt to set the hostages free. "And suppose you do succeed," said his father, "will that be the end?" Where could the liberated men be hidden? Wouldn't a raid like that be the signal for a reign of terror in the community—tortures and killings without number and in the end a wholesale roundup of the remaining men for deportation to the Reich's slave and murder camps? Who knew whether the Germans in their fury might not repeat the ferocious performance of Lidice in Czechoslovakia? Their press was always boasting of the exemplary, salutary, and wholesome effect of implacable, pitiless reprisals for acts of rebellion or even for an attempt on the life of a single Nazi boss. They might well be looking for a chance to crush the spirit of the Dutch people once and for all. To set the hostages free, Hein argued, would start a chain of events of which none could foresee the end. The time wasn't ripe for open organized resistance. Power and arms and initiative were all on the German side. The time would come, but it was not yet.

Mijnheer van Alphen nodded his head at these words, but the subject of liberating and hiding the hostages seemed to have made him thoughtful. He had made up his mind. "We can't waste any more time in talk," he said. "We have to act and act quickly. If you will dismiss the servants a little early tonight," he said, addressing his daughter, "but in such a way that they do not suspect that you want them out of the way, there is something I would like to show you children."

And so when the big old house had grown still and all the lights had been extinguished, Mijnheer van Alphen took the members of his family through the long hallway down the stairs leading to the cellar. He walked ahead with a flashlight, followed by Hein and Adriana. His grandson Dirk, carrying another pocket torch, brought up the rear. They went through the spacious cold rooms where the wine and the preserves were stored until they came to a vaulted arch. "Mind you don't hurt yourself," said the old man as he stooped to avoid the archway and the heavy crossbeams in the narrow passage they had entered. Of course they had all been in the cellar before. Adriana and Dirk had often played there as children. There was nothing mysterious or uncanny about it. The only strange thing was that the old merchant should have taken them down there at that time of night.

"As you know," said Mijnheer van Alphen, as he walked from one room into another, "this is the oldest part of our house. My great-grandfather who built here used the foundations of a former structure. These stones actually date from the thirteenth century. But of course you know all that. I have told it so often. Here on this site once stood the town house of the Seigneurs van Arkel. One thing you don't know I will show you presently."

He stopped at the end of the vaulted passageway and gave young Dirk his flashlight to hold. "This wall," he said, pointing to the stone slabs at the end of the passage, "holds a secret. It is really a door." With that he started to count the stones in the top row of the wall in front of him until he came to the fifth. This he pressed with the flat of his hand. It slid back nearly half a foot. At the same time one of the flagstones in the floor sank a few inches.

"Reach into that hole now," he said to Dirk, pointing to the spot where the flat stone in the floor had lowered itself. "You'll find a ring there on the right-hand side. Pull that ring upward." Dirk knelt down and did as he was told.

"Now," continued Mijnheer van Alphen, "you have taken the catch off that door from the inside."

He again counted the stones. "Number four in the second layer, straight down now," he muttered, "number five in the fourth, number seven in the sixth. Here we are." He leaned his shoulders against the wall. Slowly, without any noise, it opened.

A cold, musty air rushed into their faces from the opening. Throwing their lights forward, they saw a steep stone stairway leading downward.

"Down there," said the old man, "are the famous old tunnels that run under the city in all directions. This stairway connects with a passage that goes from Brother Street, where once stood the monastery of the Minor Brothers, to the crypt of the Great Church. Both exits are walled up now. Nobody knows at what point exactly the tunnels came into the church. It's so many years since alterations were made in the church's foundations. Another long burrow runs from Sister Street, where you can still tell by the façade of the houses that they were once part and parcel of a cloister, the so-called Sister House. The second passage also runs to the church.

"But this tunnel, the one we are in now, runs from the old Van Arkel mansion, from our house, that is, all the way to the Arkel Gate. It passes under the ramparts and terminates inside one of the earthen powder magazines outside the town walls. That exit too is closed, but with a secret door similar to that in our cellar. It's possible for a man starting from our house to get out of town without being observed by anybody. There are not many other persons besides myself in Gorcum who are in the secret," he added. "Two or three at the most. They are the proprietors of houses that also have a connecting passage. One is in the branch office of the Netherlands Bank. But even the director there doesn't know of its existence. Some years ago when the gas main was laid, a portion of the principal tunnel was laid bare and the workmen entered it. You remember, Adriana, how they came upon a stairway leading to the site of the old Brother House and found the skeletons of seventy monks?"

"I remember," said Hein. "We schoolboys went down, too."

"Well," continued Mijnheer van Alphen, "I was a member of the Council then and I had the tunnels closed up immediately. My father showed me the secret entry into our part of the underground city, as his father had shown him before at the time of the Napoleonic occupation. Farther back in the sixteenth century, it was from this place that patriots or Water Beggars, as they were then called, waged their war for the Prince of Orange against the Spaniards.

"But let's go down. I want to show you something," he added and leading the way, he descended the steps.

"Grandfather, be careful," said Dirk suddenly as they stood at the foot of the stairs. "I thought I saw something moving there in the distance, a light or something . . ."

"Of course, of course," came back Mijnheer van Alphen. "That's where I am taking you."

"Hey there!" he called out in a loud voice.

"Hallo!" came the answer. A light flashed on and a man could be seen walking in their direction. When he came near they recognized Hendrik Petersen, the foreman.

"Where are the others?" asked Mijnheer van Alphen.

"They're coming, sir!" said Petersen.

Another man stepped into the light.

"Well, if it isn't Ary!" exclaimed Adriana. "How glad I am to see you!"

"Dr. Brandt," said Dirk as he shook hands with the Pastor, "everybody thought you were in Germany, in some damned camp or other."

"Not yet, not yet," said Ary with a laugh. "I am still safe and sound, as you can see, thanks to your dear grandfather." Turning to Mijnheer van Alphen, he added: "Dr. Mendoza is asleep. We have just returned from a long walk to the grate near the powder magazine to get some exercise and our daily dose of fresh air. The Doctor is a little weary these last few days. He complains of the inactivity down here."

"I am showing my children the best hiding-place in the world," said Mijnheer van Alphen. "God knows how soon they'll need it." Then, taking Ary by the arm, he started walking into the depths of the tunnel, talking the while of what was uppermost in his mind: the circumstances surrounding the disappearance of Herr Meltzer and the German threat to begin executing the hostages within a few days. The others followed. Around a long curve in the tunnel they soon came upon a wooden hut built in a recess or bay. The door was open and by the light of a candle on the table inside they could see the peacefully reclining figure of the old physician. His snow-white beard contrasted sharply with the dark-green quilt he had thrown over himself. The sound of footsteps and voices awakened him and he sat up on his bunk. Adriana rushed to his side and grasped his hands.

"Is this where you are?" she said. "We all thought you had been shipped off to Germany."

"Your father decreed otherwise," answered Dr. Mendoza. "If he hadn't taken me down here a month ago, I'd probably be even farther away than Germany by now."

Mijnheer van Alphen began telling the Doctor of the latest developments in international affairs. "It seems," he said, "that Hitler is about to attack Russia. There are some enormous orders for supplies, and they are stripping our country bare."

"The time has come to fight," said Dr. Mendoza. "If Hitler conquers Russia, Europe is lost. With the resources of Russia at his command he could resist indefinitely and hold the Western world at bay. In that case even America would have to come to terms with him."

"We're going to stop as many Germans as we can from leaving for Russia," said Hendrik Petersen. "We've stopped one and there'll be others."

Before disclosing what action was taken to extricate the Van Alphens from their predicament, perhaps something should be said in explanation of Ary Brandt's and Dr. Mendoza's presence in that subterranean asylum. Both were actively sought by the Gestapo. Ary was parish minister of a large village in the extreme northern part of the province when the war broke out. He immediately drew the ire of the German military authorities by the tone and substance of his sermons. A man who preached that God rules the world, and not this or that Führer, who castigated collaborationism and the blood-and-soil theory of the Nazis, and who furthermore openly advocated passive resistance to the conquering hosts, was not likely to last long. In August 1940, three months after the invasion, he was banished from his parish and enjoined, on pain of arrest and deportation, to speak no more in public anywhere in the land.

He took his wife and children to his father's home in Altena near Gorcum and lived there for nearly a year. When he learned that the Germans intended to introduce the Nuremberg Laws in Holland, he came out of his retirement and went around the country calling on hundreds of his colleagues in the Protestant ministry to persuade them to join him in making a collective protest. He succeeded in rallying some ninety pastors to the cause. It was Ary who led the solemn procession of these men, all dressed in their Geneva gowns, through the streets of The Hague to the palace occupied by Seyss-Inquart.

Admitted to the august presence of this double traitor, Ary made a plea to spare Holland the humiliation of seeing an organized persecution of the Jews take place on her ancient, free soil. If the Germans sought to win the confidence of the Dutch people, he said, it was impolitic and unwise to set about destroying one of the noblest traditions on which the Republic of the Netherlands was founded: the tradition of religious freedom and respect for the People of the Book. He brought all his eloquence and passion to bear. He appealed to the Governor on moral grounds, on religious grounds, on political grounds, on cultural grounds. In his zeal he even overstepped the bounds of propriety and safety by uttering a threat. "The Jewish people," he said, "will live, no matter what you do. But your name and the name of Germany's thinkers and scholars, poets and states-

men, will go down in history with shame and execration."
It was of no avail. Seyss-Inquart smiled his thin, cruel
smile, shook his head, and repeated the Führer's idiotic
clichés about the Jews being the curse of mankind. They
were Bolsheviks and international plutocrats at the same
time. They must be segregated from the rest of humanity
for its sake and for their own sake. "Besides," declared the
Governor, "this is the order of the Führer himself."

"In that case," replied Ary, "Your Excellency had better
segregate us, too. The Jews are innocent. We stand four-
square with our Jewish brethren." With these words, he
and all the pastors present reached under their gowns and
took out the yellow badges of shame, which Jews were
forced to wear by way of identification, and fastened the
armlets around the sleeves of their gowns.

Ary returned to Altena, but he was soon on the road
again. He sought out Anton Mussert, an old acquaintance
of school days. He tried to persuade the leader of the Dutch
Nazi Bund to intervene in the Jews' behalf. For answer, the
Dutch Führer covered him with imprecations. He stormed
and fumed as if he were Hitler himself. He raged at the
Jews, at Gorcum, at the Gymnasium, at ecclesiastical troublemakers, and warned Ary that he would have him arrested
and sent to a place where he could do no more harm. Mussert let our friend depart, but a week later he inquired of
Zeger van Rietvelt where Ary could be located. Zeger
dropped a word about the search for Ary at the Van Alphen
home within the hearing of Adriana, who thereupon sent
Ary a message of warning. Mijnheer van Alphen, who had
also heard, quietly crossed the River Merwede one afternoon, called at Burgomaster Brandt's house, packed Ary
off in his closed carriage, and brought him to Gorcum. When
some of the most accomplished searchers of the Gestapo,
set on Dr. Brandt's trail, were forced to admit after three
months' futile search that their quarry seemed to have been
swallowed by the earth, they little suspected how close they
came to the truth.

Dr. Mendoza had been saved from the molestations of
the Gestapo in the same manner by his old friend Van

Alphen. Four or five times the retired physician had been arrested by the *Sicherheits Polizei*. He had been questioned and maltreated and then set free again, until Mijnheer van Alphen stepped in and made an end of the cruel game of cat and mouse by inviting him to the house on High Street one evening and taking him below ground to keep Pastor Brandt company. A few days after the killing of Karl Meltzer the two fugitives were joined there by Hendrik Petersen, the foreman. . . .

Now had also come the time for Dirk Dermout and his father Hein to go into hiding. Back in the house after the trip into the tunnels, Mijnheer van Alphen told his son-in-law and his grandson that the Gestapo would be looking for them in a few hours' time. "Take your clothes and blankets down," he said, "some chairs and couches, and count on staying underground for a long time. I have arranged for an increase in the food supply. Do not venture aboveground until you are notified."

They did as they were told. Mijnheer van Alphen himself led them back to the secret entrance in the basement, explained the mechanism of the contrivance once more, embraced them both, and ascended the stairs. He then went into his library, destroyed some papers, and in the middle of the night put on his hat and walked to his factory. He seems to have spoken with the night watchman for a few minutes before going into his office. From there he called the local Gestapo bureau on the telephone: "If I disclose the hiding-place of Herr Meltzer's body and give you the name of the man who killed him, will the hostages be set free?"

The answer was in the affirmative.

"In that case," said the old merchant, "send some men to the tannery and let them lift the hides in kiln number seven. The watchman will show them that particular tank, although that man, I warn you, doesn't know at this moment, and never knew, that the body is there. I am Dirk van Alphen. I killed Karl Meltzer. I did it without help from anybody."

"Where are you now?" came a voice.

"I am at my factory. I'll be waiting for you there."

Within five minutes after that telephone call, the Gestapo's sirens screamed through the dark and deserted streets and the automobiles loaded with helmeted Elite Guards came to a halt in front of the Van Alphen factory. The surprised and trembling watchman was ordered to switch on all the lights and ordered to lead the officials to tank number seven. He lifted some slabs of rotting leather: there lay the half-decomposed body of the slain Meltzer.

"Where is Herr van Alphen?"

"He was in the factory ten minutes ago," gasped the shaking watchman. "He didn't come back to the office. I was waiting there for him when you arrived. There is no other exit from the buildings at night except through the office."

"Throw a cordon around the buildings and search the place!"

The door leading to the wheel room was found to be locked. The watchman tried his key. Still it wouldn't open. It was nailed down. Axes were brought, but the very men sent to fetch those instruments sounded the alarm.

"The building is on fire!" they yelled into the tankroom. "All the lower structure is blazing."

There wasn't a ghost of a chance to save the factory. The old wooden understructure with the dried-out timbers was like a torch held below a box of matches. The flames were sucked through the stairways to the top story, where, unaccountably, all the windows had been left open. The Germans could hear the dry leather in the stockrooms catching fire like scrolls of paper. When the watchman turned in the alarm, the flames had already reached the roof. Wild billowing flames enwrapped the building on all sides. The Gestapo men hastened to bring their parked automobiles to safety from the flying sparks and the burning dislocated chunks of wood from the roof and rafters that came hurtling through the air with the force of an explosion.

As they stood waiting for the fire trucks to arrive, they suddenly saw the figure of a man moving about in the second story. The man carried a flaming torch in his hand and quietly walked past the row of open windows. Occasionally he lowered his torch. Immediately the flames leaped up behind him.

That was the last seen of Mijnheer van Alphen.

When the Gestapo men arrived at the residence on the High Street half an hour later, Adriana opened the door herself. They searched high and low. But Hein and Dirk could not be found.

From that day onward the old tunnels under the city assumed an ever-greater importance. They became the rallying center for the nascent underground movement in our part of the province. Naturally, it always remained difficult and hazardous to evade the German police in reaching the subterranean retreat, in spite of the fact that the old exits under the former site of the monastery were secretly opened by the patriots, as well as the entrance under the Sister House and the one among the tombs in the crypt of the Great Church. But once arrived underground, the partisans were as safe as if they were hidden in the depths of the Sahara Desert. They could plan and plot and talk over their condition and the condition of town and country without fear of detection or of being overheard. So long as the Gestapo remained in the dark about the entrances to the tunnels, the partisans were out of their reach. They could piece together the information men collected in various parts of the district, and give to the resistance movement both organization and intelligent method.

For nearly two years, until the glorious day of the liberation of Gorcum by the Canadian Army, the town of Gorcum was one of the irrepressible sore spots in the German system of occupation. Men sabotaged the work in the factories and workshops, and when the Gestapo began its investigation, the patriots simply disappeared. Patrols of Germans roaming in the quietest villages of the neighborhood, confiscating cattle, horses, and farm products, would suddenly come face to face with a band of determined, well-armed men who would shoot it out with them, drive them to flight, wreck their vehicles, and recapture their plunder. It was impossible for the Germans to keep a gasoline dump anywhere in or near the town. Hardly had they collected a stock in one locality, in some warehouse in town or at some lonely farm outside, when the partisans appeared on the scene, shot up the sentries, took what they required, and set the rest of the drums on fire.

The railway bridge over the canal was blown up. The canal itself was blocked for a whole year by the sinking of two bargeloads of cement. The German patrols were doubled and trebled. To no avail. The partisans changed their tactics as circumstances required. In the stillest hour of the night a jug of gasoline would suddenly come hurtling through the window of a police station. The Germans would tumble out of the post through a burst of flame and turmoil, firing their revolvers and rushing into the street. But the culprit would have flown. No use giving pursuit, for there might be an ambush around the next dark corner. On nights of storm the Bavarian garrison was tense with apprehension. Those Dutchmen of the underground staged their most daring exploits in these nights when the wind blew half a gale and the rain came down in torrents. Then they were in their element and the Germans in a dither.

The streets seemed to swarm with vengeful phantoms on such occasions; every dark corner might suddenly spew forth death and destruction. In a deserted street a pistol shot would ring out and a German would fall heavily to the pavement and lie there a huddled heap of green-gray soaking in the rain. On one such a night one of their bakeries caught fire from something that came down the chimney. When the fire trucks were brought up it was found the hose had been cut and the hydrants tampered with. It got so bad that German patrols were afraid to venture out after dark, or as one former partisan wrote me after the liberation: The Bavarian *Landwehr* men at the King William barracks were so jittery that they did not dare go to the toilet alone.

The tunnel sent forth its fighters day after day and night after night. The Dutch, in making for themselves a retreat as inaccessible as the mountain crags of Norway, had created the essential condition for a successful guerrilla warfare, as they created the essential condition for peace by their conquest of the water of the Zuyder Sea. Of course, several were caught and put to the torture. But the most fiendish torments could not make the prisoners of the Gestapo give up the secret of their comrades' hiding-place. Not one, not even the young boys and girls who served the underground as couriers and who fell into the hands of the enemy, uttered as much as a hint as to where the center of resistance was located. Neither promises of riches and honor, nor threats, nor the tearing-out of their fingernails or the crushing of their sexual organs could make those youngsters comply with the demands of their torturers. They gritted their teeth, spat in their captors' faces, and died without a word.

Adriana was, if not the silent leader of the underground, the chief inspiration of the fighters for freedom. She it was who had revealed the secret of her house to the most determined of the partisans in the first place, and who had brought them to safety. Scores of men and women had passed through her cellar into the tunnel system, not only Gorcummers but farmers from the neighborhood and some hardpressed leaders from other towns and cities in Holland. Nine British airmen and two Americans who had been forced to bail out over Holland on their way to bombing raids over Germany were found to be inmates of the underground retreat on the day of liberation.

It was she who supervised and provided the food supply for that band of latter-day Water Beggars. She had turned her house into the gayest social center in the community. To all appearances she was the most brazen collaborationist. She had all the top Nazi officials at the dances and dinners she gave at the big house on the High Street. She was seen openly walking in the streets with the bemedaled representatives of the *Herrenvolk* and their wives and sweethearts. For the entertainments she gave, she required heaps of food and wines and viands. She celebrated Hitler's birthday and Göring's and the birthdays of all the local Nazi leaders. She let no opportunity pass to stage a celebration and dazzle her guests with the "colossal" amount of food she had on her sideboards and tables. The German authorities refused her nothing; so genial a hostess, so ardent an admirer of the Führer, and all things Nazi, was entitled to the best. Most of the provisions went below into the cellar after the guests had departed.

It was Adriana in the end who was instrumental in bringing about the easy, although not quite bloodless, capture of the town by the Canadians. For six months after Montgomery's failure to get across the Rhine at Arnhem, the Canadians stood within twelve miles of Gorcum to the south in the Province of Brabant. During that time the Germans mined the ramparts and the approaches of the town so heavily that an eventual Canadian attack would have been of the costliest. However, Adriana learned from her German "friends" that the electric wires connected with the formidable piles of explosives under the ramparts all ended in a control room of the Citadel. The mere throw of a switch, she was told, at the moment of an attack, would send both the bulwarks and the men on them skyward in a series of terrific explosions. Adriana warned the underground of the German plan and of the technical preparations.

The partisans prevented what might have been a disaster to the Canadian Army by collecting all the gunpowder and dynamite they could find in the old powder magazine and piling it up in the tunnel at a point exactly beneath the site of the Citadel. When the signal came that the Canadians had crossed the Merwede a mile below Gorcum and were cautiously approaching the deathtraps under the ramparts from the land side, the Citadel itself blew up in a thunderous blast that shook the countryside.

The explosion laid bare a section of the old tunnels. But the surviving Germans had no time to investigate. The Canadians, who had been apprised of their preparations by the partisans, swarmed into the town through the five gates.

Chapter III

FAREWELL IN ROME

CROSSING the Piazza di Spagna, past the house where Keats died, past the naked and heavy pile of the Propaganda and the Virgin-topped column erected by Pius IX in honor of his dogma of the Immaculate Conception, I turned into the narrow Via Condotti and came out upon the Corso just above the Church of San Carlo, in which reposes the heart of that Carlo Borromeo, Cardinal and saint, who was. in his day one of the most spectacular adversaries of the Protestant Reformation. It had been raining all morning; the pavement was still wet, and a pleasant lukewarm sweet odor clung to the air. The afternoon sunlight had begun to tangle playfully with the jets of the fountains, and the walls of the Palazzo Chigi, visible in the near distance, swam in a burst of golden radiance. In that house of treasures the previous afternoon I had produced a somewhat amused and condescending smile on the faces of the Signors Mussolini, Mascia, and Augusto Turati when I ventured to remark that a former occupant of the same enormous room wherein we sat had been the gentle Alexander VII, who drank out of a human skull and who kept a coffin near to remind himself of the fleeting nature of all earthly grandeur.

Above the palace roof the sky was streamed with a banner of orange, or rather a thin layer of that color seemed superimposed upon the blue cloudless depth. It tempered the quality of the light and conveyed to the worn stones on every hand a soft, living polish. At that time of the year—it was a Saturday afternoon of May 1927—before the stifling summer heat and the miasmic humidity descend upon the city, Rome is often impregnated with that, to Northerners, so peculiar and almost unearthly glow which begins where the South begins—just below Lyon in France, from where it extends over the whole Mediterranean basin. This strange light of a startling white and yet of beneficent mildness reduces the tragic severity of the medieval fortress architecture of many of the city's palaces and at the same time prevents the night of ancient days from freezing the visitor's imagination. It gives him a Rome steeped in sweetness and tranquillity, an unreal, dreamlike city that at moments, when seen from the proper angle, as from the top of the Palatine Hill, seems to evaporate in the clarity of the day. On my walk to the Corso, I saw a faint bluish haze, hardly noticeable, float over the roofs of the houses in the lower quarters. It was of the thinness and delicacy of fine gauze. Beyond, in the immense Campagna the summits of the distant mountains were melting in a vapor of pale rose.

As usual on Saturday afternoons, or any afternoon for that matter, even during the tragicomical intermezzo of the Duce's reign, the Corso was crowded. It was as if the largest possible number of Romans had tried to compress itself into the narrowest possible space. As I emerged from the quiet Via Condotti, where I had not crossed a single wayfarer, it seemed hardly feasible that one more pedestrian should be able to launch himself upon that solid stream of humanity. If it weren't for the exquisite politeness of the Romans, who can always find room to make way for one more, I might have been forced to elbow my way into the crowd.

There is no street like the Corso anywhere on earth. It isn't really a street at all, it is a drawing-room in the open air where all Rome meets, as *tout Paris* met in the days of the Second Empire in a salon called the Church of the Madeleine. The crowding is almost promiscuous, but nobody takes this as a hardship. As a matter of fact, the essence of the pleasure of an afternoon on the Corso derives precisely from that crowdedness, from that enforced nearness which permits of an unexpected touch, a satisfied curiosity, a whisper, a hoped-for smile, or a dagger-sharp glance.

It is the royal road through which flows all the blood of the Eternal City as into a human heart. It offers a display without equal of vanity and curiosity-seeking. The whole city has given itself rendezvous to show off, to spy on its neighbor, to gossip, to strut, to gesticulate, to intrigue, to spread rumors and hear tattle, to salute, to bow, above all to burn up with a desire to be seen and cast about glances of admiration and tenderness with that amazing frankness of the race in affairs of the heart. A Roman who does not walk on the Corso in the afternoon is a man without a country, a man who doesn't know what's going on in the world. He is like the man in Paris or New York who doesn't read a newspaper. The atmosphere is that of a theatrical performance, of the foyer of a theater during the intermission. It is as if a storm of whispers passes by. More than once it has brought back to me a fleeting reminiscence of that moment in Gounod's *Faust* where in the last act the chorus can be heard backstage, before stamping from the wings with their *gloire immortelle de nos aïeux*. I wouldn't have been surprised in the least to hear the crowd on the Corso burst into song that afternoon as I was carried along as far as the Piazza Piombino, where I found an empty chair on the sidewalk in front of a café.

The stream went by uninterruptedly, endlessly. The Black Shirts of the epoch, with their gold and silver braid and their tasseled fezzes, of course predominated. But there were also a good many helmeted guards, cavalrymen with long blue capes, and plume-hatted Bersaglieri. There were people who knew each other and who greeted each other with a show of kindness and familiarity. In the gestures of some I recognized a touch of that dignified and solemn gravity, the *gravitas* of the poets and the conscript fathers walking and talking in the ancient Forum. The women, far more severely dressed than those of Paris, were much less numerous than the men. There were a few; tall, strong, with big tender eyes and the soft-brilliant, true Roman complexion, in whose carriage and demeanor the classic beauty has been preserved unspoiled. Who knows if the grace and loveliness of the Roman women, so disquieting to men of

Northern climes, does not go a long way to explain the recurrent invasions of this city by the barbarians? What would be their names? To me they looked so many princesses and aristocrats. Livia, Claudia, Julia, Cornelia? I found myself going over the list of the Caesars' wives. In my ear the names had a sound as sonorous and immortal as the word *Roma* itself.

Then, as if to enforce the grand-operatic mood of the moment, there came from the direction of the Altar of the Fatherland in the Piazza Venezia, faintly at first, the sound of music. At once an expectant hush fell upon the multitude. Everybody stood still. Conversations stopped; laughter was stilled. Only eyes moved with a bright childlike delight or an almost religious exaltation. It was music approaching without drums, brass, or cymbals like that of a symphony orchestra. Its notes reverberated against the façades, or rather the sound of massed violins, cellos, and flutes swelled above the crowd as if someone had started to play a great organ somewhere overhead in one of the loggias of the upper stories. The sea of humanity did the seemingly impossible and flattened itself against the walls to let a military band go by. The tune it played was the *"Marcia Reale."* Then followed a company of soldiers on the way, I presume, to relieve the watch at the King's palace. Hands were stretched out in the Fascist salute as the gold-fringed tricolor came into view. The commanding officer in front of the troop, a tall man with a pretorian face, who had his cape wrapped around his chin, walked with an unaffected triumphal amplitude that could never have been rivaled in Potsdam. So marched the tribunes of yore in front of the legions.

A Northerner cannot easily escape the appeal to his emotions when he remembers that this Corso is the old Flaminian Way. Over this road moved the destinies of Europe and of the world. Twice in the course of time Rome poured her vitality through this narrow street in an ever-spreading flood eastward and westward and northward until at last it reached even the boreal swamps of Holland and Frisia. Once the Caesars, preceded by the eagles and the trumpets, out to conquer and back to triumph, and once again the sandaled missionaries, much less noisily one imagines, the gentle forces who overcame the barbarians with quite other weapons than the sword and the javelin. When will come the third conquest? I mused, as the crowd slowly re-formed to resume its promenading pace and the last serried ranks of the infantry disappeared from view. Will there be a third time, and will it be in the nature of the first or the second triumph?

The Corso was always a place for show and circus. In the days of papal misgovernment, horse races were held here. One of the Popes, Paul II, desiring to enhance the attraction of the occasion, brought in the Jews to amuse the Christians. He ordered that the procession should open led by a body of Jewish elders followed by a cavalcade of Roman Senators. The Jews were then made to race on foot along the Corso, Jews, donkeys, horses, and buffaloes running in a confused crowd, helter-skelter, to the laughter and howls of the Italians lining the street and pelting the runners, men and beasts, with opprobrious epithets. This degrading spectacle was witnessed by noble ladies and purple-robed Cardinals while the Vicar of Christ himself looked on from his decorated balcony, applauding and shaking his sides with laughter. To add to the enjoyment, later Popes devised more humiliations for the Jews. They were ordered to run stark naked, save for a narrow loincloth, with a rope around their necks. The game was kept up for two hundred years until Clement IX allowed the Jews to buy themselves off by the payment of the prizes for the horse race, which formerly came from the papal treasury.

That was the *panem et circenses* of the Caesars translated into Christian terms. I sat down to drink my *cappucino* and to watch the ever-flowing tide. There they go again walking on the Corso, I thought, like their fathers and mothers before them for fifty generations or more. Who hasn't walked on this Flaminian Way? Cicero was there and Cato and Pliny and Virgil. Messalina, no doubt, but also the Vestal Virgins. Perhaps even that Galilean fisherman called Simon bar Jonah and the subtle Tarsiot Jew who had the strange vision on the Damascus road. 'Tis true, one cannot be sure about the Apostles. But certainly Alaric was there and Saint Augustine and Francis of Assisi and Caesar Borgia and Machiavelli and Erasmus and Michelangelo. The divine Dante walked this very ground, and that other Florentine, the somber Savonarola. Here amongst the crowd must have dawdled, too, the monk Luther one day. Didn't he say mass upon arrival in this city at the Church of Santa Maria del Popolo a little way up the street? Luther and . . . Hallo! What's that? Who? No, it can't be . . .

Suddenly in the sea of bronzed and olive-colored faces there passed one as red as a lobster. It was the face of a priest who wore a shovel hat and the usual black cassock. Where had I seen that face before?

I got up from my chair and looked after the man. Yes, that peculiar hunch of the shoulders and those arms so closely held against the body . . . There could be no doubt. . . . I motioned to the waiter to bring the account for my cup of coffee. The man was busy and I left a ten-lire note under the saucer. When I looked up again the priest had disappeared. No, there he was. But he moved through the crowd with amazing dexterity. I'll have to hurry, I thought, if I want to catch up with him. Should I call out? No, that wouldn't do. Nobody shouts in Rome. And suppose he isn't after all the man I think he is.

The priest wasn't fifty paces ahead of me. Above the heads of the strollers I could see his shovel hat dancing in and out of the crowd. I'll have to hurry some more, I thought, or he's going to escape me. There, he has turned a corner. I wish those people would get out of my way or else that I could walk on their heads and shoulders. "A thousand pardons, signori, I am in a hurry. I want to catch a priest!"

The young Fascisti laughed.

"You're in the right place for that," one man called back. "One just went by! There he goes!"

In the Via Ripetti I caught up with him. He pulled a handkerchief from his cassock, took off his hat, and wiped his forehead. I walked past him and glanced sideways at his face. If I could only see his eyes, I thought. There isn't another pair of eyes like his in the whole world. No, he didn't notice me. He didn't even look up. Now I am not absolutely sure either, and I don't want to make a fool of myself. But the resemblance is certainly striking. And that gait. I could have sworn . . .

I dropped behind. The priest was increasing his pace. He'll probably turn the next corner, I figured, or go into a doorway. I'll have one more try. I started to whistle a few bars from the *Apocalyptic Overture*, Beethoven Bis' masterpiece, the grand finale of the Free Blowers of Gorcum in Paul Smit's cowshed.

At the sound of the tune, the priest stopped dead and whirled in his tracks. Both hands went up above his head. We ran toward each other.

"Pieter!"

"Fons, old Pater, why do you walk so fast?"

Smilingly he held my two hands. A moment later we were walking arm in arm and talking in the thickest Gorcummian vernacular. I don't know where we went. We must have walked for an hour or more not knowing or caring where. At last when we looked up we were in one of those dark streets of the Borgo Nuovo, in front of a trattoria, a mere cave from whose depths gleamed strings of red peppers, swags of dried fish, clusters of oranges and lemons, presided over by a gnarled, white-haired individual who looked as old as Methuselah.

"I'm thirsty," I said. "Let's go in and drink a glass of wine. The occasion calls for a little celebration, after all!"

"Should we?" asked Fons hesitatingly, with a shy look at the amiable host and his wife on the doorstep. "Don't you think they'd find it strange if a priest . . ."

"Not they, by heavens," I reassured him. "They wouldn't think anything of it if the Pope himself dropped in to refresh himself, except that they'd probably talk about it for the rest of their lives."

"That's it, you see," said Fons. "They'd talk. You know we priests have to avoid even the semblance of evil."

"By the whiskers of old Vossius, you're not in Gorcum

now, Fons. I didn't know you had been poisoned to that
extent by the Calvinist environment."

That fetched him. He drank his wine in little sips like a
man unaccustomed to it. I had to tell him still more about
the Dalmadens and about Zeger, about Adriana and Uncle
Kees, and of course about his own mother and father, on
whom I had called in 1925 on the occasion of my first visit
back to Gorcum after an absence of twelve years. And then
about my own experiences as a divinity student in Canada
and in Paris and as a soldier in World War I in the British
Army in France and Flanders, and how I had come back
again to Europe as a newspaper correspondent and had
just had an interview with Mussolini.

"What did he say?" asked Fons, his mouth half-open
with interest.

"Among other things," I said, "the Duce told me that
there will be a redivision of the world's markets before
we are ten years older."

"What did he mean by that—war?" Fons asked genuinely
alarmed.

"Not necessarily," I said, "although it's hard to think of
any Great Power's sharing its loot with others without being
compelled to do so by force of arms, isn't it?"

"But if you publish that interview," said my old friend,
"the whole world will begin to watch Mussolini and at the
first move he makes they'll all be ready to restrain him."

"You're still as naïve as when you were a little boy in
Gorcum, Fons," I came back. "In the first place, what I
write isn't read by the whole world. In the second place,
Mussolini has already made more than the first move and
nobody has even protested. Don't you see, Pater, without
men like Mussolini the other Powers would not be able to
justify the armament campaigns they are so eager to get
under way? They all think Mussolini is a great man. And
this is not, I assure you, just because he makes the trains run
on time. Mr. Churchill, the Englishman, said only the other
day that if he were an Italian he'd be proud to call himself
'a fervent follower of the noble Duce.' As to Sir Austen
Chamberlain, he almost worships the ground Mussolini

walks on. Instead of lifting a finger to check Mussolini in his headlong course for war, Sir Austen and the British Government supplied him with a huge loan at the moment when the Fascist regime was in such dire straits that men in the know here in Rome expected its imminent collapse."

"You mean," asked Fons, "that the English Government supports a man who talks about the redivision of the world's markets, something that must of necessity involve the position of England in the world?"

"Yes, that's the way it is, alas! And the more he talks and threatens and stamps and raves, the better they like it, I think. And then there's another man on the way to power, I mean over in Germany, a certain fellow named Hitler, who is Mussolini's most perfect understudy. He wants to rearm Germany and do precisely what Mussolini talks about. When he reaches power Europe will be heading straight for another conflict."

"Monstrous!" exclaimed Father Boogaert. "Another war? I can't believe it. All the world ought to denounce Mussolini and squelch the fire before it sets the whole of Europe aflame."

"Denounce Mussolini? Yes, that's what should be done. But it isn't done, Fons. Your own Holy Father here in Rome calls the Duce 'a man of Providence.' And Cardinal Pizzardo, of the Foreign Affairs Ministry, told me that the Pope slept in peace for the first time in many months on the night when the Duce was called to the Premiership."

"Well, he has done a lot of good, too, you know, Pieter. If you had known conditions here as I knew them before the Fascisti came, you would agree with me that Mussolini has been a great reformer."

"Let's be going," I said. "Our host is listening with both ears. We talk too loud even in Dutch. If we keep on, the police will presently be here and we'll be invited to come along to the Regina Coeli (prison) to explain what we were saying. There's one name that should never be mentioned in public in this country."

"Do you think Holland would be involved in a new European conflict?" Fons asked me when we were out in the street again.

"Holland will be involved either in the next war or in the one after that. If it's a question of redividing the markets of the world, we shouldn't overlook the fact that Holland has some choice holdings in Indonesia."

"That will be terrible," sighed Fons. "I learned something of what the Belgian people suffered in the last war when I was at Roesselaere."

"Incidentally," I said, "I visited Roesselaere right after the Armistice in 1918. I was looking for you. But the principal, a certain Father Hyacinth Goemaere, told me you had left long ago for Louvain and that from there you had gone to Rome."

"Yes, I went to the Propaganda College for missionaries in this city and spent two years there."

"Aren't you there any longer?"

"Oh, no, I live in the Solomon Islands!"

"In the Solomon Islands? Then what are you doing here?"

"I'm here only on a brief visit. I came three weeks ago and I am going back again next week. I am in charge of a mission station over there. I am taking two assistants back with me next week. That was the chief object of my journey here: to find some suitable companions. We really need consecrated men out there, for the work is difficult. We encounter a good deal of opposition amongst the natives, especially on the part of their medicine men. In one of the islands, only this past January several missionaries were killed."

"Killed?"

"Yes, they were seized one night by a mob and after having been horribly tortured they were sacrificed to one of the native idols."

"Fine place, I must say. But why did you pick the Solomon Islands in the first place? Why didn't you go to the Dutch East Indies, for instance? That would seem to be the logical place for you. There are plenty of heathen there and you would have enjoyed the protection of the Government. Moreover, the Indonesian natives are by common repute the gentlest people on earth. They wouldn't torture anyone. Except for the Dyaks of Borneo perhaps, they are perfectly inoffensive. But maybe you had no choice in the matter, was that it?"

"Oh, I suppose I could have gone elsewhere if I had tried. But I simply did not want to go to any Dutch colony. Anywhere but to a Dutch colony."

"Why not? Do you want to leave that part of the vineyard to the Protestants?"

"Oh, no," he laughed. "The Catholic Church cannot leave the work of evangelization to sectarians whom she believes to be poor, erring sheep themselves. I didn't want to go to the Dutch East Indies out of deference to you and Ary!"

"To us? Why? What do you mean? How did we have any say in the matter?"

"You did," replied Father Boogaert. "Don't you remember how you often condemned missionary endeavor because you considered it to be the spearhead of imperialist penetration? I did not want to have anything to do with that. I wanted to avoid even a suspicion that my work was in the interest of any national state or of any big business whatsoever. I have no political views, you see. I want to work only for the extension of the Kingdom of God. They say the flag follows the missionaries. Well, I have no flag but the flag of Christ. There is no other cause on earth for me."

"It's hard work, you say?"

"Very hard, Pieter! But we are making a little headway. We have some devoted Christians in the Solomon Islands. Our chief difficulty is to combat old native superstitions, voodooism, snake worship. Human sacrifices are still made and cannibalism, too, is practiced."

"Cannibalism? Actually?"

"Oh, yes, I came across several instances of it. Some gruesome things happen there."

"Don't the Germans own the Solomon Islands?"

"They did until the war. Then the Australians took over. But there isn't any effective civil authority at all in some of the islands. An inspector comes once a year, or sometimes not at all. Some Japanese trading ships call now and then. But for the rest we are alone with the natives."

"I should think that the secular authorities would take a hand in eradicating such practices as cannibalism and human sacrifices."

"It would be almost impossible for the civil authorities to discover as much as a trace of these goings-on, let alone stamp them out," replied Father Boogaert, shaking his head. "The natives certainly would not give them any information, for that would involve betraying the medicine men, of whom they live in dreadful and superstitious awe. It would require a whole army of inspectors to police the islands. And even then I doubt if they would succeed. For most of that evil, you see, flourishes at night, in the pitch-dark, in secret places—some clearing in the jungle or a cabin hidden and unapproachable in the middle of a swamp. Those spots are not easily found, since the very trails leading to them are secret and undiscoverable to the white man's eyes.

"No, the only way to end those horrors," continued the priest, "lies in finding a way to the hearts of the people, to win their confidence and esteem and their love. And this can be done only by letting them know and feel beyond any peradventure of doubt that you do not want anything of them, that you are wholly disinterested and that you want nothing else but to help them, heal their diseases and save their children's lives and solve their problems. Our only approach to the natives lies in a tender consideration for their souls. Once you have them coming to the mission station, if only to sit around or to be taught something useful by the Sisters, you can begin telling them that their attempts to propitiate their gruesome idols by the shedding of blood, animal or human, are an abomination and futile, that Christ has made all the sacrifice necessary for their redemption and that His Holy Mother holds out her arms to them with such immense love that . . ."

"I see, but look, Pater . . ."

"Don't you believe that is the only way, Pieter?" he

said, forestalling the words rising to my lips. And he suddenly added: "How does it stand with yourself? Are you a little nearer?"

"Nearer to what?"

"To us, to the Catholic faith?"

"I thought you'd ask me that, Fons, old Pater. You haven't changed a whit."

"Well?"

"I am loyal to the Church of my fathers."

"The Catholic Church is much more the Church of your fathers than the Dutch Reformed body. Back in Gorcum you were always talking about primitive Christianity, about going back to the sources, to Jesus himself. Who is nearer to Jesus, we of the first century or that man Calvin who didn't appear on the scene till the sixteenth? Now?"

"Fons," I said, "I won't allow myself to be drawn into an argument with you. I remember only too well how sensitive you are on that point. Besides, I haven't the strength. We've been walking around this city for hours. I'm positively weak with hunger. Let's go and eat something first."

"You are talking like Felix," sighed Father Boogaert, shaking his head. "Remember how he told Saint Paul: *Tempore autem opportuno accersam te*—at a more convenient time will I call on thee. It is never more imperative, Pieter, to come to a decision than in the present moment. Now is the accepted time, you know it too well yourself. Still, if you're hungry we'll eat. We'll eat at the pensionat in the Piazza Mignanelli where I am staying and where you will meet some friends of mine, among them, I hope, the two men who are coming to the Solomons with me. I think you'll like them. Father van Gennep and Father Daels. They're both Flemings."

And so it came to pass that, in spite of my objections and insistence on going to a decent restaurant, I supped in a room full of Roman priests and that, Father van Gennep being absent, I met Father Daels, a young man from the neighborhood of Poperinghe near Ypres as gentle and soft-spoken as Fons himself, with porcelain-blue eyes and pale-blond hair, who turned out to be an ardent Flemish national-

ist. I was to see this Father Daels later in life, some fifteen
years afterward in America, where he told me of Fons
Boogaert's experiences. But of that later.

After a supper, chiefly remembered because of its exaggerated simplicity—I may well say, its undiluted and uninspiring insipidness: macaroni with powdered cheese and
water on the side—the three of us sat in Father Boogaert's
room for an hour or so and heard from him the story of his
experiences in the islands. As he spoke I was filled with
evil forebodings.

The people of the Solomon Islands, who are Melanesians
with a slight admixture of Kanaka blood, he told us, are to
this day the slaves and victims of their medicine men. They
are completely dominated by these wizards, who weave a
spell of mysterious awe and diabolical fascination about
their religious practices. Fons did not want to dignify their
obscene primitive cultus with the name of religion because,
as he said, instead of teaching at least one virtue, however
pagan, it catered exclusively to the basest instincts of the
natives. The medicine men frankly encourage and work on
the sensuous lusts of the people, on their bloodthirstiness
and lewd superstitions. The cultus is one of sexual voodoism,
and little more.

Most of the smaller islands have French names. The
two on which Fons worked were named Marraine and Parrain, "Godmother" and "Godfather," if the words are to
be translated. Except for a wide clearing around the mission
station on Marraine and the beginning of a similar institution on Parrain, the islands were still virgin jungle, he
said, swarming with rats and snakes and infested with
mosquitoes of a particularly poisonous kind. With the help
of the natives, he had cut a road from the seashore to the
middle of the island of Marraine, but he was obliged to
spend one day a week at least with a crew of helpers in
keeping the jungle from reconquering what he had carved
out.

"During my absence," he went on, "the nuns of Parrain
are staying with those at the main establishment on Marraine, where there are a school, a small hospital and dis-

pensary, some workshops, and of course a chapel. I could not leave them on Parrain because the situation on that island is still very indefinite. We have only a foothold there. On Marraine, it is true, they are not quite as safe as I would like them to be, either. They are under the protection of the Mother of God and of a fellow missionary, Father Lejeune. I can only hope for the best. But in view of what happened last year and in the beginning of this year 1927, when there was a wholesale extermination of missionaries on some of the islands, I live in constant fear and trembling for my coworkers and I won't stay in Rome one hour longer than necessary. I had hoped to find the time to visit Holland and see my parents, but I've given up the idea. I simply must get back as soon as possible."

"Incidentally," I said at this point, "your mother told me when I was in Gorcum two years ago that you had written her how in one place, upon your arrival the natives met you with great rejoicing and carried you in a chair over the trails."

"Yes," said Fons, laughing, "that was when I first came to Marraine. It was a happy day. The people were genuinely glad to see us. But soon after that the situation deteriorated. It seemed as if the Devil himself moved into those medicine men when they realized that their sway over the people was coming to an end. It has been war between us from that moment onward, at any rate war on their part, for insofar as we are concerned, we do not entertain the slightest feeling of hostility or resentment toward them. It's a war of nerves and of badgering and obstructionism. One night one of our cabins would go up in flames, a few nights later our toolshed would be rifled or in the morning we would find some of our animals with their throats slit, some trouble like that all the time. But never a sight did we catch of the perpetrators of these outrages. And even if we knew the culprits, what good would it be to us? We can't complain to the magistrate or to the police, for there are no secular authorities whatever on our two islands. We are alone, and must solve these problems in our own way.

"Instead of diminishing with the passage of time," continued Father Boogaert, "as I had confidently hoped, these nocturnal depredations for a time increased in frequency and boldness. And after a score of natives on Marraine came over to us, the situation grew still more tense. These native Christians—oh, they are lovable and intelligent people and their children are as adorable as little cherubs— I say these catechumens actually live in danger of their lives night and day. Especially at night they are never quite safe. The converts have all moved into the clearing or built their cabins close to us. They work the land for themselves and for us. One of us always stays up at night with two or three of the menfolk and we patrol like real soldiers."

"Are you armed?" I asked.

"Of course not," came back Father Boogaert with a scandalized look and a little curtly. "How can you ask such a thing? What has Christianity to do with arms and violence? If we cannot conquer with love, with goodness, our mission is a failure, I believe, even if we should have thousands of converts."

"Good, good!" I interjected. "Don't be angry, Pater, I'm glad to hear you say this. They are my own sentiments precisely. 'Almost persuadest thou me,' you know!"

Father Boogaert stared at me with dreaming eyes for a moment and smiled.

"Since my coming to Marraine," he continued after a brief silence, "and the initial success of the mission, the medicine men have withdrawn into the depths of the jungle. They still come down to perform the official rites of their cultus in the villages and settlements, chanting their weird incantations over sick persons and sacrificing birds and chickens and other animals such as pigs and dogs, but their real stronghold is in the interior. That's where their power lies and where the most horrible things imaginable take place. From there they continue to exercise an iron hold over the people by means of terror and intimidation. It is indeed shameful and pathetic to see how the natives quake and cower under their unseen occult influence.

"Especially toward the night of the full moon the situation on the island is not at all pleasant. Deep in the jungle the drums begin to drone. Their nervous pulsation without interruption is a maddening, intoxicating sound that chills you to the marrow of your bones and covers your body with a cold sweat. The tension becomes almost unbearable. We at the mission station can feel the approach of the monthly crisis several days in advance. Our people are seized by a secret panic. They look at us with their large beautiful eyes as if they would implore us to help them, to do something about it. They dare not speak of the anguish in their hearts, although it's written on their faces. They are too filled with dread of what's to come. They are in the grip of a nameless, overpowering evil. It is as if we were surrounded by the sibilant chattering of ghosts. The very atmosphere is surcharged with a clammy, slimy, spiritual fluid. Men in the West cannot conceive, cannot imagine, what it is like. They smile indulgently when you tell them about it and nod their heads as if to say that it is merely a matter of keeping your sangfroid and common sense, that these native superstitions should not upset a rational human being.

"Those things are easily said here in Rome or in Gorcum. But do you know what I think? You know that text in the Apostle's Epistle to the Ephesians where he writes: 'We struggle not against flesh and blood, but against the principalities of darkness, against the powers of evil in the air.' Well, I think I know exactly what Saint Paul meant," said Father Boogaert. "I found the meaning of that text right in the island of Marraine. For there on those nights when the orgies are staged in the jungle and the drums drone with a frenzy that is indescribable, I have more than once felt myself literally surrounded, hemmed in, trapped by an invisible, loathsome enemy, some fetid and putrefied influence or power that wraps itself around you like a clammy reptile. You may not believe me, Pieter, but it's so realistic, I assure you, as to be almost palpable. The evil spirits grip you by the throat until you're shaking and trembling all over and you feel your reason breaking down. It's far more dreadful than some physical danger staring you in the face.

"At first, I must tell you," he went on, "I wasn't particularly upset by the noise and fracas on those special nights of theirs. I was annoyed, of course, by the insane, monotonous racket of the drums and the wailing, shrieking chants that I heard coming from the jungle. But then I had my work to do. I was busy all day and pretty tired at night and I soon went to sleep. I didn't know really what was going on, you see. It wasn't until some of the natives came over to us that we became aware of the significance and the horror of those sacrificial rites.

"An old man was our first convert. He was a sort of outcast. In his youth he had lived at a mission station on this very island of Marraine. He had been baptized and confirmed. He told us how our predecessors on the island, a group of French Fathers, White Fathers he called them, some thirty or forty years before had been on the verge of bringing the whole population of Marraine to the feet of Christ. But then, precisely on one of those sacrificial nights, these priests were massacred to the last man. He led us to the spot where they were martyred. Not a trace remained of the earlier station. Cabins and dispensary and chapel—everything had disappeared. The jungle had covered everything.

"From him, Papa Meela we call him, we also had our first intimation that human sacrifices and cannibalism were practiced on the island. When Meela first told me about it quite casually, as if it were something self-evident and known to everybody, I was surprised, not to say aghast, as you were this afternoon when I mentioned the matter to you. I simply laughed at him. I couldn't believe it. I refused to believe it. I took it that Meela was merely trying to make himself important and interesting in our eyes by telling us some fantastic stories. I was soon to convince myself of the truth of his tales. The truth was more gruesome than Meela could have imagined.

"It seems the medicine men select at least one child—it's always a girl—to be sacrificed on the night of the full moon. Sometimes, on high holy days, more than one child is offered in a sacrifice to the obscene female divinity the natives worship. One of the medicine men goes through the villages toward the end of the month, quietly enters a cabin, and points out to the trembling parents the child he wants them to bring to the sacred clearing or cabin on the appointed night. It's most curious. The parents dread to see one of their children selected, but at the same time they seem to consider it a sort of privilege to be asked to provide the victim.

"There have been instances, Meela informed us, of parents refusing to give up a child. But those cases are very rare. Refusal is followed by a general ostracism of the parents on the part of the tribe. Their lives are not worth a cent after that. They may be slain by anyone desiring to gain favor with the medicine men and the goddess. Public opinion, you might say, forces the parents to surrender their children without a murmur, at least in public. Privately, I know, they are just as heartbroken and inconsolable over the loss of their children as more civilized people would be.

"The ceremony on the night of the full moon starts an hour or so before sundown. The trails leading to the place of sacrifice are crowded with men, women, and children. In that hour a strange unearthly silence hangs over the jungle. It falls upon your ears like a clap of thunder. All at once the drums cease their tom-tomming. They remain mute while the clans are gathering. That sudden stillness, after three days and three nights of uninterrupted droning and vibrating, is in fact the signal that the orgiastic ritual is about to begin. To us, too, it is a fearful moment, because we know what is about to take place over there in the heart of the wilderness.

"We are powerless to interfere except to pray for them —that they may be delivered from their gruesome bondage. We stay up all night and keep all our lamps burning. This we do chiefly for the sake of our converts and the friends who have taken refuge with us. For our people are very nervous on nights like that. They are frightened. They tremble in every limb, sometimes shriek in fear, and toward morning they are exhausted with the suspense. There is always a possibility, you see, that the medicine men will whip their people into a frenzy of fury against us and bring the mob down howling for our blood. That's the way the other missionaries were massacred in the past. I mean those White Fathers, those Marist Fathers of whom Meela spoke, as well as those who were martyred this very year. It's always on a night of full moon that these killings occur.

"Out there in the gathering dusk in the sacred clearing the natives group themselves around a huge fire while others are arriving every minute. Fuel is constantly heaped on the fire until it is a roaring pile of which we can see the glow reflected against the sky at our station several miles distant. When it is quite dark the drums start up again and the medicine man makes his appearance. The chief wizard on Marraine is a huge, powerfully built man, as tall as our Ary Brandt, with a fierce look on his face, and long hair. He is usually dressed in some crudely tinted costume and exhales an odor that nauseates you at a distance of ten paces. I have often seen him, and I have spoken with him on several occasions. On the night of the ceremony, when he first comes upon the scene his face is covered with a black wooden mask. This mask represents the face of the goddess. It is a horrible caricature of a human countenance with white painted circles around the eyes and a broad red smear for a mouth. The top is adorned with long strings of matted dark hair, the hair of the medicine man's dead predecessors.

"The people receive the medicine man with shouts and shrieks that can be heard for miles around. As he seats himself by the fire they break into a dreary, monotonous chant, lamenting the passage of the good old times and the coming death of the moon. While they chant and clap their hands in rhythm with the drums, a pair of goats or sheep is led into the enclosure. And then pandemonium really breaks loose. I do not know," Father Boogaert said, interrupting his description, "the reason for the alternation of sheep and goats at succeeding festivals. There is some significance attached to it, of course. I have not been able to discover what it is.

"At any rate," he continued, "the animals are led around the fire a number of times, then all at once the medicine

man darts forward and pierces their throats with a long
knife, or rather a dagger of razor sharpness. In one thrust
he severs their heads and holds them in his two hands high
above his head. The blood pouring from the bodies is
caught in earthen vessels and this is mixed with a liquor the
natives distill from the leaves of certain palm trees. It is the
strongest aphrodisiac known in the East. The pots of mixed
blood and liquor are passed around and almost at once
produce intoxication. The bodies of the animals are put on
spits to roast on the fire, and the feast commences.

"In long circling chains, the one nearest the fire moving
to the left and the next one to the right and so on, they now
begin to dance around the fire holding each other by the
hand or shoulders. The drums quicken their rhythm. The
fire throws a red sheen on the dusky glistening bodies and
they whirl around ever faster and scream at the top of their
lungs. The chant turns into a long sustained howl that
makes the gooseflesh come out on the people gathered with
us at the mission station.

"This goes on for a time until the medicine man, who
stands with his back to the fire looking on, is given a pair
of roosters. He holds the cackling birds at arm's length
by their feet and cuts their head off. As they flap their wings
the blood is spattered over his mask and body and over the
hands and shoulders of the crowd whirling around him.
Circles then re-form. The one farthest from the fire now
comes nearest to it, and the dancing resumes. Four or five
times the performance with the roosters is repeated after
intervals of dancing and wailing, until every dancer present
is bespattered with blood. The headless chickens are thrown
on the fire to roast with the sheep or goats.

"Then after the pots of liquor and blood have been
passed around once more the crowd, with ear-piercing yelling and battering and pummeling and trampling one another, throws itself upon the bodies roasting at the spit.
The flesh is still raw, of course. But they tear it off the bones
with their teeth and for a moment there is relative calm as
they gorge themselves with the meat.

"Two more goats or sheep are brought into the clearing

and the whole thing starts all over again. They drink the blood, they dance, roosters are killed and the dancing bodies are besprinkled with blood, and finally the animals are torn apart and devoured. As the night wears on the participants grow staggering drunk. But they do not, as you might think, drop with exhaustion or stupor. To the contrary, it seems that with each repetition of the rite their strength increases and also their excitement. It's the aphrodisiac burning in their veins. They work themselves up to the insane, frenzied climax that is going to come just before dawn.

"For then the girl victim is at last brought from the cabin near by and is led within the so-called sacred circle. She is immediately given a cup of the blood-and-liquor mixture. The medicine man draws his snakes, three or four big yellow and black reptiles, from a box and wraps them around his neck. This is his badge of office, so to speak. When he puts on the snakes, it means that the supreme moment is near. The drums are silent and the crowd of sweating, gleaming bodies presses close, breathless with expectation. As the snakes, startled by the roaring flames, coil and uncoil around the man's arms and neck and head, he intones a low moaning chant. He is dedicating the little girl to the goddess.

"The monotonous, quavering chant continues for a while as the crowd sways silently to and fro. They are thoroughly drunk by then, and the liquor seething in their veins whips them up to a boundless lust. The medicine man seems to be working himself into a trancelike state, then all at once he breaks off with a terrible scream. He opens some baskets that have been placed at his feet and takes out some chickens and throws them high into the air. The people break into yelling, grab the fluttering birds, and tear off their heads. Greedily they drink and suck the fresh blood from the decapitated bodies. All this time the little girl has been forced to drink one cup after another of the mixture, so that her senses are drugged and she stares with wide-open eyes at the man with the gruesome mask.

"The wizard then places his arms around her shoulders and with elaborate gestures puts a crown of flowers on her head. At that moment the tension is terrific. It's the beginning of the sacrifice for which the people have been preparing all night. The ceremony with the flowers lasts a few minutes, for the medicine man has to end the song he is singing to her. With a wild yell he breaks off at last, tears off his mask, flings the girl to the ground, and violates her. Then he lifts her up high and from all sides the crowd presses forward, screaming and howling like possessed devils. The child is literally torn limb from limb and eaten. Only the head is preserved, and is placed on a pike near the fire.

"Having devoured the child, the crowd goes mad. They claw and bite at each other, possess each other, roaring like animals. It's a heaving mass of intertwined bodies, snarling, scratching, tearing at each other like beasts. But then it's dawn too, and they lie exhausted on the ground, some severely wounded. The medicine man has disappeared. From all directions come groans and moans. Not seldom there are several dead among them. We of the mission station approach the place after the ceremony is over and bind up their wounds."

Father Boogaert was silent for a moment and sat staring in front of him seemingly absent-minded. Through the open window came a soft breeze that stirred the curtains. Father Daels, the young Fleming, got up from his chair and poured himself a glass of water from the decanter on the table. I looked at the fine ascetic face of Fons Boogaert and in a flash my thoughts ran over the course of his life. I saw him again in his poor shoes and in the butcher shop in the Melkpad quarter; his mother, their quick walks together through Gorcum in the ice-cold dawn when they went to pray for the recovery of his father; the incident with Yssel Ponthieu and the last day of the examination when he refused to translate those excerpts from Seneca that seemed to him blasphemous. I had always thought of him up till then as a meek, self-effacing, quietistic sort of individual, almost feminine in character, who should not be exposed to the rawness of life but who would be best off and happiest perhaps in a cloister or a bookery leading a contemplative, meditative life. I suddenly saw him in a new light. He wasn't weak. He was a fighter in the forefront of the battle against ignorance and darkness. He was one of the Militia of Christ. . . .

The hooting of a taxicab outside and the sound of laughing voices in the street below dispelled the silence in the room. Father Boogaert looked in my direction.

"And is this still going on?" I asked him. "I mean what you told us just now, that grisly business in the jungle?"

"On Parrain and some other islands, yes," he replied. "But not on Marraine, except perhaps, I am afraid, now and then in the greatest secrecy. And even then only animals are used. Still it's no longer a public affair, that's certain."

"You stopped it?" I asked.

He nodded with a smile. "It was stopped," he said.

"How did you do that? I'd think the medicine men would have killed you first."

"They certainly would have liked to do away with me," agreed the priest. "And they may still want to. But on our island their power is broken. After I learned precisely what went on at those sacrificial ceremonies from having witnessed some of those diabolical scenes from a distance, I knew that the practice would have to be discontinued or else that I myself would have to go. There was no room for us both. I could not have stayed on the island knowing that each month one of the children was to be slaughtered right under my nose, you might say."

"Well?"

"Well, I simply kidnapped the girl who was designated for the next holocaust," he smiled.

"You did? But that was the most risky thing to do, I should imagine."

"It did involve a certain risk," he nodded his head. "I had, of course, spoken to the people whenever I could of the evil of the practice and of the grievous sin they committed. I begged them to desist, hoping that my pleas would cause some of them to give up. My hopes were vain for quite a while. The people were in dread of what might happen to them from the side of the medicine man if they should challenge his authority. One day, however, a mother came to us, a young woman with a kind and lovely face. She told us that her only child had been selected to be immolated on the next night of the full moon. She trembled and wept and implored us to save her little one.

"Then and there I took a resolution to have it out with the medicine men. I told the good woman to come to our mission station and bring her child. She came and brought not only the child but her husband as well. This was, of course, like giving an ultimatum to the wizards—I mean bringing that child and her mother to our station. In an hour everybody on the island knew. But once it was done it was irrevocable. We had to face the consequences whatever they might be.

"A day before the night of the sacrifice," he went on, "a few more people came in, fathers, mothers, and children, all asking for protection. These people were fearful that at the last moment, finding his originally designated victim had escaped him, the medicine man would pick one or more of their children as a substitute."

"Yes?"

"Well, that brought on the crisis. I knew we were in for it. I fully counted on being attacked. And so, on the night when the sacrifice was scheduled, I crowded all the inhabitants of our station into the little chapel and I lit all the lamps. We had besides some fifty candles burning—a heavy expense, but it was the final battle. Lejeune was at the altar, where he was served by Papa Meela and a young boy we had adopted three years before. I placed a burning pitch torch on either side of the door and, putting on my vestments, I stood guard there."

"Did you have at least some kind of weapon, Pater, to defend yourself?"

"I had a crucifix, yes," he said simply.

"Mass was said about one in the morning," Father Boogaert continued. "Just as Lejeune sang out the *Ite, missa est,* I heard the mob coming down the road and saw them pouring into our clearing. I turned around and told the people to stay in the chapel and be quiet. 'The Great

Mother,' I told them, 'will help us and protect us.' Father Lejeune joined me at the door. He carried the Holy Sacrament.

"The crowd stopped at the sight of us. In front was the medicine man wearing his odious mask. I said to Father Lejeune, 'Let us go!' Slowly we walked forward, Lejeune holding high the monstrance and I my crucifix. Instead of attacking us the crowd stopped yelling. They looked awestruck. Suddenly the medicine man bolted. Pieter, I was petrified. Two or three of the women fell on their knees. I ran forward and put my arms around their shoulders and around the little children and brought them into the chapel. That was the end.

"Isn't God great?" he said, his eyes suddenly transparent as daylight. "Not a child, as far as I know, has been troubled since."

It had grown late. As I rose to leave the missing Father van Gennep came in and we exchanged a few pleasant words. He was a few years older than my friend, more portly, too, and spoke with an accent suggesting the neighborhood of Ghent. Fons Boogaert put on his hat and said he would accompany me part of the way to my hotel. Actually he took me right to the door. Then, without any forethought, I walked him back again to the Piazza Mignatelli. It was like the old days, or rather the old nights, in Gorcum. Then, too, there had been no end to our walking to and fro in the deserted streets. An hour later, still holding discourse, we found ourselves crossing the bridge of Sant' Angelo and a little later stood gazing into St. Peter's Square, at that hour wrapt in silence and solitude. In that spot hallowed by the ashes of the martyrs we sat down on the edge of the colonnade on the Vatican side and did not stir till the darkness of night was dispelled by the first rays of the rising sun. He made me promise to write his mother of our meeting. It was close to five o'clock when we walked back in a hurry to Fons' hostelry. At the corner of the piazza we parted. I waited till he reached the door. On the threshold he stood still and waved his hat in a last greeting.

In the month of October 1942 while riding on a train near Chicago I read in one of the weekly news magazines the brief announcement that a Dutch priest had been crucified in the Solomon Islands by the Japanese. The man's name had been garbled in transmission. Upon inquiring a few days later at the head office of the magazine in New York, I was shown the original dispatch, and sent a cable to the correspondent in the Solomon Islands asking for the priest's exact name. A week later came the confirmation. The martyred man was indeed Father Alfons Boogaert.

In the early part of 1943 I was informed that several nuns and priests from the Solomon Islands, having been rescued by American troops, had been landed in Seattle and were recovering from their harrowing experiences in a nursing home on the Pacific coast. I searched till I found them. The Sisters referred me to Father Guido Daels, who had made the journey with them but who was recuperating elsewhere.

Never have I seen a man so aged in so short a time. He was almost a youngster when I met him in the Eternal City. Now he was a dazed shadow, tottering on his feet. His hair had turned white. He spoke slowly, with some difficulty. His face was grooved and his once fresh boyish complexion had turned the color of parchment. At first he was reluctant to speak of his experiences and of the last days at the mission station on Marraine. He was particularly anxious that I should not repeat our conversation to the newspapers, as he desired no publicity whatever.

The Japanese, he began, sent but a small detachment ashore on Marraine, perhaps two hundred men in all, under the command of a certain Captain Itake Yamamuro. This officer's first action on the island was the dismissal of the administrative council set up by the Australian Government in 1929 and the arrest of the white officials. In conformity with the Japanese policy of destroying the myth of white superiority in Asia, the Europeans on Marraine, the missionaries included, were at once set to work on the most menial tasks, and made subject to the old native ruling caste, which in the case of Marraine signified that the clan of wizards and medicine men, who were the undisputed masters before the advent of the missionaries, came to the top again under Japanese military protection. Since the island was invaded for the specific purpose of laying out a few airstrips, the natives were promptly organized into forced labor gangs. The first to be pressed into service were the men and women who had embraced Christianity.

With the approval and, it seems, to the intense delight, of Captain Yamamuro, the old ritualistic practices, involving the monthly sacrifice of one or more children, were also restored. Inasmuch as the military had taken over the mission compound and had confined the missionaries and the nuns to the chapel building under strict orders to cease all proselytizing activity, the medicine men selected the first victims for the restored cultus from the children of the native converts with perfect impunity.

"We were compelled to look on," said Father Daels, "as some of the loveliest children of our community were dragged off by the Japanese soldiers to their cabins and by the medicine men to the place of slaughter.

"One of the priests, Father Lejeune, was thereupon dispatched in secrecy to the neighboring island of Parrain. He rowed over one dark night and learned from Father van Gennep, who was in charge on Parrain, that there were no Japanese on that island, that Australian seaplanes had occasionally landed there, and that they would probably be back in force to prevent the Japanese from coming ashore.

"This intelligence gave us the idea," continued Father Daels, "of making an attempt to evacuate our people and the nuns to Parrain. Naturally, we had to proceed with the utmost care and caution. We could make no official announcement of our plans, of course, and ask for candidates to accompany us. That would have been disastrous. It would have betrayed us to the Japanese or to the medicine men, which would amount to the same thing: strict incarceration for all of us, and probably death. Moreover, we owned but three native proas that could be used to send the women and children to safety.

"One thing favored us," said Father Daels, "the fact

that our people, the converts, had been driven from the mission compound. It was their cabins the Japanese commandeered the moment they set foot on Marraine. Most of our people had gone into hiding after that in the jungle. In this way the Japanese and their native collaborators could not tell at once when some had left the island. We were successful in evacuating some one hundred and forty two of our people. This included all the children of the converts, and the Sisters. An Australian destroyer was hovering off the shores of Parrain at night and facilitated our escape; that is, its presence somewhere in the dark gave us a certain sense of security.

"Father Boogaert and I stayed behind. Boogaert made a resolution that he would not leave until the last child and the last nun were safely on Parrain. We went about our usual business in the daytime, working on the airstrips, and at night supervised the removal of the refugees. This was not as easy as it sounds." Father Daels smiled wanly. "We had to be extremely circumspect, as the main beach, at the end of our road, was patrolled and the Japanese had guards roving over the island in all directions at night. In addition we had to be on the watch for the native collaborators.

"Even so, the work was done. On the northern end of Marraine there is a small cove. It was from this point, after a two-hour march through the jungle, that we shipped off our people, one proaful at the time, each proa in charge of Papa Meela and one of the Sisters. We had seen off about a dozen of our friends one night, the party including the last nun on the island, when on our way back to the chapel we ran into a Japanese patrol. They seized us and brought us to Captain Yamamuro.

"The officer was half-drunk when we were brought before him in Father Boogaert's own cabin. He was lying fully dressed on the bed. The floor was littered with empty bottles and remains of food. Father Boogaert's books had been piled in a heap in the corner and were being used, I could see, as fuel to heat the cookstove. He asked us where we had been so late when his men met us in the northern end of the island. Not wishing to betray the relatively safe retreat of our friends, we refused to answer. He said that he was aware that some natives and the nuns had disappeared from the island. He wanted them returned at once and he was going to force us to tell him the location of their hideout, even if he had to kill us. He then sent for the chief medicine man, and when this individual arrived asked him how best he could force us to give up our secret.

"The medicine man suggested a most diabolical torture," went on Father Daels. "We were taken into the chapel and there by the light of pitch torches Father Boogaert was stripped bare and tied to the altar. Then they brought in a metal cage filled with huge rats and this cage was placed upside down on Father Boogaert's stomach. One of the soldiers opened the trapdoor in the bottom of the cage and held it in such a way that the rats could not escape. The beasts immediately started to gnaw at Father Boogaert's body. He groaned once or twice, but that's all the sound that came from him. When he had fainted with the pain, my turn came. I soon lost consciousness. When I came to my senses again, I was lying outside, at the rear of the chapel. My hands and feet were tied to a stake, but Father Boogaert was gone.

"The first daylight was coming through the palms when I heard voices and saw a group of soldiers and the medicine man bringing Father Boogaert back. His face was horribly swollen and his whole body one open sore. I realized at once what they had done to the poor boy. They had tied him up to a tree trunk in one of the swamps to allow the mosquitoes to feast on him. His eyes were closed, so I called out to him: 'Boogaert, Boogaert, I'm here!'

"He tried to smile at the sound of my voice. Captain Yamamuro followed behind. He carried a bottle of liquor in his hands and said to me: 'We are going to finish your pal and you will look on. If you won't talk after that, you'll have the same treatment tomorrow.' "

Father Daels was silent. He struggled with his emotions and the memory of that ghastly night. "That I escaped in the end," he said, "is due to the fact that after Father Boogaert's death Papa Meela and Father Lejeune came back in search of us and packed me off to the proa and to Parrain."

"And so they killed Fons Boogaert," I said, "one of the best men that ever lived."

"Yes, they crucified him," said the priest.

"Crucified him?"

"Yes, they crucified him against the back wall of the chapel. They drove nails through his wrists and feet and let him hang there. I was not a dozen yards away from him, tied to my stake. After they had done that, they left us there. I still thought my turn would come the next day.

"I spoke to Father Boogaert and gave him absolution," continued Father Daels. "I know he could hear me, although his eyes were closed. As the sun grew hot, his naked body with those hideous wounds was covered with flies. No sound came from him except some deep sighs. Later in the day Captain Yamamuro returned once with some soldiers. They looked at Father Boogaert. I prayed them to take him down. But they paid no attention to me. One of the soldiers kicked me in the face.

"Shortly after they left, Father Boogaert opened his eyes. I do not think he recognized me. He moaned and several times I heard him say: 'Jesus, be not unto me a judge, but my Saviour!' Then his voice sank to a whisper. At last as the pitiless sun sank to rest he suddenly cried out with a loud voice: '*Moeder, Moeder, ik kom!* Mother, I am coming!' Thus he went to God."

Father Daels made the sign of the cross and wept.

Chapter IV

THE END OF THE ROAD

FOR the first sixteen months following the occupation, the members of the Jewish community of Gorcum, some one hundred and thirty souls in all, were confined in the local synagogue. They were rounded up within a week after the entry of the Germans, who seem to have been in as great a hurry in our town as they were everywhere else to possess themselves of the Jews' property and to carry off everything portable. Inasmuch as the Jews of Gorcum were for the most part people in humble circumstances of life, the loot from their homes cannot have been very impressive. I knew their plush chairs and horsehair sofas, their commodes, chiffoniers, crockery, and jingle. If all that poor stuff had been put together it wouldn't have made a decent auction sale. The Germans pounced upon it as if they had struck a long-hidden treasure. The vacated Jewish houses were occupied by officials of the Gestapo, the *Sicherheits Dienst*, the Labor Department, and by functionaries of other administrative branches who brought their families from the Reich to settle down, for good as they thought, in the conquered land.

The synagogue in which the Jews were herded together stood in a narrow street, not far from the Roman Catholic chapel, a short distance from the sidewalk behind an iron grill in a brick-paved small square that was separated from other buildings on either side and at the rear by a high whitewashed wall. As I remember the tiny late-Gothic structure from the single visit I paid it on the occasion of a special service—I think it was on the Day of Atonement in 1910, when David Dalmaden invited Ary Brandt and myself to hear a sermon by a renowned rabbi from Haarlem—it was not much larger inside than a good-sized drawing-room. The subject of the sermon has escaped my memory entirely, but not the impression of austerity and solemnity I carried away from the service. I do recall, however, our amazement upon being told by David that the women sat upstairs in the gallery behind screens of latticed woodwork of the kind one sees to this day in mosques and in the upper stories of prominent Muslim houses before the harem apartments.

On the wall above our seat hung a large disk of marble with a gold-lettered inscription praying God to bestow blessings without end on the people, the rulers, and the country of the Netherlands for having provided a refuge to the Jews of Spain and Portugal in 1492 and the following years of their "great tribulation." I also seem to remember that upon entering the synagogue we were asked to take off our shoes and leave them in the vestibule. For the rest, I can still hear in my head the plaintive, sobbing voice of the cantor as he stood in his white prayer shawl, the upper part of his body swaying slightly to and fro, before the Scroll of the Law.

Beneath the hall of worship proper in the basement was located a library in which burned night and day a row of finely-wrought brass lamps of remembrance that were suspended from the ceiling by long, brilliantly polished chains. There was, furthermore, in that basement a robing-room for the officiating rabbi and a ritual bath, reached by a steep stone stairway, that was used by the women on appropriate occasions.

Thinking back to that synagogue, it seems almost incredible to me that more than a hundred human beings, men, women, and children, could have been forced inside it to take up their abode. Still, it was done—that and worse! The terrors of the first days were swallowed up by yet greater horrors as time went on. The occupants of the synagogue, or we had perhaps better say the prisoners, were forbidden to leave the grilled enclosure on pain of death. Only during one hour in the morning and for another hour after sunset were the Jews permited to send two or three of their number to the local shops to buy provisions for their hapless community. But since Jews were not, on orders of the Gestapo, supplied with ration tickets and most of the shops in town closed in the evening, the buyers often returned empty-handed.

Some did not come back at all. On their way in the streets, where they were easily recognized by the armlets with a yellow star that they were compelled to wear for identification purposes, the Jewish buyers were often stopped by the police to show their passports and papers, or else they were taken along to the station for questioning. There they were made to wait until the hour of their leave of absence from the synagogue was up, and then arrested for overstaying it. This was generally the last seen of them. Without any further ado they were packed off as transgressors of the law, as malefactors, to the concentration camps of Eastern Europe. Curious alone in this connection was the German punctiliousness in preserving a certain semblance of legality. They could have killed the Jews outright. Later they made no bones about it, beating Jewish men and women to death without the slightest provocation. They did it for sport or for a lark. In the beginning they still lodged formal charges against them, trumped-up charges to be sure, and went through the lengthy procedure of law to convict them formally and deport them.

In the first weeks after the occupation the Germans repeated in Gorcum on a small scale what they did in Berlin and in other cities of the Reich shortly after Hitler's appointment to the Chancellorship. They would select a few old men from the synagogue corral, shave half their heads and beards, hang signs around their necks saying: "I am a Jewish swine," "I am a ritual murderer and a drinker of Christian blood," or "I am an Asiatic *Untermensch*," and other degrading inscriptions of that kind and parade them through the streets. This was part of the regular, codified procedure with Jews wherever the Nazis installed themselves. It was done, I suppose, to reveal to the Dutch people what criminals and scoundrels they had unwittingly harbored in their midst for so many years. The Germans were bringing the Hollanders enlightenment at last on the subject of Jews and Judaism. It also served to justify, in German eyes at least, the war the Führer had unleashed upon "Judaism and Bolshevism" and the heavy sacrifices he demanded from the German people to rid Europe of a sinister menace that was everywhere present, even in so small and out-of-the-way a place as Gorcum.

Thereafter parties of Jewish prisoners could regularly be seen moving through town, under the watchful eye of Elite Guards of course, on their way to and from work. Employees of the street-cleaning department and the sanitation service had been given other occupations and their former tasks assigned to the Jews.

"You saw," writes a friend from Gorcum, "tottering and emaciated old men and boys carrying shovels and pushing handcarts and doing the most menial and filthy tasks. For instance, Mr. Dalmaden the umbrella-maker, whom you surely remember, a man in his eighties, I saw one day on his knees washing the pavement of the parade ground. With him were several other Jews. A soldier stood guard over them and a *Feldwebel* directed operations. Another man of your acquaintance, Mr. Pimentel, a public schoolteacher, was ordered to descend into the sewers on Kortedyk Street to retrieve a piece of wood that an SS man had thrown in there. When Mr. Pimentel reappeared through the manhole, covered with ordure, the Germans held their noses and pushed him back with sticks, clamped the metal cover over the hole, and left him there. The following day the other Jews were summoned to recover his body and take it to the synagogue, where it was left for a week before permission for interment was given.

"At the Jewish cemetery the Jews themselves were forced to knock down the tombstones bearing the names of their ancestors, and carry them to the river (more than a mile distant). A Jewish painter was directed to put huge swastika signs on the public buildings. But the bulk of the Jewish men were employed in the latrines of the King William barracks, occupied by a regiment of Bavarian *Landwehr*, and at the garbage dump outside town. In the evening, exhausted and hungry, you could see them drag themselves back to their synagogue."

Since I had expressed surprise in a letter to my friend at the relatively large number of Jews apprehended in Gorcum, wondering if perchance some men and women from other communities were included in that number of one hundred and thirty, she replied that a number of individuals were suddenly added to the Jewish community in 1940 upon their inability to show documentary evidence of "a clear, unsullied Aryan descent" from the year 1795 onward. "Men and women," wrote my friend, "who had, or whose ancestors had, abandoned Judaism generations before, who had adopted very Netherlandish-sounding names, who had intermarried with Gentiles to such an extent that scarcely any trace remained of their Jewish identity, were all at once classed as Jews when the Nuremberg Laws were applied in Holland. As often to their own cruel surprise," she adds, "as that of their Christian neighbors. Baptism, complete merger with their Dutch environment, repudiation of religious beliefs, disassociation from Jewish folkways, civic honors, learning, age, or prominent standing in the general community—nothing availed these people. To the Germans they were Jews, and as Jews they were treated, that is to say, they were squeezed into the synagogue of which they had probably never seen the interior before."

Rich and poor, old and young, sick and well, the Jews and half-Jews and quarter-Jews were thrown together in a stifling promiscuity. At nine o'clock in the evening the doors were locked and the windows closed, and a German sentry was placed at the grill. Lights were not permitted, and since the only water closet was in the back of the yard, pails had to be used during the night, causing an insufferable stench. In a short time half the prisoners were ill and the interior of the synagogue, where straw was used for bedding but seldom refreshed, resembled one of those medieval lazarettos or pesthouses of which Saint Vincent de Paul has left us a description and where death came as a welcome release.

Nineteen persons out of the one hundred and thirty died during the first sixteen months of hunger and destitution. Most of these were old folk and very young children. Baruch Dalmaden was one of them. Only when the sixteen months were over, and the misery and human degradation in the synagogue seemed to have reached its lowest depth, did a change come. But it was not a change for the better. Then only began the real road of sorrows. What followed must have made the survivors often think back to their incarceration at the synagogue as a relatively pleasant holiday.

In the late summer of 1941 the Nazis weeded out all the young men and women from the Jewish compounds they had established all over Holland. They sent the boys to the sulphur mines of Germany and Hungary and the girls to the military brothels that were set up all over Eastern Europe in anticipation of the Führer's forthcoming Russian campaign. Seventeen thousand Dutch Jewish youth were deported in that way in the month of June. In December of the same year only nine thousand of these were alive. The rest had perished, as a cynical note in the *German Gazette* for the Netherlands announced on December 15, 1941, "as a result of their inability to get accustomed to the change of climate." The sinister truth is that most of the eight thousand died of the effects of the brutal and purposely careless operations for sexual sterilization to which they were subjected. Of the thousands of girls and young women who were deported simultaneously with the boys no one was ever heard of again.

Insofar as the Jewish community of Gorcum was concerned, this weeding-out process of the youth meant a reduction in their number to seventy-two souls. This remnant was transferred to the local penitentiary for women, from which the former prisoners had been removed to Dordt. The Jews were lodged in the upper stories, the ground floor being occupied by a detail of the infamous Schutz-Staffeln or Elite Guards especially assigned to the liquidation of the Jewish problem in our community.

The thick medieval walls of the prison and its remote location in a little-frequented neighborhood of abandoned warehouses and junk yards, where a tomblike silence reigned at night, made it an ideal retreat for the Elite Guards to practice their most bestial erotomaniac experiments on the bodies of those helpless men and women. It seems that the synagogue, which stood in a rather populous quarter, had been too accessible a place, too much in the public eye and ear. Few passed through the prison neighborhood in the evening to hear the screams and moans of the tortured prisoners coming through the barred windows.

The SS Standart Gruppe stationed at the prison was in charge of a certain August Deffner, a thin, aenemic, long-nosed fellow, who was like Horst Wessel the son of an evangelical pastor from Elberfeld-Barmen and like that prototype of Nazi satyriasis a frustrated intellectual who had become a follower of Hitler in the days when the movement's leadership swarmed with pimps, pederasts, homosexuals, and white-slavers. I knew the Nazi leaders, as well as Horst Wessel, in the days of the party's rise to power. I know whereof I speak. I can well believe the accounts of the few survivors of that episode in the Gorcum prison when they declare it to have been an unadulterated, unimaginable hell.

Deffner took his private pleasure in selecting a few Jews when the sadistic lust came upon him, chaining them up to the wall and crushing their bare toes with the heels of his hobnailed boots. He would bring in his friends and cronies to watch the spectacle of two Jews, who each had been given a dagger, fighting one another. If he could manage, he preferred to have a son oppose his father. The Elite Guards sat around the ring with whips to urge and drive the men on to cut and wound each other. Refusal or showing halfheartedness in the duel brought the severest punishment, a beating with lead-loaded sticks in the region of the kidneys that left the victims unable to walk for days.

In that prison took place unmentionable things, things compared to which the horrors of the Inquisition are mere innocent childish pranks. Every conceivable atrocity, and some quite inconceivable to a normal mind, were perpetrated there virtually under the eyes of the Christian people of Gorcum. For everybody knew what was going on in the upper stories of the jail on nights when Herr Deffner and his company of Elite Guards were carousing and amusing themselves. Word of it was whispered from house to house. Turnkeys and wardens and orderlies at the penitentiary were Dutch fellow citizens. They knew. They saw day by day to what indignities and torments the Jews were subjected. They talked, be it in guarded language, of what they saw and heard.

Yet what could the people do about it? What could anyone do? Go and lodge a protest at the local Gestapo headquarters? Write a letter to the newspapers? Tell Herr Deffner to his face that he was an uncivilized barbarian, a sadist, a neuropathic pervert? Hit some lone German over the head in retaliation on a dark night, or push him into the canal as the youths of Rotterdam were doing?

All very well! But not every man is a hero. Not every man will take his life in his hands and brave a power that has made a specialty of ruthlesness and *Schrecklichkeit*. The repressional apparatus of the Germans in Holland, as everywhere else, was a machine of formidable might and relentless vindictiveness. It was not something to fool with lightly. It had teeth. It brooked no interference, allowed no criticism or admonition to compassion, no whisper of dissent or appeal to reason. It struck, crushed, mangled, annihilated anyone daring to raise himself in its path. The least overt act or word of opposition to the New Order was answered with totalitarian Nazi thoroughness and dispatch. The people were overawed by the might of the system, by its cruelty and by its machinelike heartlessness. They were themselves in a fog of terror.

And then, yes, and then, the victims were only Jews after all, weren't they? Those horrible things were not happening to Catholics or to Protestants. They were happening only to Jews. The others, Catholics and Protestants, were indeed punished just as severely as anyone else when they committed what was a crime in Nazi eyes: an act of opposition, a display of disrespect by word or deed of the Führer's august person, sabotage, intelligence with Germany's enemies, hoarding of valuables, *Zerzetzung der Wehrmacht* —interference with the task of the German Army. But Catholics and Protestants were not singled out for the most fiendish tortures imaginable and for wholesale extermination for the mere fact of their being Catholics or Protestants. Ninety per cent of the inmates of the Nazi murder camps in East Europe were Jews. Six million noncombatant Jews were done to death. The Jews alone were made to suffer not for anything they did do or did not do, but for what they were: Jews.

Few, very few Protestants or Catholics in Holland, in France, in Czechoslovakia, or in any other occupied country were ever molested by the Nazis, let alone made to suffer and die, for the sake of their faith alone. Except for the Salvation Army, which was forbidden to carry on its activities under the Nazi regime because of its founder's Jewish blood, not a single Christian church, chapel, or shrine was closed anywhere in Western Europe. But all synagogues were. Every other man, Protestant or Catholic, Buddhist or Muslim, was left free to worship God in his customary way. But not the Jew. The Jew was doomed a priori. Whether good or bad, rich or poor, old or young, male or female, radical or reactionary, orthodox or modernist, circumcised or baptized, speaking Yiddish, Hebrew, or the idiom of other peoples, peasant or poet, scholar or idiot, believer or unbeliever, the Jews were earmarked for destruction by decrees of Hitler promulgated as early as 1930.

That would have been the time for the civilized world to protest and intervene. That was the right moment to prevent Hitler from carrying out his foul designs. Those years from 1930 to 1939 are now completely forgotten, it seems, by the planners of Germany's future and by the most vociferous champions of democracy. Those years were the blossom hour of fate when the fascist dragon was incubating

in the egg, so to speak, and when Hitler could have
been driven from power by a mere word spoken in
London, Washington, or Paris, by the institution of
a boycott of German goods, by withholding financial
help, by a moral embargo on the Reich, by challenging
the Führer's initial and preliminary moves in the
international field, in Spain, in the Rhineland, in Austria and Czechoslovakia.

Why wasn't it done? Why was the act of protesting
against the incipient Nazi terrorism left to a few
isolated individuals, to radicals, to the Soviet Union,
to a handful of Christians in the Anglo-Saxon and
Scandinavian countries? Where was the Christian
Church, the Pope, the Roman hierarchy, the Protestant world federations, all those who after the deluge
of innocent blood were to demand the re-education of
the German people along democratic lines?

At that time, in those decisive years when the Nazi
party was being supported and kept alive by financial
contributions from Dutch, French, Czechoslovak,
British, Belgian, and other industrialists, munition-
eers, and bankers—because Hitler had promised to
rearm the Reich, and the rearmament of Germany
was the condition sine qua non of a general rearmament campaign—in those days the murder of the
German Jews, if it caused any discussion or any concern at all, was generally attributed to or dismissed
as some cold-blooded, tigerish, sadistic trait in the
German character.

It never was a secret that Hitler was the creature
of international finance and that for him were lifted
the burdens of the Versailles Treaty that preceding
German statesmen had sought in vain to have lifted
in London and Paris. The record shows that he was
helped over critical periods in the growth of his
movement whenever democratic opposition in the
Reich seemed on the verge of sweeping him into
limbo, by financial donations from the big French,
Czechoslovak, British, Dutch and other armament

and oil trusts; that he was allowed to remilitarize the Rhineland when one French Army corps could have stopped him on the Lunenburger Heath; that he was allowed to annex Austria without interference or protest from anybody at a time when the *Reichswehr* was far from the formidable military machine it later became; that he was handed the Czechoslovakian fortress, which barred his way to Russia, on a silver platter by Messrs. Chamberlain, Runciman, and Daladier; in short that everything possible was done to facilitate the Führer's going to war, including his extermination of democratic elements in the Reich. He was allowed to proclaim anti-Semitism as an official government policy without as much as a diplomatic intervention by the self-styled saviors of civilization.

He was allowed with perfect impunity to begin murdering the Jews and to turn Germany into a vast prison camp the moment Hindenburg appointed him Chancellor of the Reich. He was allowed to turn the schools of learning into drill halls. He proscribed free thought, destroyed the co-operatives, closed the progressive schools, muzzled the theater, put the press in step. He, an upstart politician who would have been discredited and have sunk into oblivion if powerful foreign interventionists had not revived him and his party time and again, a loud-mouthed vulgar demagogue, half a lunatic, was permitted to destroy every vestige of democracy in Germany.

For six long years, Hitler drove into exile, imprisoned, tortured, broke the spirit of, or assassinated every German democrat, every man of independent mind, every pacifist, every antimilitarist, every intellectual, every labor leader, every progressive economist, every social worker and social theoretician, every single German who had not bent or who would not bend the knee to the Baal of fascism. Three hundred thousand German liberals and democrats, it is said, had been killed or been driven into exile or suicide by 1939 and three hundred thousand more were in concentration camps. Where would American democracy be if half a million of its leaders and thinkers were eliminated? Are there half a million?

While Hitler was killing off everything decent, humane, and forward-looking, he reared a new generation in the cult of pitiless inhumanity and war. He ruled the leaderless German masses with an army of gorillas and plug-uglies, gangsters and sadists. What was called the marvel of German efficiency and organizing ability was in reality the dictatorship of brutality and inhuman, satanic perversity. This army of black cutthroats and gangsters, picked from the sinks and the stews of Berlin, Hamburg, and other large cities, was unleashed on the conquered countries. The Nazi "elite" set its stamp of frightfulness and bestiality on everything the Germans undertook.

Who allowed that army of Jew-killers and torturers to come into existence? Who lauded, encouraged, supported, and egged on the Hitler gang for years as the protectors of Christendom against Bolshevism and as the potential destroyers of the Soviet Union? Wasn't it international big business and its flunkies: the prelates, statesmen, journalists, diplomats, educators, molders of public opinion in the so-called democratic countries? After the termination of World War II the Archbishop of Canterbury solemnly asked whether we could ever forgive the Germans. A more pertinent question would be: Can we ever expect to be forgiven ourselves? Do we repent now for our sins of commission and omission in having allowed everything decent and democratic in Germany to be covered by the Nazi slime?

What all the laurels of glory cannot hide is the Cain mark on our own foreheads. The word that is spoken flies, we know, irrevocable: no less, but more, the action that is done. The thing once done, Carlyle says somewhere, is always done, cast forth into endless time; and long conspicuous or soon hidden, must verily work and grow forever there, an indestructible new element in the infinite scheme of things. . . .

Were all those sorrows and horrors of World War II endured to no other end but that imperialism, with the help of its victims, might eliminate a few of its most desperate rivals, only to resume with the same ruthlessness and callous inhumanity its old game of blood and guile through dismal years to come?

The termination of World War II has not brought agreement between the Great Powers. What they have reached is not even a compromise, but an approximate ascertainment each of what is in the other.

It is now clear that World War II was but a fraction of the great battle that started long before 1939, and which goes on uninterruptedly in this day of nominal peace. Man has not stopped exploiting and oppressing his brother.

The embers of war are still smoldering, and from a thousand editorial offices, academies, and pulpits comes the wind, the poisoned breath, that seeks to blow them into flame again. In public, mincing, grimacing statesmen with plausible speech and brushed raiment talk of peace and goodwill and international collaboration. Inside the council chambers, behind closed doors, with menacing brow they whisper of security, of aerial bases, of hemispheric defense, of bigger navies, of standing armies, of markets, of spheres of influence, of more scientific instruments of death and destruction. Yesterday's so-called aggressor nations are defeated. They lie humbled in the dust, their armies shattered, their navies sunk, their industries wrecked, their commerce in ruins. They are reduced to such impotence, to such depths of destitution and misery, that they are unable to raise themselves an inch. Yet security is the chief topic of international conferences. Who can be threatening security and the peace of the world now that Germany and Japan have been eliminated? Who? Where is the culprit?

Napoleon, who had harnessed the tremendous

driving power of the French Revolution, said one day in 1815: "When the kings and prelates of Europe talk of security and of establishing order, it isn't me they envisage. They have in mind the Revolution."

That's what the statesmen and prelates have in mind today. They are trying to head off the European revolution and the revolution of the peoples living in the traditional areas of colonialism. They are jockeying for positions, shaping cordons sanitaires, balances of power in East and West, building bases and springboards for attack and strategic routes, and establishing military control posts for vast regions. As in the days of the French Revolution they are hammering together a new Holy Alliance. They are even now paving the road that will lead to the pit for millions more.

If man disregards the signs of the times, if he does not heed the call for the unification of mankind on a new basis, if he turns a deaf ear to his own intuition, if he silences the very God within his heart who bids him begin the new era now, institute without delay the holy commune of mankind, now that the inconceivable destructiveness of atomic energy hangs over his head as an ever-present threat, if he should allow greed and egotism and lust of power to blind his eyes and stop his ears, if he persists in defending and maintaining at all costs the chaos and violence of imperialist capitalism—then the solemn warning sounded two thousand years ago in Judea may well be fulfilled in our day and generation. For it was Jesus who said that the human race will not accept the divine plan of peace and order until violence shall have reached its ultimate degree. Only, said He, when dread and terror shall have mounted their utmost crescendo, when people in the immensity of their anguish, at their wits' end cry out: Mountains, fall upon us, and hills, cover us—only then shall appear the sign of the Son of Man.

David Dalmaden was not at first subjected to the full rigors of the Nuremberg Laws. As a physician he was permitted to continue visiting those of his patients who still desired and dared to avail themselves of his professional services. In public he was merely required to wear the usual yellow armband, plus a cardboard notice hanging around his neck saying: "I am a Jewish quack." He had been chief surgeon at the local infirmary and clinic before the occupation. There the Nazis came to take advantage of his skill and science after they installed themselves in our town. At the end of a hard day's work in the operating room, Dr. Dalmaden went to the synagogue to be locked up for the night with the other Jews, among whom were his two sisters, Rebecca and Esther, his brother, and for a time his father, as well as his wife Yetta and his two daughters. David's house, the former residence of his predecessor Dr. Mendoza whose practice he had taken over, had been confiscated. Deffner, the chief of the Schutz Staffel, occupied it with some women friends he had brought from Barmen.

David had learned through Adriana of the hiding-place of his friends, Dr. Mendoza and Ary Brandt. Although she insisted time and again that he join the fugitives in their underground retreat, David just as insistently refused. He feared that his disappearance would cause the Nazis to take reprisals against his relatives. This contemptible system of pressure and intimidation was indeed one of their strongest weapons. When I say, from having in my possession the sad documentary evidence, that dozens of non-Jewish Dutch persons were actually tortured and some assassinated for being related to myself, "one of the most implacable enemies of Germany in the world," according to the late Dr. Goebbels, or for merely having been acquainted with me in my younger years, it will be understood how well justified David Dalmaden was in fearing that his defenseless kinsfolk might become the victims of an eventual escape on his own part. Even after his two young daughters were caught in the Gestapo's continent-wide dragnet for future prostitutes for the Eastern armies, David still resisted Adriana's urgings to save himself. Yetta, his sisters, and one brother were still among the prisoners.

On several occasions Adriana let him through the secret door in the cellar of her house on the High Street to see his old friends for a brief moment. It was on one of those visits that he informed Dr. Mendoza and Ary of the rumors circulating in town that the Jewish captives were to be moved for a second time. In other Dutch towns the exodus was already in full swing. Thousands of Jewish citizens of Amsterdam, The Hague, and Rotterdam had been transferred to the Reich and to Eastern Europe. Jews from all over the Continent were being assembled in territories lying within the jurisdiction of the new German-sponsored Government General of Poland.

The Führer, it was said, was of a more generous turn of mind on the subject of the Jews after his phenomenal victories in Russia. He had relented; the Jews would be allowed to live. He had arrived at a definite decision with regard to the Jewish problem. To begin with, there was to be an end to their being shuttled to and fro aimlessly from one country to another. They were to be collected from all the occupied countries and given a permanent abode in a fixed place. Jewish manpower was not to be wasted any longer. Jews were to be put to work on some useful task and thus contribute to the victory of the Reich.

Segregated areas in the vicinity of the Polish city of Lublin and other localities were being put in readiness to receive them. A million or more had reached that destination. Trainloads of Jews were speeding across the Continent in the direction of the new Jewish national home. Thousands were arriving every day. Hitler was going to show the world how to settle the Jewish question. Other states and nations were continually holding conferences and debates on that subject and pouring out a mass of sentimental drivel but in the final analysis did nothing practical about it. The Germans dispensed with international conferences. They wasted no time on hypocritical democratic palaver. They were going to act. They were going to settle the Jewish question once and for all.

Most of the Jews of Europe were now under German domination, and with a victory over Russia assured the majority of the Jewish people in the world would come under the Nazi sway. It was time to apply a radical solution to the problem. The first arrivals in the Lublin area, it was said, were already building roads and barracks for the reception of the mass of their brethren. Now the turn had come for the Jews of Holland to join the new colonies, which were to be administered by the Jews themselves, of course under German supervision. It was to be an experiment that would have valuable lessons for the eventual transfer, collection, and segregation of other racial minorities with whom the *Herrenvolk* should have no contact but whose services should nevertheless not be dispensed with.

This was in substance the news that David Dalmaden conveyed to his friends in the underground retreat. He warned them that he was not likely to visit them again, inasmuch as the official notification for the Gorcum Jews to move off was apt to come any day and he himself was most likely to accompany the exiles in his capacity of physician. The Germans were going to clean house. Not a single Jew, he said, was likely to remain behind. On the whole David was glad that he was leaving, for he did not want to be separated from his wife Yetta. "Who knows," he said hopefully, "whether we Jews haven't come to the end of our trials? If we are left to our own devices in the Lubliner reservation, as they say we will be, we may be able to manage somehow. It will not be easy. But we will be together. Maybe we will be forgotten in the awful turmoil that's coming. Maybe the Russians will stage a comeback and liberate us."

Dr. Mendoza did not take so optimistic a view of the situation. The idea of collecting the remaining Jews of Europe in one locality, he felt, was only another cruel trick. The Nazis would probably offer large batches of Jews for ransom once they had them in their Polish compounds. Then, in order to justify their continued imprisonment, they would cite the British Government's refusal to furnish immigration certificates for Palestine and the opposition of all

the other civilized nations to allowing mass immigration of
Jews. It would be the same story all over again. The Germans could be counted upon to find a very plausible reason
for shifting responsibility in continuing to oppress the
Jews.

That the Russians would eventually overcome the German Army and drive it back, of that Dr. Mendoza had no
doubt. But therein lay a new and greater source of danger
for the Jews. Hitler might be in a somewhat more lenient
mood for the moment now that his campaign in the East
was going from one success to another. But what would happen when American industry and American military might
were at last fully mobilized? Then Hitler was bound to
meet with reverses. The whole of Europe was hoping and
praying for that moment. And it would come. The Continent would be invaded. The old Doctor felt certain of that.
Hitler would then be caught between two fires. He would
be in a trap, a deadly trap, with the Americans and the
Russians bearing down on him from opposite sides.

What would happen then? Would Hitler in that moment
forget the Jews? No, in that moment precisely he would
remember them very much. He would vent his wild rage
for the defeats on the most helpless of his victims. It would
be to easy to shift responsibility and guilt for the debacle
to the Jews, who had always been designated as the archconspirators, as the cause of all Germany's woes. Instead
of hope, the liberation of Europe would bring the Jews
their final and greatest disaster. The defeats would not be
attributed to the superior armament and fighting power of
the enemy, but to Jewish international plotting, to Jewish
intrigue. The Jews in their Polish compounds would be held
responsible and would feel the full fury of the Führer's
resentment. That was the Doctor's view, and proved to be
the correct one.

He was also right about the German blackmail propositions. For a German offer to set a number of Jews free,
upon payment of ransom money, from Poland and later
from Hungary and Romania, was indeed subsequently
made. Since the Jews have perished, it is futile and immate-

rial to speculate on the question whether the offer was made
in good faith or not. At the time when the proposition was
made at certain diplomatic back doors in Europe, it evoked
not the slightest response. The only repercussion was that
the democracies held a conference or two on refugees and
decided, virtually unanimously, that the moment wasn't opportune to lift their immigration barriers by so much as an
inch. The British Government had its information bureaus
in various lands plead that no ships were available for the
transportation of refugees and that the introduction of still
more Jews into Palestine would inevitably cause the Arab
world to explode. The negative reaction in the West to the
German offer had the same effect as if Hitler had been given
carte blanche to continue solving the Jewish question in his
own way. . . .

"But when you do leave," said Dr. Mendoza to David,
"I will not stay behind. Old as I am, I am coming along.
I belong with my people. Whatever their fate, good or bad,
it is my fate."

A few days later indeed he left his hiding-place and in
spite of Adriana's tears and prayers walked out of her
house on the High Street. He took a last look at his own
house and then quietly gave himself up at the local office
of the *Sicherheits Dienst*. He was immediately transferred
to the prison house where the fifty-five surviving Jews were
under orders to be ready to move off at a moment's notice
and start the long journey to Poland.

But then Ary Brandt, too, could no longer bear to remain
a distant spectator of the Jews' woe. As long as there had
been a bare chance that help might arrive before they were
driven out, he considered it his duty to remain with the
underground movement, to work with the fighters for freedom. He was the inspiration and the counselor of the group
that actively resisted the Nazis in our part of the country.
He planned one action after another, and participated in
raids on Nazi food hoards and munition depots. Through
Ary's action the Linge Canal was blocked for an entire
year, stopping all water transport. He personally lit the
fuse to a charge of dynamite that blew up a section of the

cement factory when the Nazis began building their West
Wall along Holland's coast and drew a large part of their
supplies from the Gorcum plant. Besides publishing a clandestine newssheet, he also ran a small hospital in the tunnels and was in charge of the liaison service with the groups
that made it their business to save Allied airmen from the
clutches of the Nazis and ship them back to Britain.

When he learned from David Dalmaden that the hour
had struck for the Jews' departure on what was to become
their death march, he decided to come into the open and
make a last attempt to prevent or hold up their leaving.
"The thought," wrote Adriana, from whom I have the details of this painful episode, "of the Jews being shipped off
to Poland, where, as Doctor Mendoza said, an impenetrable curtain would hide from the civilized world the horrors the Nazis would inflict on them, gave him no rest.

"He came into my house every night," she goes on to
say, "through the secret door in the cellar, although the
main channel for communication with the people in the tunnels had been transferred to the ruins of the Netherlands
Bank building after the partisans set it on fire. He had
drawn up dozens of big red-lettered posters and went out to
paste or nail them up on walls and billboards. Every time
he went into the street he took his life in his hands, for
there was a price on his head and the surveillance at night
was far more severe than in the beginning of the occupation.

"On those posters he called upon his fellow citizens to
signify by a ringing act of protest their condemnation and
their repudiation of the persecution of the Jews. 'It must
never be said in later years when the sun of freedom will
shine again in Holland,' he warned, 'that the Dutch people
in any way connived at, had the least share in, or even approved by their silence the unspeakable horrors perpetrated
by the Nazis on the Jews. Now,' he wrote further, 'is the
time to show your solidarity with the victims of German
fascism. Your regrets and disapproval in later years, when
the Jews are no more, will have no value. The persecution
of the Jews is politically unjustified, morally an outrage,
patriotically a betrayal of Holland's ancient traditions, and

from the Christian point of view a sin before God. Silence at this time,' wound up his appeal, 'means approval of the Nazis and will so be interpreted by them. Therefore speak out now and demonstrate against the deportation of our Jewish fellow citizens!'

"As he had done before, he again went to see several prominent men in town and in the neighborhood," Adriana continues her letter. "Circumstances compelled him to do most of his traveling on foot and by night, inasmuch he could ill afford to be seen in any public place or conveyance, such as railway stations, river boats, train coaches, bus stations, which were either heavily guarded or crowded with *Moffen* of one sort or another. His idea was to have a number of influential citizens sign a joint protest with him, or failing that to address an appeal for mercy to the authorities in behalf of the Jews. He did not think that anyone would object to making at least a politely worded appeal.

"I need not tell you," the letter goes on, "that he did not get very far with this project. His own appearance frightened people. Everybody knew that the *Moffen* were looking for him and that he was wanted by the Gestapo as 'an incorrigible enemy.' People were afraid to let him come into their homes. It amounted to sheltering a fugitive from justice and carried the death penalty. Ary expressed himself to me bitterly at times," says Adriana, "over the kind of reception he received from various men he had thought good loyal friends. He made small account of the danger in which he placed his friends by the mere fact of calling on them.

"One of the men he saw again was Zeger van Rietvelt. Zeger enjoyed the confidence of the *Moffen* because of his zealous collaboration. It was for this very reason that Ary thought Zeger could be more helpful than many another. Zeger's influence and friendship with some of the top Nazis, he imagined, would be an ideal instrument to make the persecutors relent or consent to some mitigation in their treatment of the Jews. How he could muster the courage to face the Squire at all, I do not understand. Ary overcame his repulsion for the sake of the victims. 'After all,' he said to

me, 'Zeger and I know each other. He is not unamenable
to reason. He has a good heart au fond and has suffered a
good deal himself. I know he can be generous if you appeal
to him in the right way and flatter him a little.' I predicted,"
Adriana goes on, "that the second attempt with Zeger
would have no better results than the first. But nevertheless
he started out one evening for Asperen in a pouring rain
storm.

"Zeger seems to have been greatly upset at first by Ary's
visit. He took him upstairs into his bedroom and made sure
that the servants did not suspect his visitor's identity. He
talked to him for an hour. First he tried to persuade Ary
to give up his plans. There was no use, he told him. There
was not the slightest hope of bringing the German authorities to change their minds. They were determined that the
Jews were to perish as fomenters of revolution and social
unrest. They were the allies of Germany's enemies. They
were camouflaged Bolsheviks, even the seemingly inoffensive and harmless Jews of Gorcum. They were this, that,
and the other thing, the cause of all Europe's ills and wars
and so on, all the old anti-Semitic drivel and nonsense. Ary
listened in silence, which was, you will admit," says Adriana,
"a tremendous achievement on his part when you think of
his stormy, impetuous nature. Then he answered Zeger
point by point.

"Zeger seems to have been irritated by Ary's calm. He
began to reproach him for his opposition to the New Order. He called Ary's attitude unpatriotic and inconsistent.
Unpatriotic because the Dutch people's interests, now that
Germany had as good as won the war, lay entirely with the
Reich. Britain would never recover from the blow admin-
istered at Dunkirk. Her empire was tottering to a fall. The
German armies even then were cutting its lifeline in Egypt
and at Suez. British losses in the Far East were staggering.
Of British possessions only Australia and India remained,
and these would soon fall into Japanese hands. What could
Holland expect from a defeated and broken England?

"As to America, her entry into the war was a gigantic
bluff. Zeger knew. He had visited America more than once.

It wasn't a nation you dealt with over there. America was just a huge boardinghouse without any spirit of coherence. The Americans would work for the British and supply them with war necessities as long as they could make a profit. As soon as British credit was exhausted, and that day was not far off, America would simply shift to the other side. 'Do you think,' he asked Ary, 'that American businessmen want to see Bolshevism installed in Europe?' The Americans would soon recognize the Führer's greatness and acknowledge the justice of his attack on Russia. For that was the essence of the war: the attempt to crush the Bolshevik regime. The rest was a mere sideshow, an unavoidable, unfortunate miscarriage of fundamental plans. Once the Great Powers realized what was really at stake they would thank Hitler for having shown the way and they would back him to the limit.

"Ary's inconsistency, Zeger said, lay in the fact that he had always been a dreamer and a champion of European unification. Now that the Führer was welding the heterogeneous elements of the Continent together by abolishing frontiers and tariffs, by instituting a common system of jurisprudence, by reforming the schools and giving the jarring and clashing nations one common language and outlook, sweeping aside all the impediments and hurdles that formerly kept the peoples apart and at dagger's point, now that the Führer was fulfilling that ideal, how could Ary resist and urge others to resist? His attitude was really shameful and he deserved to be punished for it.

"In the end Zeger grew abusive and threatened to call the police. When Ary, who had steadily maintained his sangfroid during the interview, thereupon began to remonstrate and appealed to their old friendship, the Squire suddenly blurted out that he knew perfectly well the hiding-place from which Ary and the others carried on their illegal activity. 'If I ever hear again of the slightest incident, Brandt,' he said to our friend in parting, 'I will denounce the whole business and have you strung up, you and all that Communist rabble that's with you in the sewers. I am not going to cover you any longer with my silence.'

THE END OF THE ROAD

"When Ary returned shortly before dawn through by-ways and alleys, disheveled and haggard and soaked to the skin, I was as upset as he about Zeger's last words. We could not take a chance and let the secret get out to the Gestapo. We had lost thirty-one young men and three girls up to that time. They had fallen into the hands of the *Moffen* in the course of various assignments. None had betrayed the secret of the tunnels, in spite of the most excruciating torture. One girl was choked in mud. She was literally killed inch by inch. Another succumbed under the application of red-hot smoothing irons to her bare skin. Not a word came from her lips.

"But now it was different. We were at Zeger's mercy. If he spoke, it would mean a mass execution. There were no less than two hundred men and women hiding in the tunnels at the time. They would all be caught. Ary and I debated the issue just after daylight that morning. We realized that we could not go down into the cellar and advise our people to flee. For where could they have fled? We therefore descended into the cellar and told the leaders calmly what danger was hanging over their heads.

"It was decided to act without a moment's delay: Zeger was to be put out of the way. He had condemned himself. There was no other issue. It had to be done. Some were in favor of executing him that very morning. But this was not done. I do not know what trick or ruse they used to get him to leave his house that same night. They probably had one of the girls lure him to a place of rendezvous. The fact is he did leave Asperen by automobile shortly before midnight. The car ran into an ambush set by the partisans, and Zeger was arrested. He was gagged and bound and taken through my kitchen right into the cellar. I advised the partisans to hold a drum court-martial that very night and be done with him. This advice was not followed. Zeger was incarcerated along with a few other gentlemen we had down there and was kept alive for the day of liberation to be dealt with by the regular authorities. He is at this moment in the prison at Dordt awaiting trial on a charge of collaborationism.

"That's going to be the end of Zeger van Rietvelt," writes Adriana. "The firing squad, probably. That is, if he doesn't manage to get some influential friends in high places to pull him out of the scrape. I learn that he has hired the ablest lawyers in the country to defend him. We shall see. . . .

"Our friend Ary, however," she continues, "had then and there also come to the end of the road. He took part in Zeger's kidnapping and it was he who advised the partisans to disregard my counsel to try the man summarily. He was utterly dismayed over the fact that he had been able to collect only a dozen signatures for his protest, his appeal for mercy in behalf of the Jews. If his own brethren in the ministry turned him down, what could be expected of Zeger? Zeger after all wasn't supposed to be a champion of a religion of mercy and compassion. Zeger had merely acted in what he thought were his own best interests.

"The orthodox dominies refused assistance with a piece of sophistry so contemptible that I must write you about it," Adriana goes on to say. "One and all, every one of these fundamentalists on whom he called invoked the Bible, or rather the Gospel story. The cause of the world's unredemption, Ary was told by one prominent neo-Calvinist, lay in the fact of the Jews' denial of Jesus' divinity. It was not a struggle between light and darkness, between progress and reaction, that unsettled the times and caused the tumult in the world. It was another question entirely. For two thousand years the Jews had refused God's outstretched hand. From that affront to the Divine Majesty derived all the world's ills: the wars, the revolutions, the social unrest, the decline in morals and in faith, everything evil. It wasn't strange therefore that the Jews were suffering. They had themselves called down God's wrath by that shout of the mob before Pontius Pilate about letting the guilt for shedding Jesus' blood be upon them and upon their children.

"In other words," writes Adriana, "the Jews of Holland, two thousand years after that event, which as Ary believed was of extremely doubtful historical authenticity—in fact he said that particular text is one of the most obvious

frauds in the New Testament—the Jews of Holland were
to suffer for that spurious word of their ancestors in Jerusalem. I have never heard anything more absurd or shameful! What a God! What a conception of divine justice!
Compare to that God of the Calvinists, Torquemada was
holy innocence personified. At any rate the Jews' suffering
was preordained. God willed it. Hitler was merely the divine
instrument in the execution of God's will.

"This subterfuge or pretext, or white lie, or whatever
else you want to call it, so exasperated our friend Ary, I
might well say it so infuriated him, that his voice trembled
with rage whenever he spoke about the matter. He seemed
a different man. All the suavity and gentleness and calm
resolution that had characterized him during the long
months of underground activity seemed to have left him.
He spoke with a strange, somber fierceness. His seamed and
dusky face radiated his passion for the right. Sometimes I
thought he was mad, not insane, but mad with a sacred
madness. I could not help thinking of the time when he
challenged Yssel Ponthieu in the classroom, that time when
he suddenly called out: 'That was a most unfair remark to
make,' and when he said that not to have spoken out would
have been like a self-inflicted dumbness. Do you remember?
As then, it seemed that he would burst if he did not speak
out.

"He did nothing but write, write, and write those last
days and nights, as if the Furies were at his heels. He said
the time had come for him to cease being a dead letter. He
felt, he said, that now had come the moment to be a living,
visible, and audible witness of the mind that was in Christ
Jesus. If he didn't speak out, he felt he would lose his own
soul. What was the use of mumbling creeds and theorizing
about abstract theological conceptions and preaching literary sermons on the subject of man's brotherhood and God's
fatherhood if these theories were never to be translated
into action? Facts alone, he said, can give concrete worth
to these moral ideas. I saw that he was heading for trouble
of the worst kind. I pleaded with him to go slow, to be
cautious. I pointed out the dangers he was running and the

perils to which rashness on his part might expose the whole community. But he would not heed me, nor his old father, nor anyone else.

"He almost deliberately put his neck in the halter when he persuaded one of his liberal colleagues whose turn it was to conduct the service in the Great Church the following Sunday morning to let him, Ary, occupy the pulpit. He was prohibited from speaking anywhere in the land, don't forget. I still wonder how he could expect to brave the Gestapo by preaching that sermon and escape the consequences. But then, as I said, he was rushing headlong to his own destruction. He had thrown all caution to the wind and would not hear of compromise. On the very Sunday morning when he left my house while the bells were ringing for the service, I made my last effort to stop him. 'Wait,' I said, 'wait, maybe there will come a more opportune moment, when you can do something really effective for the Jews.'

" 'The Jews are beyond help and beyond tears now,' he replied. 'I go to speak for my own sake, to redeem myself from the guilt in this tragedy. I must speak, if I am to be torn in fragments for it. . . .'

"I did not go to the service myself," Adriana goes on to say, "I stayed home. I probably prayed for the first time in my life. I feared that an incident might occur during the service. Incidents of pastors having been arrested, of ministers having been dragged out of the pulpit in the middle of the service, had occurred in several places and I was afraid Ary would be the victim of some such raid that very morning. But nothing of that kind happened yet.

"Ary, I learned from his father a few days later, took his text from Jesus' words: 'Be of good cheer; I have overcome the world.' He spoke first of the meaning of the Kingdom of God, and that it is man's task to lift conditions, social, political, and economic relations, to its level and in its direction. Jesus' victory over the world was one of principle only. To look at the world in its present state might well lead one to think that Jesus had been defeated. But that was an optical illusion. His victory awaited the participation of man in the struggle. Man had to carry out the task in the practical sphere if the Kingdom of God was to be achieved. 'If the people do not work and are not vigilant,' Ary said, 'God cannot work either; He falls asleep.'

"I do not recall everything he said," remarks Adriana. "I only have it from hearsay, after all. The subject of the Kingdom of God, as you know better than I do, had been a favorite with Ary for several years. It was his exclusive interest. But of late it had become more than a visionary doctrine, or shall I say more than a theory. It was a reality to him, a fact as obvious and tangible as a cow in the field. He bore witness to it not merely in argument but in his whole way of thinking, feeling, and acting. The Kingdom of God, he said that morning, was something of the will as well as of the perceptions. We must be of it in order to see it. We can only see it when we are of it. And since it is a reality in which we all must be a part if we are to achieve the Kingdom of God among ourselves and in our time, it follows that we must aim at the Kingdom politically, socially, economically, and by all kinds of concerted effort.

"Since the Kingdom is a reality, he said, we must dare all the things it requires in order to be part of that reality. We must not believe or hanker after another reality, for the alternative to the Kingdom of God is a non-sense and darkness, emptiness and chaos. The word must become flesh if it is to be the word. It is we who must incarnate the word, change it from a dead letter by our lives and our acts. Phrases, the most pious and noble-intentioned, are of no value. They are tinkling brass and empty noise if they are not clothed with reality. Words by themselves, he said, are often a denial of the Kingdom of God even if they have the Kingdom for their subject. He cited as an illustration the case of Russia, where the words God, Christ, love, and mercy are seldom uttered, but where the cause of the Kingdom of God, which is man's cause, the cause of the weary and heavy-laden, has advanced so immeasurably in our lifetime that the old social order and all its ecclesiastical appendages snarl and hiss at Russia like evil beasts driven in a corner.

"The abolition in Russia of racial discrimination, of anti-Semitism, and all the other tricks whereby the exploitation of man by his brother is sought to be justified and kept in existence, has advanced the Kingdom of God more than all the prayer and goodwill meetings of the Western churches in the last century, Ary said. In the end he called upon his hearers for an act, an act of faith, an immediate and necessary act, the only act required by the circumstances and by the ideal of the Kingdom of God: he asked the congregation to accompany their Jewish fellow citizens to the railway station on the day of departure. By that act, he said, they would show their solidarity with the victims of fascism and prove the brotherhood of man a reality and the Kingdom of God a living force yet capable of conquering the world.

"And so it came to pass," writes Adriana, "that we saw what can be the potency of a man's word on the souls of other men. On the Thursday following at two o'clock in the afternoon the factory whistles suddenly started blowing and the great bell in Sint Jan's tower, old Roelandt, you remember, whom we hadn't heard since that night of All Souls many years before, began to toll. It was the eeriest, awfulest sound I ever heard. It was as if heaven and earth had joined in a moaning, wailing lament. I ran outdoors to see what was going on. Everywhere doors and windows were opening and people were looking out and stepping out into the streets. I soon learned that the Jews were to be entrained for Poland that afternoon.

"Literally everybody in town was in the streets. Through the Arkel Gate and the Chancellory Gate came the workers. They had struck work. I wish you could have seen them, or that your Uncle Kees could have been there to see them. How proud he would have been! In their ragged working clothes, wearing their wooden shoes, bareheaded, a great silent mass of men tramped by our house. I never was so proud in all my life of being a Hollander, of belonging to that people, when I saw the procession of the workers; an endless, grim, tense, silent multitude. That was Holland going by. I confess frankly that I wept at the spectacle, as many others did.*

"Then I noticed that the children were in the streets, too. The schools had been closed. Even the inmates of the alms-house and the home for the aged and the orphan asylum were out—everybody. There were people at the windows, on the roofs, on the lamp irons, on the branches of trees.

"At three o'clock the Jews came into sight. What a horror! Slowly and wearily these men and women dragging themselves forward, many of them sick and having to be supported. Nobody could look on that little group of about fifty men and women with dry eyes. Our people stood mute, heart-stricken. They saw the calamity going by and for the first time fully realized its bitter magnitude. History tells us many things; but for the last thousand years or more, what thing has it told us of a sort like the Jewish people's agony? Albigensian Crusades, Nights of Bartholomew, Sicilian Vespers, all are like spluttering firecrackers, tame and colorless compared with that explosion of hatred.

"Right in front, with Dr. Mendoza and David, walked our friend Ary. Hein and Dirk were out of the cellar and watched through the crevices in the shutters. My heart shrank when I saw how heavily the Germans were armed. If only our people keep quiet and do not start jeering or hissing, I thought. If they do, it will be too bad for words. Two armored cars rode in front of the procession and two more brought up the rear, ready for action.

"The Germans apparently did not know what to make of it all. They looked ill at ease and worried. Had there been any show of violence they would have known what to do. Perhaps they would have welcomed an outburst of the popular wrath. But that tremendous, spontaneous silence, that simple dignity under the threat of machine guns and overwhelming power, the *Herrenvolk* men could not fathom. It frightened them. The crowd formed behind the Jews and walked to the station. I joined them. Only once did I

* In striking contrast with the oppression of Indonesia by Dutch imperialism, stands the fact that more than forty thousand of the common people of the Netherlands were sent to concentration camps by the Nazis for sheltering and hiding Jews.

hear an outcry. That was near the Chancellory Gate when
Lode van Nierop, the printer, looking out of the top window of his house suddenly shouted to the Jews: 'The God
of Daniel still lives! The God of Daniel still lives! He will
bring you out of the lions' den!'

"For an instant the crowd seemed confused, startled, and
on the verge of breaking. The German soldiers grew rigid.
But immediately the people's self-imposed discipline as-
serted itself and they resumed their slow silent march.
There was something so inexorable, so implacable, in that
measured step of thousands of wooden shoes that it made
you shiver. I said to Hein after I returned home that the
Germans seemed stunned. The calm and solemnity of the
crowd unnerved them. They must have felt something of
what the Duke of Alva felt after he had boasted that having conquered a people of iron, the Turks, he would make
short shrift of the Dutch, a people of butter. But the butter
slipped through the fingers of his mailed fists. The spirit of
the Dutch remained free. It was the same again. The Ger-
mains, too, could shoot and crush and terrorize us. But
they could not conquer our souls. They realized it that
afternoon.

"Before the Jews entered the depot they were loaded
with bread and foodstuffs and clothes. Everybody seemed to
have brought something. The poorest gave the most, as is
usually the case. By going to the side of the station we could
see the Jews crossing the platform and getting on the train.
Ary climbed on the fence and began to speak to them. But
by that time the Germans had enough of it. Four or five
Gestapo men seized him just as the whistle blew. The train
began to move slowly. David and Yetta and Dr. Mendoza
stood at one of the carriage windows and waved their
hands. Ary, who was being led away by the police, turned
around and held his hat high in the air. Then they fastened
the irons around his wrists, pushed him into one of the
armored cars, and he was seen no more.

"We learned from his father that he was sent to that
murder camp in Vugt. Nobody was permitted to visit him.
He was not allowed to write. We don't know how long he

lived. But when the Canadians entered the camp, a note was found appended to his name on the scroll of the camp's inmates. It said: Died: December 25, 1944; cause of death: pneumonia."

Doctor Mendoza's somber fears were justified even before the party of Gorcum Jews reached their final destination. As long as they traveled through Holland and Western Germany all went well. In order to give foreign public opinion no further occasion to criticize Germany's handling of the Jewish problem, Jews en route to the Eastern concentration camps were not to be unduly subjected to indignities or violence. Consequently the Gorcum Jews were treated almost humanely. They merely occupied a segregated section on the train. They had room enough and more than sufficient food. They were not molested. But in Dresden, where they were to change trains, things became different. They were lodged in a partitioned corner of the baggage department next to the railroad station and placed under heavy guard. Within an hour of their arrival they were given post cards and urged to write to their friends and acquaintances in the old town telling them that their journey had been quite comfortable, that they lacked nothing, and that they felt highly encouraged in their favorable expectations of the new homes to which they were going.

No sooner were the messages written and collected than the attitude of their guards and guides underwent a complete transformation. The mask was off. The Jews were deprived of every scrap of foodstuffs they had brought with them. They were told they were to remain in that shed at least a week and to make themselves at home on the floor. They were not allowed to keep any baggage whatever. Blankets and all clothing except that on their backs was taken away. Then came a four days' wait without anything to eat or drink until the morning when they started on the last lap of the journey. Instead of the passenger coaches in which they had come from Holland, they were now taken to a long string of cattle cars standing on a siding. All the Gorcum Jews were squeezed into a single truck, while par-

ties of other Jewish men and women who had been gathered
at the Dresden assembly point were distributed over the
other trucks. They were crushed so close together that their
bodies supported each other, and they could neither sit nor
lie on the floor. No food or drink was supplied. The doors
were locked. After an interminable wait on the siding the
train with its human cargo at last started off for the human
abattoirs.

I was once on a British patrol boat cruising off the coast
of Somaliland when the captain sighted an Arabian ship
which upon investigation proved to be loaded with young
Negroes and Negresses from the interior of Ethiopia destined for the markets of Yemen and Hamadraut. The slaver
had been out to sea but two days when they were halted.
When I looked into the hold and saw that mass of sick
and suffering humans, the stench drove me back, and I
thought I had seen a patch of hell. I know now that I was
mistaken. That dark, filth-steaming hold in the slave ship
was an Elysian idyl compared with the chloride-of-lime-
strewn cattle trucks in which millions of Jews were transported to Poland. After all, the Red Sea cargo was valuable
merchandise to be kept alive and to be sold. But the more
Jews died en route to Poland, the less work there was for
the butchers of Lublin, Oswiecim, Kolumya, Treblinka,
Belsen, and other such places.

Once in Silesia the Gorcum Jews passed behind that impenetrable curtain of horror of which Dr. Mendoza had
surmised the existence. They were delivered up, defenseless,
physically exhausted, and without hope, into the hands of
men who had shed the last vestige of humanity. Darkness
and the shadow of horrid cruelty envelops them. Clear it is
only that many, that millions, entered, that few have returned. Three men and two women out of the original one
hundred and thirty Gorcum Jews came back to tell the tale
of the Polish slaughterhouses and crematories, the tale of
shame of our twentieth century of Christian civilization
when the Nazis carried the Christian sin of anti-Semitism
to its logical conclusion.

"The gods themselves," says Pindar, "cannot annihilate

the action that is done"—action done, in this instance, with
our knowledge, action done while we kept silent, while we,
the peoples of Britain and America, in the callousness of
our hearts cut off any and every avenue of escape to those
Jews. Do you think, reader, that their blood will not be
upon our heads and upon the heads of our children? Have
you not seen that the mills of the gods, even if they do
grind slowly, do grind in the final accounting, and that
they grind exceedingly small? . . .

The details I have on the further experiences of Doctor
Mendoza and David Dalmaden came from various sources.
Letters from one of the surviving Gorcum Jews tell of what
happened to the old physician. The chance reading of a
dispatch in the *Journal de Genève* in the winter of 1944
gave me a glimpse of the role David Dalmaden played in
the revolutionary movement of the Polish underground.
This information was verified later by men who had known
him and seen him at work, men who had been his comrades.
There are many things that cannot be written down, so
abysmal and incredible is their sordidness. Deeds were done
for which language has no name. Few things in the history
of carnage are more painful. The horrors of the Polish concentration camps where millions of Jews were done to death
cannot be grasped by the human mind. I can well believe
my correspondent, a well-known pharmacist in Gorcum,
when he writes that as soon as he arrived in the Kolumya
camp Doctor Mendoza seemed in a daze from what he
witnessed.

He and the pharmacist were separated from the others
in Camp Kolumya and put to work in a neighboring village
from which the former Polish inhabitants had been deported. German settlers, most of them veterans, had taken
the place of the Polish farmers and peasants. A thriving
agricultural community had come into existence. Because of
his reputation as an obstetrician, the Doctor was pressed
into service. Hitler was preparing to fill the conquered Slav
territories, in which the indigenous population was method-
ically decimated, with Germans. Doctor Mendoza had a
small shanty for an office and the pharmacist, my corre-

spondent, was his assistant. They were required to answer rollcall at the camp five miles away, but they seldom walked that distance, since there was generally a farm wagon or a truck going their way. On busy nights they merely had to telephone the camp administration to be excused from returning before the lights-out signal was sounded.

Of course they knew everything that was going on at the reservation, where there were no less than thirty thousand Jewish prisoners. They were the daily witnesses of the atrocities or else upon their return at night learned from the other inmates what new barbarity had been visited upon them in the bygone twenty-four hours. They saw the pathetic separation of husbands from their wives. They saw the victims of scientific experimentations, men and women inoculated with typhus germs or cholera bacilli, dying in their bunks. They witnessed the daily selection of those who were to be gassed. They heard the German band play light Viennese music to render inaudible the agonized cries of the victims in the gas chambers. They saw the piles of ghastly bare corpses being soaked in kerosene and set aflame, and the death chambers being put in readiness for the next day's batch. They learned of the wholesale raping of Jewish children in the night and watched these little ones deposit their toys and shoes in front of the crematorium before being scalded to death or having their lungs burst by means of ammonia fumes. They saw those things. Day by day they shared an unimaginable anticipation with their fellow Jews.

Shortly after his arrival in Kolumya, which lies in that Teschen district that Poland seized from Czechoslovakia in 1940, Doctor Mendoza seems to have begun to entertain and nourish a notion that the outside world—America, Britain, Sweden—was not fully aware of the sufferings the Jewish people were undergoing. That the Jews were discriminated against and persecuted wherever the Nazis introduced the Nuremberg Laws, that was known, of course. But he thought the world did not begin to realize to what gruesome extents the Nazis were going. How could the American people, for instance, he wondered, believe that the European kinsmen of their German-American neigh-

THE END OF THE ROAD

bors, those sentimental, choral-singing, *gemütliche*, genial beer-drinkers and small businessmen, have turned into ferocious beasts? It was incredible. He himself, Doctor Mendoza, would not have believed it had he not seen it with his own eyes. The Dutch at home, he felt, in spite of the mounting hatred for their oppressors, would remain very skeptical if told of what went on in such camps as the Lubliner reservation and Kolumya. How could anyone believe that these Nazi officials who ran the camp, slow-going, middle-aged men, fathers of families themselves, members and probably officers of their church in their home towns—schoolteachers, bookkeepers, druggists, printers, carpenters, in civil life, quiet unassuming fellows all—should here reveal themselves as murderers and rapists?

"Take Herr Michael Yost, the assistant camp superintendent, for instance," said Doctor Mendoza. "He told me himself that he was secretary to the Burgomaster of Wesel, that he occupied that position for twenty-seven years, celebrated his silver jubilee two years ago. He has a wife and three grown-up daughters. He has grandchildren. He carries their photographs in his portfolio. He says he cannot sleep at nights because of *Heimweh*, of his longing for home. He belongs to a literary club. He is an official in the Evangelical Church. He once made a trip to the Holy Land and told me how that visit had confirmed his faith, he having seen all those places where Jesus and the Apostles and the prophets lived and walked. And yet that man sits down in the evening and calmly marks the names of the Jewish children who are to be done to death tomorrow morning. It is unbelievable. He rejected David Dalmaden's plea the other day to spare Yetta. 'No,' he said curtly to David, 'no, your wife's turn has come,' and glancing casually at the list on his desk, he added: 'Yes, here she is, Yetta Dalmaden. Yes, that's right, I did mark her down for the second batch for the gas room tomorrow morning at ten-twenty.'"

The Doctor thought the German people were sick, sick spiritually, because their country had for a long time been sick economically. Their minds were being warped and

twisted by a regime that had repudiated all the humanistic
virtues. When he studied at Leipzig and Halle in his youth
he had found them the kindest and most sympathetic people
imaginable. What had come over them to bring about this
violent change? If he could only get out and tell the story
of what he had seen and observed. He felt certain that if an
authentic witness of the cruelties practiced on the Jews
could tell the Western world, if such a man could impress
the plight of the Jews upon the great democratic Christian
nations, there would be such a burst of indignation that the
Nazis themselves would be stunned by it.

Some kind of help will yet come, he often said. He was
sure that some sort of an arrangement between the Western
Powers and Germany could still be brought about. He did
not believe Herr Yost, who had told him repeatedly that
the Jews were not wanted anywhere. "The Führer does not
want you Jews in Germany," said Herr Yost, "and the
Western Powers reproach the Führer for his intolerance.
But Britain herself bars the Jews from Palestine. The whole
American hemisphere has lowered its immigration barriers
against them. Australia says she has far too many Jews as
it is. Only Russia takes in Jews if they can get through
across the battlefields."

Doctor Mendoza wanted to go and see for himself. If
he could only get out of Kolumya. Ah, if he were a younger
man he would have been on his way long before.

"Where to?" the pharmacist asked him.

"From here I'd go straight south," he said. "I would try
to reach Turkey and from there I am sure it would be easy
to get into the Holy Land. There at least I could tell my
story and I would persuade the Jews there to stir up world
public opinion. I would set up such a roar that the world
would be compelled to listen."

"I tried to tell him," writes the pharmacist, "that the
Jews of Palestine and the Jews everywhere else knew very
well what plight we of Europe were in, that they had done
their best to rouse public opinion, but that the Christian
world was apparently too busy with its own troubles and
problems to bother about us. But I could talk as I liked; he

would go nevertheless. He must go. It was an idée fixe with him.

"You'll be captured the day after you leave Kolumya," the pharmacist told him. "You will be brought back and you'll go into the gas chamber."

That prospect did not deter the Doctor. What difference would it make, a day earlier or later? He was an old man. He expected nothing more from life. But the thought of establishing contact with the outside world obsessed him. He was willing to make any sacrifice to acquaint foreign public opinion with the harrowing plight of his people. He had the opportunity to slip away unobserved, an opportunity denied to thousands of others. He convinced himself that it was his duty to flee. His task was ineluctable.

And so those two men, the Doctor and the pharmacist, telephoned the *Kommandantur* at the camp one evening that they would be busy all night and probably the next day in the new German villages of the neighborhood where several births were expected. They asked to be excused from answering the rollcall. They received permission to stay away as long as necessary.

Shortly after sunset on the fifth day of December they set out on their journey. They made a detour of the town of Kolumya and then followed the railway line in a southeasterly direction toward Cernauti, fifty miles distant. Deep snow was on the ground and their clothing was of the scantiest. They walked all night. At daybreak they halted in a pine forest and built themselves a fire from twigs and tree branches. They ate sparingly from the small stock of provisions they had saved up for the day of their expedition, and then fell asleep.

They did not have a very clear notion of where they were. The information they had been able to gather on the geography of the territory they were to traverse was limited to mere elementary details. All they knew was that if they walked in a general south-southeastern direction they must sooner or later strike the Romanian border. The first big city inside Romania was Cernauti. There they would find Jews. They wanted to avoid towns and villages as much as possible, for they figured that the alarm would be raised soon enough at the camp and that pursuers would be on their trail. The difficulty of crossing the frontier entered little into their calculations. Somewhere or other in the Transylvania hills, they thought, they would be able to slip across.

But their journey was not prosperous, the pharmacist writes me. The cold was intense and Doctor Mendoza grew weary. He had shrunk to a mere skeleton, his legs were feeble, and it was harder to keep warm at nights than it is to twist rope from sand. Painfully they advanced a few miles each evening. But every succeeding night the distance they covered became shorter. Their provisions were low. Nothing remained but one loaf of black bread from the Kolumya camp. Even so, on the seventh day they had covered twenty miles and the Romanian border was in sight. They halted on the edge of a steep ravine at the bottom of which flowed the Prut River. In the distance across the valley they could see the frontier post with the Romanian flag flying. Near by was the railway bridge connecting the two countries. They walked to and fro through the forest looking for a place where the rock wall of the ravine was not too steep, permitting them to approach the river's shore. Their search was futile. Everywhere there was a sheer drop of five, six hundred feet to the valley. They decided to camp once more for the night, remain in hiding during the following day, and attempt to cross the bridge on the following evening in the darkness. They came as close to the Polish frontier post as they dared. They could see the lights in the barrack room and the sentry pacing up and down at the entrance to the bridge.

That night they almost froze to death. The pharmacist stamped about to keep the blood circulating in his veins. Doctor Mendoza dozed off peacefully. He had to be awakened time and again and be forced to move about. His eyelids were heavy with drowsiness. So that night waned slowly. Daylight was long delayed by a heavy snowstorm, which grew more intense as the day wore on. Around five o'clock in the afternoon they started for the bridge. They slipped past the frontier post unobserved and actually gained the bridge. They were on it. In a few minutes they would be in Romania. A train passed them and they decided to wait till it should have moved out of the Romanian border station. They were numbed with the cold and so weak that they had to support each other. At the end of the bridge they were challenged by a sentry. They could not understand the man, who pointed a bayonet at them while he blew a whistle that brought an officer and several other soldiers from the guard-house. The officer spoke German and asked for their pass-ports. They had nothing to show.

Doctor Mendoza asked permission to go into the guard-house to warm himself. The officer replied that the guard-house was on Romanian territory, that without a passport and a valid visa no stranger was allowed to set foot on Romanian soil. The Doctor said he was dying with the cold, that his hands and feet were frozen, and that he could scarcely remain standing with the pain. The officer replied that he was sorry but orders were orders. "Will you allow me to telephone to the authorities in Cernauti or Bucha-rest?" Doctor Mendoza asked. The officer said the use of the telephone was restricted to military men and matters. "What are you Jews thinking of?" he exclaimed suddenly. "Go back to where you came from or I'll have you thrown into the river. How did the Poles let you pass in the first place? I will telephone the guard post on the other side to see what they know about you."

The two men trudged back across the bridge without a word. The Poles, warned of their coming, were waiting for them. They were again asked for their passports. Unable to produce the least scrap of identification, the two were in the selfsame predicament they had faced on the Romanian side. They could not come into Poland. There was a war on. They were ordered back to the Romanian side. But Doctor Mendoza could no longer move. He sat down on the side of the bridge leaning his back against the railing. The Polish officials returned to their barracks. Only the sen-tinel remained outside and stamped up and down to keep warm. The snow had stopped. The stars were out. The two

Jews were alone. They were literally hanging in the air, between heaven and the river, stopped from going either backward or forward. From below came the sound of the ice clinking and clattering against the piles of the bridge. On either shore were houses with lights in the windows. The smoke from the chimneys rose candle-straight into the pale-blue evening sky.

"A sharp wind that cut to the marrow of our bones whistled through the railing of the bridge," writes the pharmacist. "Doctor Mendoza talked to me about Gorcum. He did not regret that he had left his hiding-place to come to Poland with the other Jews. He regretted that he could not continue his journey. 'I had hoped to reach the outside world,' he said. Then his head fell on my shoulder and he was asleep. When the Nazis came from Camp Kolumya next morning, he was dead and I had to be lifted in a truck, as my feet were frozen. . . ."

How the pharmacist returned to the prison camp, how both his feet were amputated, how he was finally liberated by the Red Army on the eve of the day when he was scheduled to go into the gas chamber, and how he got back to Gorcum in the end, is a tale that does not belong in this chronicle.

Here, before the book is closed, shall only be told the story of David Dalmaden, who had lost his wife and both his children, his father, sisters, and brother to the Nazi barbarians.

In the fall of 1943 David was transferred from Camp Kolumya to Warsaw and attached to the Jewish medical service in that city. Forty thousand of the original three hundred and sixty thousand Jewish inhabitants of the Polish capital had survived the deportations and the pogroms. They lived in a walled-in enclosure, the remnant of the old ghetto located in the Walewski quarter behind the ruined Church of Our Lady of Cracow. Most of these remaining Jews were tailors and garment workers who had been permitted to buy themselves a few months of life by manufacturing uniforms and greatcoats for the German Army. They had seen their kinsfolk slaughtered and deported in batches of tens of thousands. They had no illusions as to what might be in store for them once their usefulness to their tormentors came to an end. They did not know when that moment would come, but they knew that it merely depended on a signal from Berlin to the Gestapo forces in the city. There was no chance for evasion. They were in a trap from which escape was impossible. The streets of the quarter were patrolled. Every move of the inhabitants was controlled from morning till night. Barbed-wire fences charged with high-tension electricity had been strung around the ghetto. At stated intervals on the walls were watchtowers equipped with searchlights and manned by guards with the eyes and claws of falcons.

And yet those Jews revolted. Over their black doom flits an immortal glory. They fought regular German Army troops in a nine-day battle, which for sheer heroism and defiance of death must rank with—yes, and outrank—Thermopylae and the charge of the Light Brigade. Those Jews fought without hope of victory, even without a gleam of hope of saving their lives, with no weapons to speak of, without food, dressed in rags and often barefooted, but with a courage whipped up by desperation to something almost superhuman. For nine long days and nights they held three divisions of the black, demonized Elite Guard at bay. Time and again with little more than their bare hands they drove back tanks and armored cars and troops equipped with the most modern killing instruments. Smoke enveloped them in the day, in the night, fire. Death was ever present. Their revolt was like a dumb, dread force of nature. It smote the Germans like a sudden bolt of lightning. . . .

When David came to Warsaw, the resolution to fight had been taken by the leaders of the Jewish community. All the inhabitants of the ghetto were in the secret. Only the date when the rising was to take place remained undecided. David, white-haired and bent according to those who saw him in the Polish capital, prematurely aged, his face scathed and desolate by suffering and want, seemed a man broken in spirit and body when he arrived. He did his work listlessly and spoke little. He, too, had no more illusions. But when he was taken into their confidence by the leaders and told that they planned to stake their all on a last-ditch stand against the enemy before accepting death, his spirits revived. Not that he counted on salvation or liberation. He had learned to abandon all hope. But he was willing to fight. He was glad to go down fighting with the rest of his people.

The hospital where he worked became one of the centers of the conspiracy. On one pretense or another men and women presented themselves there to confer with David. Often they left with him whatever information they wished to convey to their fellow partisans who were working in different shops and factories, whereupon David would transmit the intelligence. Delays in the rising were occasioned by the lack of weapons and the necessarily extremely slow collection of material that would be required on the great day. Stocks of food had to be pilfered. Material had to be gathered for barricades. Entrenchments had to be dug. A careful distribution of manpower had to be arranged for the different sections of the ghetto where the Germans would inevitably counterattack. A thousand and one details had to be devised, decided, and attended to. Chief among these was, of course, the acquisition of arms. Without arms, the ingenuity and courage of men would crack, and become the fatuity and futility of shorn lambs led to the slaughter. A quantity of small arms and ammunition had been smuggled in and hidden in the ghetto in the course of several months, but the big catch of machine guns and automatic rifles was made only a day or two before the actual rising.

One morning three hundred carefully picked Jewish young men put on the German uniforms they had manufactured and marched to the arsenal in military formation. It appears from the aforementioned article in the *Journal de Genève* that "a Dutch Jewish physician, Dr. David Dalmaden," impersonated a German officer on that occasion and that he presented the military storekeepers with a forged order to deliver into his hands without delay all the machine guns, hand grenades, demolition bombs, and tommy guns his three hundred men could carry. The Germans at the arsenal hadn't the least suspicion; the order was formal, duly signed and countersigned. They handed over the stocks without any difficulty. The three hundred marched off an hour later loaded with the spoils.

They were scarcely back in the ghetto when their ruse was discovered. Yet the Germans, knowing what valuable weapons had been sequestered, were not so imprudent as to give chase immediately. The Warsaw Commandant consulted Berlin. For the time being he withdrew the watch at the ghetto gates and from the watchtowers and threw a cordon of troops around the walled district, out of reach of eventual Jewish gunfire and snipers. For two days a grim silence reigned in the approaches to the ghetto. Then arrived the three divisions of Elite Guards and the battle was on.

It was on a Tuesday morning that the first German tank rumbled into the Jewish quarter after smashing the gate. It rushed through the narrow street for a quarter of a mile and then disappeared in a cloud of smoke and dust. It had run into a thinly-covered ditch in which lay a charge of dynamite. Five other tanks followed. Unable to turn around in the alley where they had followed their wrecked predecessors, they started to back up when the façades of the tenement houses behind them on either side of the street toppled forward and buried them under a mass of smoking masonry. The first German attack was stalled. Tanks and armored cars were, obviously, of no use in dislodging the Jews. The Germans consequently changed their tactics. There was nothing for it but to go in with the bayonet and machine guns. Before their next assault they subjected the ghetto to an aerial bombardment with high-explosive and incendiary bombs for twelve consecutive hours until whole streets lay in ruins and buildings were flaming high in all directions. But the Jews were not intimidated. It was as if they were rooted to the ground. They didn't give way an inch. They hammered, schemed, dug ditches, drew up barricades, lugged ammunition, sent death volleys bursting from the walls, so that when the German infantry moved in in mass formation, it was mowed down and sent reeling back to where it came from.

Another day followed of incessant bombardment by

artillery and dive bombers combined. Entire streets were pulverized under that tornado of steel and fire. But when the tempest was over the Jews rushed from their cellars and dugouts firing their guns and hand-grenading their way forward out of the ghetto, and actually succeeded in capturing some of the German artillery pieces. Again the Germans retaliated with a bombardment. On the fifth day they were inside the ghetto and advancing step by step, sniper-wise, harrying, massacring, encircling the last Jewish street, the houses of which were fringed and maned with red fire.

The fighting was uninterrupted. Bands of Jewish men and women, in terror and rags and frenzy, would dash from cover and hurl themselves upon the enemy in fierce desperation. They were annihilated by the German troops that swarmed in from all sides. Other Jews, their faces covered with sweat and blood, took the place of the fallen. No prisoners were taken. It was man against man, lunging, stabbing, cutting throats, fighting till the last. One Jew ran forward with a belt loaded with hand grenades tied around his waist and flung himself into the midst of a group of German soldiers resting around a corner. Another jumped from a roof on a party of Germans assembling for the assault of his house and destroyed them and himself with the dynamite he carried. The Battle of the Ghetto must be reckoned with whatsoever is most savage and most hideous in the annals of warfare. Sorrier misery was never enacted in this world.

The night brought no respite. By the lurid half-light of burning houses the Jews fought on, in groups and individually, in a terrible, silent stubbornness of will and courage. They fought on stairways, in cellars, on the roofs. They rallied in the very sewers. . . .

On the ninth day the last Jewish defenders, a band of twenty-two men and women, were gathered on the roof of a four-story house. They had hurled their last hand grenade and had fired their last cartridge. But they still had a box of dynamite. With this they blew up the house and took with them into death the company of German soldiers who were crowding and storming up the stairs for the kill.

In the ruins of that house, amid the dead and dying, in the glare and gloom of that fire-ocean, lay the body of the Jewish boy from Gorcum.

Unhappy David! I would weep for him were there not a whole world to weep for.

Finished writing in Bronxville, New York,
on Reformation Day, October 31, 1945.